TREASURY OF LITERATURE—READTEXT SERIES

ADVENTURE LANDS

Selected and Edited by
ELEANOR M. JOHNSON
Editor-in-Chief
My Weekly Reader
and

LELAND B. JACOBS
Professor of Education
Teachers College, Columbia University
Specialist in Children's Literature

CHARLES E. MERRILL BOOKS
Columbus, Ohio

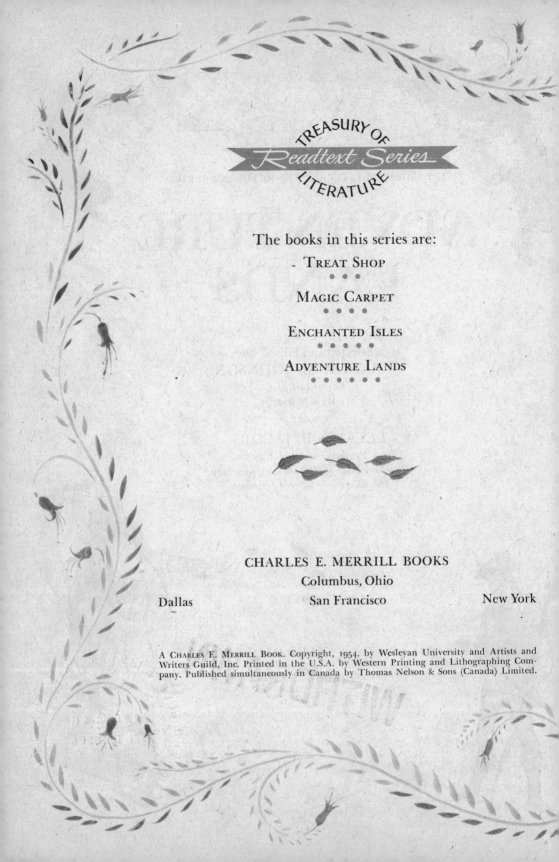

TREASURY OF
Readtext Series
LITERATURE

The books in this series are:

- TREAT SHOP

• • •

MAGIC CARPET

• • • •

ENCHANTED ISLES

• • • • •

ADVENTURE LANDS

• • • • • •

CHARLES E. MERRILL BOOKS
Columbus, Ohio

Dallas   San Francisco   New York

A CHARLES E. MERRILL BOOK. Copyright, 1954, by Wesleyan University and Artists and Writers Guild, Inc. Printed in the U.S.A. by Western Printing and Lithographing Company. Published simultaneously in Canada by Thomas Nelson & Sons (Canada) Limited.

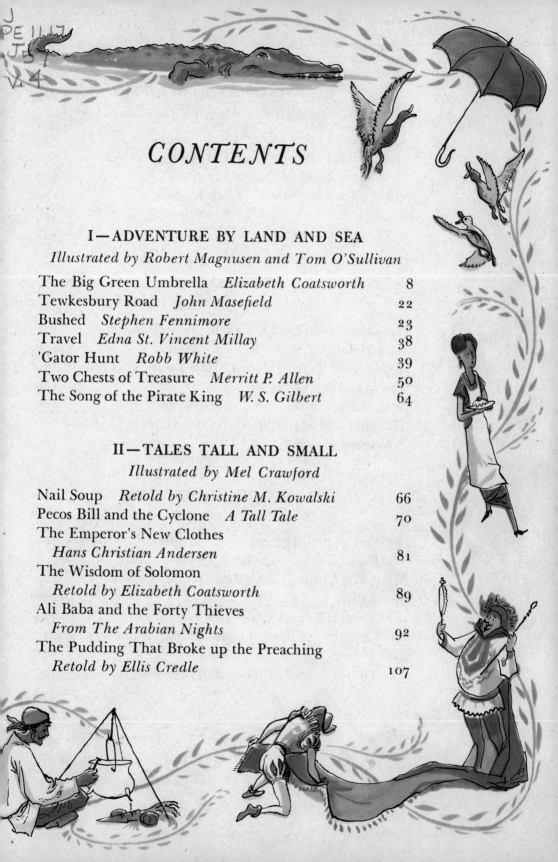

CONTENTS

CONTENTS

III—WINGS AND FOUR FEET

Illustrated by Maurice Robertson

IV—OTHER TIMES AND OTHER PLACES

Illustrated by Brinton Turkle

V—SING HIGH, SING LOW

Illustrated by Decie Merwin

CONTENTS

VI—YEARS OF OUR LAND

Illustrated by Tom O'Sullivan and Gordon Hake

CONTENTS

VII — STRANGE AND WONDERFUL
Illustrated by Grace Dalles Clarke

VIII — DOWN OUR STREET
Illustrated by William de J. Rutherfoord

Adventure
by Land and Sea

Adventure by land, adventure by sea—
Pirates or Indians, adventure for me!
I'll go to Tibet, I'll go to the moon,
I'll sail in a junk through a roaring typhoon;
I'll follow a rainbow, follow a star,
Follow a beckoning tune from afar,
Off to wherever adventure may be,
A book for my passport, conveyance, and key.
—*Dorothy Hall*

The Big Green Umbrella

Elizabeth Coatsworth

This is a true story of the early 1800's.

Mr. Thomas Thomas had an umbrella. It was a very fine umbrella, made of dark green silk, with an ivory tip, and a round ivory handle.

Mr. Thomas's umbrella was a very large umbrella. It was really like a small silk roof. It would keep Mr. Thomas and Mrs. Thomas and young Tom and little Amanda all dry on a rainy day. At least if the rain came down straight, they would be dry.

On rainy days the whole family walked together, under Mr. Thomas's big green umbrella. The umbrella would keep them dry, going to church, or going down the street in the little town of Newcastle, Delaware, past the big Green with its elm trees, past the little red brick houses with their small-paned windows. People looking out from upstairs windows would say, "There goes Mr. Thomas's big green umbrella!"

Everyone knew it. There were many big umbrellas in Newcastle, but Mr. Thomas's was the biggest, the greenest, and the silkiest. He was very proud of it, and so were Mrs. Thomas and young Tom and Amanda.

But one day the umbrella seemed to grow tired of its life in Newcastle. It grew tired of keeping the rain off the Thomases on rainy days and on sunny days standing in the dark corner behind the door. It had heard the talk of the winds from far away. It had listened to the whispering of raindrops which had seen all the world at one time or another. Goodness knows what thoughts the umbrella had been thinking during all the long hours behind the door! But when the moment came, the umbrella acted.

It was a Saturday morning in April. The wind blew fresh, the clouds raced overhead, the sun shone brightly when it shone at all. The birds sat among the budding trees and sang for joy, though sometimes they had to stop their singing when a sudden gust of wind almost blew their tails inside out. It was a wild day, but a lovely day. The dogs barked, the little boys flew their plunging kites, the horses trotting over the cobbled streets threw up their heads at the blowing bits of paper, and the Thomas family went for a walk. Mr. Thomas took the umbrella along, because in April a shower may come up at any minute.

When people in Newcastle went for a walk, they always went to the river, the Delaware River, whose wide waters ran along the back of the gardens of the red brick houses on the shore. There were always things to be seen on the river, a flock of wild ducks bobbing about, or fishermen in their small boats. Or it might be a big clipper ship with its white sails spread, sailing down the river for South America, or the ports of Russia, or far-away China.

On this April morning, such a ship was standing off

the shore, its sails taut with wind, its figurehead gallantly rising and falling.

"She's from Philadelphia," Mr. Thomas remarked. "Probably bound for the Pagoda Anchorage."

"I wish I were on her," said young Tom.

"So do I," said little Amanda.

"Pooh, you'd be sick!" cried Tom.

"No more than you!" cried Amanda.

"Hush, children," said gentle Mrs. Thomas. "See, it's beginning to rain." Yes, the clouds had suddenly gathered. A minute ago the sun was shining, and now the rain was falling!

Mr. Thomas put up the big green silk umbrella, and all the Thomases gathered under it, like chickens under a bush when the rain begins. Had the umbrella heard what the children said? Who will ever know?

Suddenly an unexpected gust of wind arose, stronger than any of the others. It pushed its way under the green umbrella. Umbrella and wind together struggled to pull the ivory handle out of Mr. Thomas's grasp.

Mrs. Thomas smothered a scream. The children

knocked against Mr. Thomas's elbows. The umbrella, like a thing gone mad, whacked against Mr. Thomas's fine beaver hat and sent it spinning. As Mr. Thomas reached one hand out to catch his hat, the umbrella gave a wicked twist, and it was free!

Above the meadow the umbrella went, now near the ground, now high in the air, like a big green flower, like a tumbling toadstool. Now it floated like a jellyfish, now it soared upward like a kite, now it turned head-over-heels like a boy at play.

It was soon over the river, frightening a flock of ducks, which flew up quacking and spattering water in their wake. A fisherman saw it and began to row desperately after the flying umbrella. But he and his little boat were left far behind.

The rain had stopped now. The sun was out again. In a row, the Thomases stood and watched the great green umbrella, which had been their pride, dancing and bowing and twirling above the river. It was scarcely larger than a thimble now. Sometimes they couldn't see it, and then they would catch a glimpse of it again, dark against the white sails of the clipper ship which it seemed to be approaching.

Then they could see it no more.

"If only my hat hadn't blown off!" sighed Mr. Thomas. "I might have held it."

"No one could have held that big umbrella in such a wind," soothed Mrs. Thomas.

"We'll never have another umbrella like that," whimpered Amanda.

"There's not another umbrella like it in the world," said young Tom solemnly.

"The wind's gone down," said Mr. Thomas. "I suppose our umbrella's in the Delaware by now."

"It will float for a while," murmured Mrs. Thomas. "And then I suppose it will sink."

"And scare the fishes," Tom suggested hopefully.

"Perhaps it will keep the sunshine off the fishes as it used to keep the rain off us," said Amanda.

"Anyhow, it's at the bottom of the Delaware by now," said Mr. Thomas. "I'm sorry, for it was a fine umbrella. We'll never see it again."

Mr. Thomas was an upright man, the head of a good firm of lawyers, a deacon of the church, a kind husband, and an indulgent father. He set the children a splendid example by never making a remark unless he was sure that he was right.

But on this fine blowy April Saturday morning, Mr.

Thomas was as wrong as wrong could be. The umbrella was *not* at the bottom of the Delaware, or even on the top of it among the waves. And he was mistaken in other ways besides.

By Clipper to China

Captain John DeWitt of the clipper ship *Commerce* was walking the deck on this fine April morning thinking what a fine ship his was, and what a good crew he had signed on, and how well the first mate was handling the business of sailing the vessel down the river.

Off for China! That was an exciting thought at the beginning of each voyage. To sail half-way round the world to trade with the Chinese, to fill the hold with sweet-smelling tea and to buy fine dishes and embroidered shawls for his wife, surely that was a fine kind of voyage to make. It was much pleasanter than bringing iron ore from Archangel, or hides and tallow from the Spanish Missions on the coast of California. The day was part of his mood, very gay and bright and wild. Suddenly, something caught his eye. It bobbed and winked at the captain.

"That's a funny bird," he thought. But his sharp sailor's eyes told him immediately that it was no bird.

"A kite?" But it hadn't a kite's shape.

Dancing, leaping, tumbling, the thing approached nearer. "An umbrella!" exclaimed the captain, and laughed.

The umbrella seemed to be on a frolic, so full of high spirits that it couldn't behave the same way for two seconds on end. Now it appeared about to leap into the river, now it changed its course to skim over the masts.

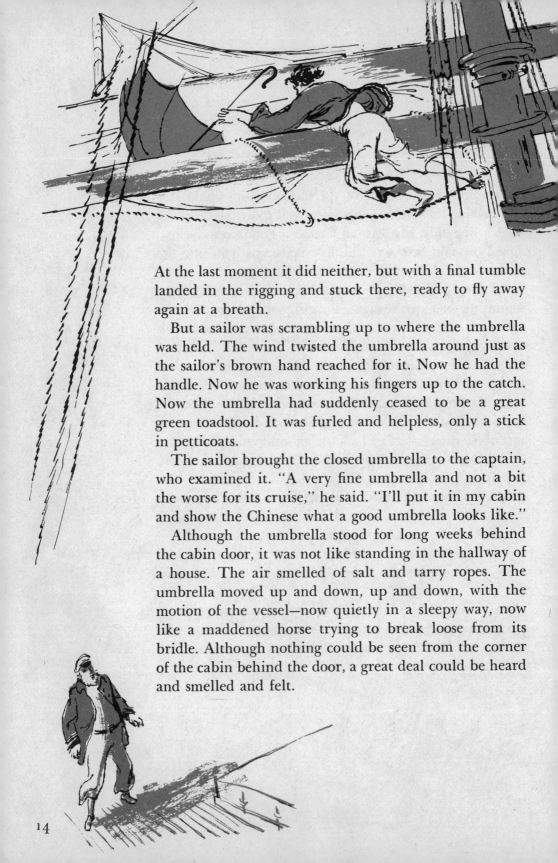

At the last moment it did neither, but with a final tumble landed in the rigging and stuck there, ready to fly away again at a breath.

But a sailor was scrambling up to where the umbrella was held. The wind twisted the umbrella around just as the sailor's brown hand reached for it. Now he had the handle. Now he was working his fingers up to the catch. Now the umbrella had suddenly ceased to be a great green toadstool. It was furled and helpless, only a stick in petticoats.

The sailor brought the closed umbrella to the captain, who examined it. "A very fine umbrella and not a bit the worse for its cruise," he said. "I'll put it in my cabin and show the Chinese what a good umbrella looks like."

Although the umbrella stood for long weeks behind the cabin door, it was not like standing in the hallway of a house. The air smelled of salt and tarry ropes. The umbrella moved up and down, up and down, with the motion of the vessel—now quietly in a sleepy way, now like a maddened horse trying to break loose from its bridle. Although nothing could be seen from the corner of the cabin behind the door, a great deal could be heard and smelled and felt.

Land air has a different smell. First come the sea birds on the borders of the ocean, and then come the land birds, singing and twittering. The *Commerce* moved smoothly now on a quiet river. There were cries of rivermen, unlike the sounds of American voices, and smells of gardens and incense and dead fish.

When the *Commerce* came to anchor there were temple bells, too, in the distance, and Chinese voices conferring with Captain DeWitt in the cabin. But still nothing could be seen.

Then one day it rained, slats of rain falling on the cabin roof like a bamboo curtain falling with a sharp sound. And that day the great green umbrella with the ivory handle came out of its hiding and saw China.

If I should tell you all that the umbrella saw, I should have to tell you all about China. For it saw everything. It saw the blue-clothed crowds, with pigtails hanging down their backs, the women with bound feet in little embroidered slippers, the children in bright clothes. It saw the river boats with big eyes painted on each side of the prows, the dark temples opening on streets so narrow that the umbrella touched walls on each side. Indeed, the streets were so very narrow, and the green umbrella was so very large, that hundreds of Chinese had to pass under it as it moved along, and they all gave it a glance of interest and admiration.

An Umbrella for Peach Blossom

The merchant who was in charge of loading the *Commerce* looked at the umbrella with interest and admiration, too. "A very fine umbrella," he said in Chinese.

"A very fine umbrella," the interpreter repeated in English.

"It is yours," declared Captain DeWitt, for the captain and the merchant were always giving each other presents.

So that afternoon the umbrella started off with a slim yellow hand on its ivory handle, and a grave Chinese face like an old idol's in its green shade.

When the merchant reached his home, he went directly into the part of his house where the women of the family lived, to show them the new umbrella. The women liked to see things which came from across the sea. They were used to smaller parasols made of glazed paper. They laughed and stared at the great big green umbrella as large as a little, little house.

Peach Blossom, the merchant's youngest daughter, was more interested than any one else. "It is so strange," she exclaimed. "I have never seen such a thing."

The merchant smiled at her. "It is yours," he said. "But you must have one of the servants hold it for you when it rains. It is too large for your little hands."

So the umbrella became Peach Blossom's. It went out into the garden in the courtyard to keep her dry when it rained. A big peasant woman held it, while Peach Blossom tripped along on her tiny feet, bringing food for the goldfish in the rain-speckled pond under the

moonshaped bridge. More rarely, the umbrella took her
to a temple or to visit at some other house where her aunts
lived or her father's cousin. Then all the children crowded
under the umbrella and laughed because they had seen
nothing like it before.

A month went by. One morning, the merchant noticed
that Peach Blossom was looking more thoughtful than
usual.

"What are you thinking about, Peach Blossom?" he
asked.

"I had a dream last night, my father," Peach Blossom
replied, bowing.

"Tell me," he said.

So Peach Blossom bowed. "In my dream," she went on,
"I was walking out in the rain, holding the foreign
umbrella in my hand. And I heard it sigh and I looked
up. It seemed now that it was a bird which I was holding
by its leg, a huge bird which struggled to be free. But I
was not afraid.

"'Why do you sigh?' I asked it. And it replied, 'I am
weary for my own place and my own people.'

"Then I looked again and it seemed to be only the foreign umbrella. But this morning when Green Bamboo, the servant, held it over me during a shower, it tugged and struggled so that she could hardly hold it."

The Umbrella Goes Home

The merchant nodded slowly. "It is homesick," he said. "Things can no doubt be homesick, too. I will take it back to the captain and explain. If it stayed here it would not be lucky. Fortunately the *Commerce* has not yet sailed."

So that was how it came about that the big green umbrella found itself once more behind the door in the captain's cabin. Once more it smelled and heard and felt the life of a ship, leaving the port for the open sea. Once more it shared in the life of a long voyage, heard the talk, and felt the rise and fall of the vessel beneath it. Once more it came through storms and calms to the quiet of a great river. But this time, the odors that blew from the land and the far-off sounds of the shores were familiar as sun and rain to the umbrella.

Then once more the ship came up into the wind, and the anchor chains rattled. The captain's gig was lowered and the captain and the umbrella were rowed ashore.

At the little Newcastle customs house, the officer bowed politely to Captain DeWitt. "I trust that you had a good voyage to China, sir. Are you putting goods ashore at Newcastle this trip?"

Captain DeWitt laughed. "Only this stowaway which signed on from here without papers." And he held out the big green umbrella.

"Good heavens, sir, that's Mr. Thomas's umbrella,

which blew away over a year ago. It was the biggest umbrella in town. He never expected to lay eyes on that again, I do assure you."

So the captain explained how the umbrella had chosen to come aboard, and the customs officer laughed and nodded and called a boy. "Here, Jim, take this to Mr. Thomas Thomas's house with my compliments. Tell him that it went on a voyage to China along with Captain DeWitt on the *Commerce*. In China, it was given to a little Chinese girl who had a dream and sent it back because she thought the umbrella was homesick. Amanda will like to hear that."

"Tell Amanda that the little girl's name was Peach Blossom," Captain DeWitt joined in.

The boy, Jim, started up the street toward the Green, whistling and swinging the big green umbrella by its ivory handle. It was so tall that he had to keep his hand nearly up to his shoulder so the ivory tip wouldn't hit the paving stones.

"What have you got there, Jim?" one of his friends asked him. "Look out or it will run away with you."

"That's Mr. Thomas's green umbrella and it's been on a cruise to China," Jim explained.

"Whew!" said the boy, falling in beside Jim. "What do you know about that?"

Just then, a lady who was passing stopped, looking sharply at the umbrella. "Isn't that Mr. Thomas's big green umbrella?" she demanded. "What are you doing with it, boy?"

When she heard the story she nodded her head a couple of times. "I'll go along to see that you don't break it," she declared. "I do want to see Mrs. Thomas's face

when she comes to the door. I've seen that umbrella too
many times from my window to be mistaken about it."

So the umbrella went on its triumphant way, and more
and more people joined the procession. There were
children, and dogs, of course, and grown-up people, too,
just to see what the Thomases would say when they saw
their big green umbrella returned from far-away China.

Jim knocked on the big shiny knocker on the white
door. The maid came, and was soon followed by Mr. and
Mrs. Thomas and young Tom and little Amanda, pouring out onto the steps to see the big green umbrella. Mr.
Thomas opened it, and there it was, as big and sheltering
as ever, and not a tear or wear in all its dark green surface.

Mrs. Thomas kept repeating, "Well, I never in all my born days!"

Young Tom grinned and went out into the street to see the *Commerce* standing off shore, with her sails set for Philadelphia. But Amanda went over when no one was looking and kissed the handle of the runaway umbrella to welcome it home again. It was she who found fastened below the ivory handle a colored cord from which hung an embroidered peach with a tassel at its end, filled with sandalwood, as a remembrance.

But Peach Blossom must have been right; the umbrella apparently wanted to be home where it belonged. For never again did it attempt to leave Newcastle, where it lived in great splendor as the umbrella that had been to China—yes, and had come back again.

Tewkesbury Road

It is good to be out on the road, and going one knows
       not where,
Going through meadow and village, one knows not
       whither or why;
Through the grey light drift of the dust, in the keen,
       cool rush of the air,
Under the flying white clouds, and the broad blue lift
       of the sky.

And to halt at the chattering brook, in the tall green
       fern at the brink,
Where the harebell grows, and the gorse, and the fox-
       gloves purple and white;
Where the shy-eyed delicate deer troop down to the
       brook to drink,
Where the stars are mellow and large at the coming
       of the night.

O, to feel the beat of rain, and the homely smell of
       the earth,
Is a tune for the blood to jig to, a joy past power
       of words;
And the blessed green comely meadows are all a-ripple
       with mirth
At the noise of the lambs at play and the dear wild cry
       of the birds.

—*John Masefield*

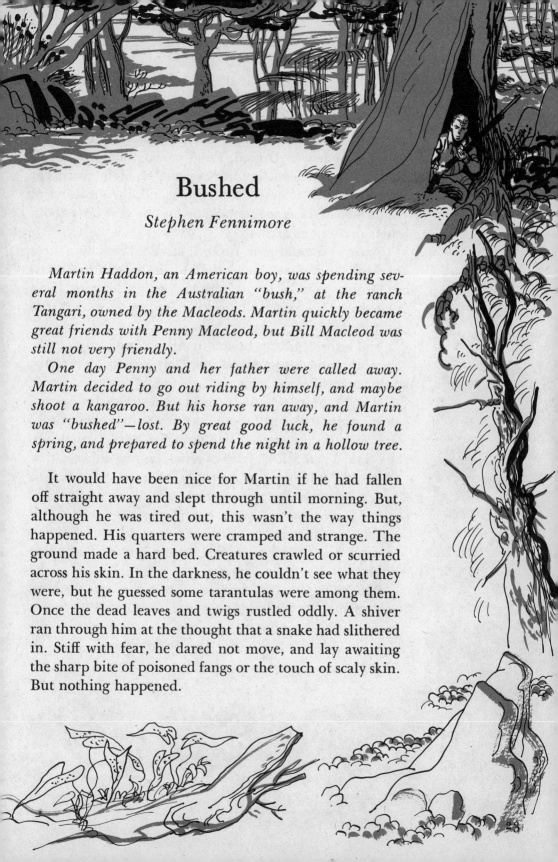

Bushed

Stephen Fennimore

Martin Haddon, an American boy, was spending several months in the Australian "bush," at the ranch Tangari, owned by the Macleods. Martin quickly became great friends with Penny Macleod, but Bill Macleod was still not very friendly.

One day Penny and her father were called away. Martin decided to go out riding by himself, and maybe shoot a kangaroo. But his horse ran away, and Martin was "bushed"—lost. By great good luck, he found a spring, and prepared to spend the night in a hollow tree.

It would have been nice for Martin if he had fallen off straight away and slept through until morning. But, although he was tired out, this wasn't the way things happened. His quarters were cramped and strange. The ground made a hard bed. Creatures crawled or scurried across his skin. In the darkness, he couldn't see what they were, but he guessed some tarantulas were among them. Once the dead leaves and twigs rustled oddly. A shiver ran through him at the thought that a snake had slithered in. Stiff with fear, he dared not move, and lay awaiting the sharp bite of poisoned fangs or the touch of scaly skin. But nothing happened.

23

Outside, the noises of the bush had changed entirely. There was an eerie sense of much activity by unseen creatures. The mopokes called, and a bittern boomed on a lonely note. Possums squeaked and scampered. A dingo howled and foxes barked. Frogs croaked and some bird he had never heard before screamed as if in pain. Far from going to sleep when the night fell, the creatures of the wilderness seemed to wake up and be very busy about their mysterious affairs.

Once, in the starlight, two bright, tilted eyes, like those of a wolf in a picture book, looked in through his screen of saplings, and he heard inquiring sniffs. Martin's hand closed on the barrel of the gun. But as he moved, the visitor vanished.

And again, turning in an attempt to find a more comfortable position, he saw a ghost. It floated in mid-air, pale and white and glowing in a misty way.

Hastily, Martin shut his eyes. But when he opened them again, it was still there, burning with a kind of cold fire. His teeth chattered. He wriggled farther back into the tree. Then, with a gulp of relief, he remembered that Penny had told him that some of the big bulges of fungus which grew on the trees shone weirdly at night, as if they'd been covered with phosphorescent paint. This simple explanation of what had seemed so terrifying cheered him up a lot. He fell asleep, hoping that when he woke it would be daylight.

But it wasn't. The dark still pressed down. Possums were fighting. Something snored loudly. Wild geese passed over, honking sadly. From up there in the sky they would be able to see the Yedda River, even by starlight.

He dozed again, woke again, dozed. The night seemed endless. A breeze came and set the millions and millions of leaves whispering and sighing. Branches creaked.

No glimmer of light yet, no sight of dawn. His eyes ached with staring into the darkness. Closing them, he fell into uneasy sleep again.

And when he awoke the next time, he was delighted to find that the night was over and the day had come. It seemed a shame that he had missed the long-awaited dawn. Still, the great point was—

His thoughts broke off and his mind went blank.

Coiled up against his stomach, looking rather like Bill's stock whip when he gathered it in, was a snake. It was asleep, triangular head resting on its folds. Martin was too paralyzed at that moment even to connect it with the rustlings of the night and his fears. Rigid, numb, he lay there with that awful bedfellow, staring, horrified. He could have sworn he had not moved a fraction of an inch. But perhaps his muscles contracted without his knowing it. The snake felt something, woke up, raised his head, and looked into Martin's face with sharp, cruel, beady eyes.

Martin wanted to scream and leap up. No sound came from him. He couldn't move. If the snake struck now —at his face—he would die an awful death alone.

It didn't. It swung away, uncoiling as it did so, and rustled off through the screen of saplings.

Martin let out his breath in a hiss. The blood, which had seemed to freeze in his veins, began to flow again. He couldn't imagine a snake's being grateful, or having any good qualities. But certainly this one, having enjoyed the warmth of his body through the night, at least had the decency not to pay for his lodgings with poison.

After such an escape, the mere business of being bushed seemed nothing. Martin pushed the saplings aside and crawled out, feeling fit and almost gay.

Bush Breakfast

Mist drifted about. Leaves and grass were bright with dew, and the birds warbled their happy morning songs. Martin's spirits rose higher, and he looked about, almost expecting to see Hero nearby, cropping the grass, waiting to take him home. But of course the pony wasn't there. Hero was back at Tangari.

Martin flicked finger and thumb. That was something! When the pony returned without his rider, a search would begin. A point to remember, and he'd have to think about it. But first he was thirsty and hungry.

He went down to the spring and drank and washed. The water was beautifully cool and refreshing. The rabbits out feeding, including the golden one, popped into their burrows. That reminded him. He needn't go hungry. The rabbit he had shot with his last lucky bullet hung safely in the hollow tree.

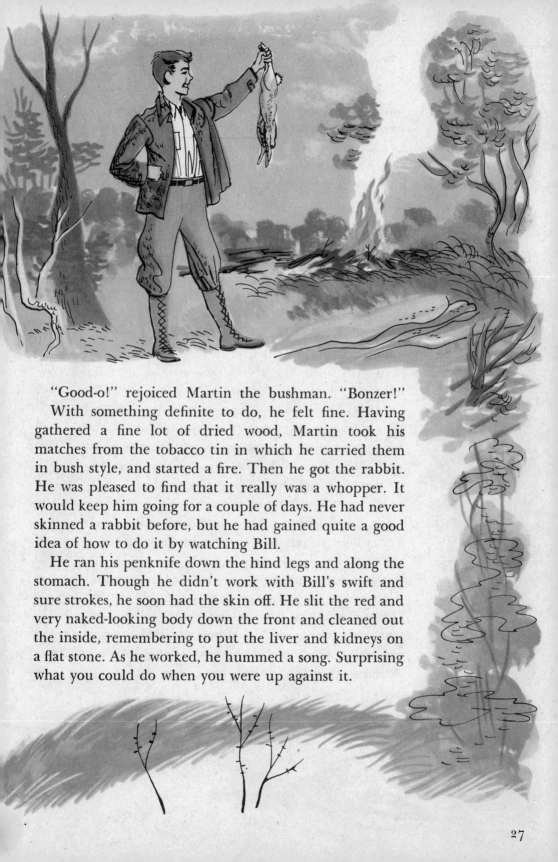

"Good-o!" rejoiced Martin the bushman. "Bonzer!"

With something definite to do, he felt fine. Having gathered a fine lot of dried wood, Martin took his matches from the tobacco tin in which he carried them in bush style, and started a fire. Then he got the rabbit. He was pleased to find that it really was a whopper. It would keep him going for a couple of days. He had never skinned a rabbit before, but he had gained quite a good idea of how to do it by watching Bill.

He ran his penknife down the hind legs and along the stomach. Though he didn't work with Bill's swift and sure strokes, he soon had the skin off. He slit the red and very naked-looking body down the front and cleaned out the inside, remembering to put the liver and kidneys on a flat stone. As he worked, he hummed a song. Surprising what you could do when you were up against it.

Having let the fire die down into nice red embers, he laid the rabbit over it. Soon an appetizing smell of cooking rose into the fresh morning air. He found his nose twitching to it, like a hungry animal sniffing. As the body baked, he turned it from side to side with a stick. On another pointed stick, he toasted the kidneys and liver. These tid-bits were done first, and he popped a kidney, hot and good, into his mouth. He had never been so ravenous in his life. The other followed, and the liver. The rabbit seemed to be done now. He took it off the fire and scraped the ash from it with his knife. A hind leg completed his breakfast, and it was the best meal he had ever eaten.

"Yankee, eh?" he shouted in triumph. A kookaburra laughed happily with him.

Martin hung the rest of the carcass up in the tree, wrapping it carefully in his shirt so that the flies couldn't get at it. The shirt wasn't very clean, but details like that didn't matter any more. Then he washed the grease off his hands at the spring, using mud for soap. When the spring had cleared, he had another drink, and felt equal to anything—even to finding the Yedda River.

He was about to gather his things together and set off, when he paused suddenly, sat down, and really thought. Yesterday had taught him that just imagining you knew the way wasn't any use when you were bushed. A whole day's tramping might only take you farther into the wilderness. He might never find the Yedda or the Badger. He mightn't have the luck to chance on another spring just when he wanted it. When the rabbit was done, he would be out of food. He might be able to wing a parrot or some other bird with a stone. But that wasn't so easy as it sounded. He'd tried for fun in the past and he knew.

What was the right thing to do? He puzzled over the problem, which was the greatest he had ever had to face. He knew quite well that it was, really and truly, a matter of life and death.

The solution came quite suddenly. Stay put! While he wandered on blindly, he would be much harder to find than the smallest needle in the greatest haystack. But if he stayed where he was, with food and water, and didn't budge, sooner or later he would be found. If he put damp wood on his camp fire, a great column of smoke would go up. The search parties would see it and understand.

A great weight lifted off his mind. Again he had work to do.

He gathered wood and built up the fire, dampening it with water from the spring. The breeze had died down. A tall column of blue-gray smoke rose into the still air. He rubbed his hands in glee.

A sudden noise in the trees, a sound of hoarse, gruff chatter, caused him to look up. On every branch perched great black cockatoos. They had proud crests the color of flames and strong black beaks which looked as if they could bite through a good-sized bough—or a finger. They were interested in Martin and his fire, and peered down with red eyes and talked the matter over in raucous voices.

Yesterday, the arrival of this strange company would have made him sad. Today, it was different. Having done so much for himself, and worked out his own plans, he was not bothered. He found the black cockatoos handsome fellows and good company.

Something Martin had read came back to his mind.

Native people made signals with puffs of smoke. It struck him that if he could break up his column it would be more likely to catch the eye. He wet a sapling at the spring and waved it slowly to and fro. The idea worked. Now there were spaces between the smoke, and no one could mistake it for just a smoldering tree. He watched with pride as the big woolly balls floated up into the blue.

The sun climbed high, and the hours passed. His arms ached, and he had to rest at intervals. But he saw to it that the smoke went up whether he was signaling or not. The day grew hot. The orchestra of insects burred and buzzed. He fell asleep for a time, worn out after his disturbed night. Awakening, he could not imagine, for a moment, where he was or how he came to be there. When his wits returned, he felt very lonely. The black cockatoos had moved on. The trees drooped under the weight of

the noonday heat. He longed for the sound of a human voice. Living among people as he always had, he had never realized before that ears could ache for the sound of just ordinary words saying any old thing.

For lunch, he had the other hind leg of the rabbit. He could have eaten more, but by now the rabbit wasn't looking so big as it had before. There was no saying how long it might have to last.

In the afternoon, he passed some time trying to kill birds with stones. It was even harder now than when it didn't matter. He couldn't even hit a fat wood pigeon that sat cooing at him but rose knowingly into the air as soon as the stone drew near.

Another Day, Another Night

And still nobody came to answer his signal fire. Another night was drawing near. He dreaded the thought. The certainty that he could find Tangari, or at least the Badger or the Yedda, swept up in him again. A great temptation to start out, with that feeling that he only had to go straight ahead to get somewhere. But he reminded himself that it wasn't even possible to go straight ahead—and won the battle. Between times of waving the

bough over the smoke, he filled the floor of the tree with leaves to make a softer bed. He put up a kind of fence of sapling trunks across the entrance, which, he hoped without much certainty, would keep out the snake.

The sun began to drop down into the west. Surely, before it went, he could find the river or the creek! Even if he had to camp again for the night, he would be on his way home in the morning. Once more, a stubborn streak in him conquered the urge. Though it was so boring and tiresome, this was the right thing to do. And, by golly, he would go on doing it!

He ate the two small forelegs of the rabbit for supper, and was left with only the back and the head. Even they seemed to have shrunk. He threw more wood on the fire and signaled more eagerly than ever.

Down went the sun, and down. The air grew cooler. The birds of the day began to prepare for bed. Martin built the fire higher, and clouds of sparks danced up. It was a bitter disappointment that what had seemed such good sense hadn't brought any reward. The twilight was sad. He took a burning branch and inspected his bedroom. Things scurried up into the darkness above. They would come down when he was asleep and run over him. He felt thoroughly miserable.

And then—a dog barked!

Martin didn't believe his ears. It barked again. A fox? A dingo? Some mimic, like the lyrebirds? He turned back from the black hole of the tree, and piled the last of the fuel he had gathered on the fire.

"Coo-ee!" he called. Though he still couldn't get it right, it was heartening to hear his own voice going out toward the barking dog—if it were a dog.

"Coo-ee!" An echo from the empty hills? No, that wasn't his own feeble effort flung back to him. It was a genuine coo-ee, crisp and sure as the crack of a whip. He had been found.

The relief of it brought tears to his eyes. But he wasn't going to be rescued blubbering like a—like a scared townee. He threw on the fire the barrier he had made against the snake. The flames roared up, burning a great red cave in the darkness.

Into the red cave bounded Blotto, Bill's dog. He was a one-man dog, but now he was delighted to see Martin. He leaped up at him and woofed and stroked him with his paws. No need to save the rabbit now. Martin darted into the tree, unwrapped what was left from his shirt, hacked the head off, and gave it to Blotto, much to Blotto's delight. He himself began to gnaw the back. He was still eating when Bill rode into the brightness of the fire. Bill looked very grim and savage, sitting up on his big mare.

"Crikey," he growled. "You're ten times more trouble than Uncle Luke."

But though he sounded cross, he was delighted to see Martin, and immensely relieved. To Martin's amazement, Bill, the tough bushman, drew his finger across his nose and gave a big sniff. His eyes were bright and shining. They took in the whole scene—the hollow tree with the leaf bed spread in it, the fire which had been burning for hours, the blackened branches which had been waved through the smoke, and Martin still automatically munching away at the last of his roast rabbit.

"Water?" he asked.

"There's a small spring down there. That's why I

decided to stay here, particularly after I'd shot the rabbit."

"With that rifle?"

"Yes," said Martin. "I aimed at a yellow one, but I hit the one next to it."

"Then that must be the secret of that worn old barrel—aim six inches to the side, whichever side it was." Bill jumped down from his horse. He looked big and fine and every inch a bushman. "You shouldn't have gone and got bushed, Mart," he said. "But when you'd done it, you certainly showed some sense. Tell us what happened."

So Martin, feeling almost as tall as Bill, told him the whole story.

"Well, kid," Bill said at last, "you're not a townee any more. Shake, cobber." And he put out his hand and gripped Martin's. "Have I been in a flat spin, with Dad

away and all! I'll tell you this, Mart, there aren't many
bush kids would have done as well. Most of them would
have been sure they could find the Yedda and gone wandering on and on until they'd been lost for good. Good on
you, Mart. When I saw your smoke signals I couldn't
believe my eyes."

"Did Hero get home?" asked Martin. It was fine to
be talking to Bill as man to man.

"Yes, last night. I knew then, of course. But I couldn't
do anything. I was out at break of day—had no one to
send for help down to the farms or anything, didn't know
which way you'd gone, didn't know nothing. I ought to
hate you worse than ever, but somehow I can't. In fact,
everything's oke now, Mart, and I'm sorry for not liking
you before. I'll show you how to handle a stock whip
tomorrow—if you like."

He said it shyly, almost apologetically, looking aside
into the fire.

"Will you really?" gasped Martin.

"Dinkum," said Bill, so Martin knew he would. "Well,
we'd better be getting back. Dad and Penny weren't there
when I left, but they may be by now."

"But we can't possibly get home tonight, can we?"

"Can't we just?" said Bill. He began to trample the
dying fire into the ground, so that there wasn't so much as
a spark left. "Put on your shirt and grab your rifle. Wait
till I take you in hand." He swung himself into the saddle.
"Hop up, Mart," he said, freeing a stirrup so that his
cobber could climb up onto the big mare. "Hang on to
me," he said. "Come, Blotto."

He spoke to the mare, and they started off. Martin
sat bareback behind the saddle and held onto Bill. They

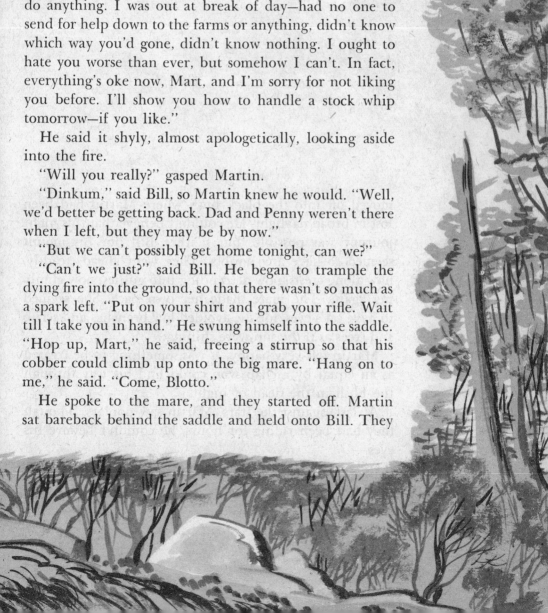

moved off into the black bush where Martin had been
lost in broad daylight. He couldn't believe that this night
journey was possible, but neither Bill nor his mount
seemed to have any doubts. They went ahead steadily,
now along crests, now descending into gullies, now climbing again. The mare made her own pace. She seemed
to have cat's eyes, for she avoided low branches and scrub
and trees as if the sun were shining.

Martin felt very happy. It was something to be treated
as an equal by a chap who could find his way through
the bush in the dead of night.

At last, against the stars, Martin saw poplars. Though
they had been riding for hours, he couldn't believe his
eyes.

"That's not—that's not Tangari, Bill?" he said.

"If it isn't, we're bushed, Mart," laughed Bill. Though he sounded pleased with himself, you couldn't blame him for that.

As they cantered across the home pasture, Bill glanced about. "Good! they're not back. Just as well. Getting late now. Old Marjorie will have some tucker. Turn in as soon as you've had it. I got a few things to see to, having been out all day."

He jumped down and threw the reins over the picket fence outside the house. Martin scrambled down, too. He still couldn't believe that they were really back at Tangari.

"I'm sorry for being such a fool, Bill," he said, with a bit of a lump in his throat.

"Forget it," Bill said, giving his shoulder a heavy thump. "I'm only glad you were so sensible. Dad wouldn't half have given me a tanning if he'd come back and found the crows picking your bones back in them there hills."

Travel

The railroad track is miles away,
   And the day is loud with voices speaking,
Yet there isn't a train goes by all day
   But I hear its whistle shrieking.

All night there isn't a train goes by,
   Though the night is still for sleep and dreaming
But I see its cinders red on the sky,
   And hear its engine steaming.

My heart is warm with the friends I make,
   And better friends I'll not be knowing,
Yet there isn't a train I wouldn't take,
   No matter where it's going.

—*Edna St. Vincent Millay*

'Gator Hunt

Robb White

Nick and his sister Penny were sailing with Ben on Ben's sailboat, the Lion's Paw. *The boat was taking the inland water way through Florida's lakes and swamps. One morning, Ben had to go ashore to do some errands. Nick, who knew almost nothing about alligators but hankered to capture one, saw his chance.*

As Ben started out, Nick put on an innocent expression. "Ben, can I go rowing in the dinghy while you're gone? I want to practice."

"Go ahead," Ben said.

Nick rowed Ben over to the bank and then went back to the *Lion's Paw*. He rowed innocently around as long as Penny was on deck. As soon as she went below, he changed course and started purposefully up the creek. In the bottom of the dinghy he had stowed a boat hook. Concealed in his pocket, he had a length of rope with which to make a noose. Nick had a very determined look in his eye.

Soon the winding creek hid him from the sloop. The water was shallow enough so that he could stand up in the stern and pole the boat along with the boat hook. As Ben had done on their first try, he went very slowly and silently and kept watching for alligators.

In a little while, he saw one lying in the mud of the bank. Nick almost turned right around and went back. The 'gator was ten feet long. As he went past, it turned its head and looked at him with clear, pale yellow eyes. It opened its jaws wide, and Nick could see the rows of long teeth and the white, flabby-looking inside of its mouth.

Farther on, he saw another one. But it was big, too. As soon as he got close, it waddled slowly down across the muddy bank and slid into the water. For a little while, he could see where it was going by the hump it made in the water. and the trail of mud. Finally, it disappeared altogether.

He saw three more, but they all slid off into the water before he could get near them. At last, he was so far up the little creek that there was hardly room enough for the dinghy to move. When it finally stopped, stuck in the mud, Nick stood for a moment half disappointed and half relieved. He had to admit that he was a little afraid of the alligators, especially hunting them this way all by himself. Maybe he ought to get Penny to help him.

Nick pushed the dinghy out of the mud and turned it around. As he started to go back, he saw, in the mud of the bank, some tracks. They weren't like the others he had seen, which had big sloppy footprints on each side of a' wavy slick line where the alligator's tail dragged.

These were little. The footprints were clear where the
toes dug into the mud. The line the tail made between
them was just a slick place on the mud. The footprints
went away from the creek.

Looking around to be sure that there were no big ones
watching him, Nick pushed the bow of the dinghy into
the mudbank and climbed out. He sank into mud almost
to his knees. But, as he followed the little claw marks, the
mud got better—down to his ankles. He lost the little
track in some leaves. Then he found it again. In one
place, the alligator had just wandered around. Then it
had started on.

Nick followed the tracks until they led him to a
little pool of water left by the rain. As he came toward it,
he at last saw the alligator. It slid down into the water.
It was about eight inches long. Its scales, unlike those of
the big ones, were clean and yellow with blackish spots
on them.

Nick slogged his way to the edge of the pool and looked
down into the inch-deep water. The alligator had made
a curving line of mud out to the middle of the pool.
There it ended, in a little cloud of muddy water.

Around him, the woods were silent. Far away, in a
circle, Nick could hear things—bugs and birds and a

squirrel. Right where he was, there wasn't a sound and nothing moved — not even the little green leaves at the tops of the trees.

Going very slowly and trying his best not to muddy the water, Nick waded out into the little pool. He stopped a foot or so from the last trace of the alligator and waited, standing perfectly still, until the mud had settled like wet brown dust to the bottom.

Looking down through the clear water now, he could see where the little alligator had gone under the mud. It had made an outline of its body in the smooth mud. He could see where its head was, and there was a thin line marking the tail.

Very carefully Nick reached down, his fingers open and ready to grab. As his fingers touched the mud, he suddenly shoved down hard.

He had it. Through the oozing mud he felt the rounded body thrashing back and forth. Jerking his hand out, he held the muddy alligator up. Its little feet on the short legs clawed uselessly at his hand. Its little mouth opened and snapped shut as fast as it could, the yellow eyes blazing at him. Nick was surprised by the grunting noise the little 'gator made.

Holding the 'gator tightly, Nick washed him off in the pool. Then, feeling jubilant, he began slogging his way back to the dinghy. The alligator kept on grunting.

'Gator to the Rescue

He had almost reached the boat and was floundering in mud up to his knees when he heard the noise behind him. It was a loud, abrupt, hissing sound. He twisted around to see what it was.

Coming toward him through the mud, its pale yellow eyes fixed on him, was an enormous alligator, hissing through the two little nostrils on the end of its bony snout!

For a second, Nick stood in the mud, petrified with fear. Then, with all his strength, he plowed toward the dinghy, his legs fighting the clawing mud, his hands and arms waving around to keep him from falling off balance. Once he looked back over his shoulder. The alligator was moving much faster than he was.

When Nick half fell over into the dinghy, the 'gator was only a few feet away. Dropping the little alligator, Nick grabbed an oar, shoved the dinghy's bow out of the mud, and swung it downstream. As the big 'gator came hissing down the bank and into the water, Nick grabbed the other oar and fitted both of them into the oarlocks. For a moment, the alligator disappeared in the muddy water. As Nick began to row, he thought that it had gone. Bracing his feet, he threw all his weight against the oars. The dinghy began to slide away.

Then, behind the dinghy, Nick saw the moving hump of water. At first it was just rounded and smooth, but then it began to stretch out, getting thinner and thinner. Suddenly the 'gator's long head and scaly back broke through the surface. The knobs where the eyes were made two long ripples, and its beating tail sent waves of muddy water against the bank.

Nick rowed harder. His breath was dry as dust in his throat. He could hear it rasping back and forth as he tried to breathe. His arms and legs began to feel like bagfuls of water, with no strength in them. The pumping

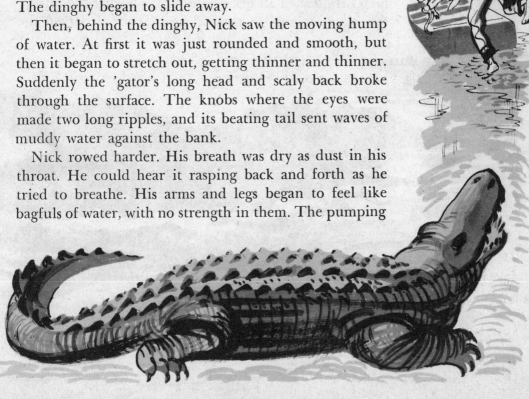

of his heart felt as though it would break through his ribs.

With easy, powerful strokes of its tail, the 'gator gained on him fast, the little eyes sliding toward him and watching him.

Nick stopped rowing and grabbed the boat hook. It was of white oak, with a handle about six feet long. It had a spike ending in a little ball, and a curved brass hook. Crouching in the stern of the boat, Nick clubbed the boat hook and waited.

The alligator came straight at him, the little eyes evil and steady, the tail making a swishing noise in the water. With all his strength, Nick brought the boat hook down on the snout. The brass fitting banged the hump where the nostrils opened, making the pole shiver in Nick's hands.

The 'gator disappeared in a mass of foam and mud. It seemed to hump up in the middle and thrash with its whole body. Nick reached for the bottom with the boat hook. He leaned all his weight on it, shoving the dinghy fast downstream. He reached again, shoved, jerked the

end out of the clinging mud, and shoved again, the water getting deeper and deeper, the dinghy going in sudden leaps and gliding stops.

The alligator appeared suddenly right astern. It came whooshing up through the muddy water. As it broke the surface, it opened its jaws and came for the dinghy.

To Nick, it seemed that everything stopped moving except the rushing jaws of the 'gator. The creek, the woods, the sky were silent. The sunlight made everything crystal-clear. He saw muddy water in the bottom of the dinghy. He saw his little alligator lying motionless but still grunting. He saw a turtle, its shell glossy, sitting on a log.

He saw the teeth of the alligator's upper jaw and saw a silver drop of water fall from one of them. The inside of the thing's mouth was soft-looking and dead white and wet. It hung in smooth folds from the top jaw, sagged in the bottom of the mouth. Back where the throat was, the

white, folding flesh looked as though it were puckered up a little, closing the throat.

The gaping jaws seemed to grow bigger and bigger as they swam straight toward him. For long seconds, Nick squatted perfectly still in the dinghy as the jaws slid swiftly toward him. He couldn't breathe. He couldn't move a muscle.

Out of Death's Jaws

Then everything broke apart like an explosion. In the woods, jay birds began suddenly to screech. The turtle slid with a splash off the log. The little alligator scurried up the side of the dinghy and fell back on the oar. Nick lunged forward with the boat hook. He watched the brass fitting, bright in the sunlight, go in between the two jaws, go on until it disappeared into the puckered folds of the white flesh back where the throat was.

The top jaw came down with a crash which tore the boat hook out of Nick's hands. The creature whirled it around, banging it against the dinghy. Again and again and again the jaws opened and crashed shut, sending showers of water away from the head. Then three feet of the handle of the boat hook floated away on the wild water. The alligator began to whirl over and over, its great tail rising from the water and beating down again, thrashing the stream into a froth of mud and water.

Hanging on with both hands to the wildly pitching dinghy, Nick got back to the thwart, shoved the oars out, and began to row. Sweat and muddy water streamed into his eyes. He rammed the boat against the bank, backed it off, and went ahead again. He was half blind, but he could still hear the thrashing of the alligator.

Missing a stroke, Nick clawed the sweat and water out of his eyes and looked up the creek. The beast was still whirling around and around, the little legs clawing the empty air. He could hear the squashy snapping of the jaws as they opened and shut.

When he was fifty feet from the *Lion's Paw*, Nick began to yell for Penny. He kept on yelling even after he had heard Penny answering him.

Then, when the dinghy bumped into the side of the sloop, Nick collapsed. He turned loose the oars, and one of them slid out of the oarlock and floated away.

"Nick, what's the matter? What's the matter?" Penny asked. Her voice was full of fear as she leaned over the side of the sloop.

"Alligator—got—me," Nick said, gasping for breath. "Big—jaws—bite—chased—me—boat—hook right in two."

"What? What?" Penny asked.

Nick took a deep breath and looked up into the frightened face of his sister. "I said a 'gator got me," he said.

"How? Where?" Penny asked, her voice rising.

Nick tried to stand up. But his knees had gone, and he sat down again with a wet thump. "The boat hook's gone," he said in a low voice. "He bit it right in two."

"Nick," Penny said sternly, "get out of that boat and come up here."

"I can't," Nick said. "I haven't got any knees."

"Are you crazy? What happened?"

"An alligator tried to eat the dinghy," Nick said. "While I was in it."

"Oh, Nick!" Penny said. "You ought to have your mouth washed out with soap."

"He bit the boat hook right in two. He's back there now, going around and around."

"Really?" Penny said, her voice low.

"He was huge," Nick said. "He was as long as the *Lion's Paw*, and his mouth was white inside."

"Is he coming?"

Nick shook his head. "I fixed him. I put the boat hook all the way down his throat."

"Nick, *please* get out of that boat and tell me what happened."

"All right." Nick got back the floating oar. Then, as he was about to climb out, he remembered the little alligator. It had disappeared. He began frantically searching for it in the bilge water and under the oars.

"What's the matter now?" Penny asked.

"I've lost my alligator."

Penny straightened up and looked down into the dinghy. "Nick, what's the matter with you?" she asked slowly.

Then Nick found the little alligator far up in the bow. When he got it by the tail, it whipped around and tried to bite him. He grabbed it with his other hand and held it up.

"See?" he said.

Penny looked at the little alligator in amazement. "You really did," she said slowly.

After Penny and Nick had got the dinghy cleaned out, the alligator in a basin with some water in it, and Nick had removed some of the mud, the story about the alligator had been told five times. And when Ben came back in the afternoon, it had to be told two or three times more. Finally, all three of them went back up the creek to see where it had happened.

Nick, who was afraid that maybe they didn't believe all of it, was happier after they found the end of the boat hook, the oak handle chewed through.

They found nothing else.

Two Chests of Treasure

Merritt P. Allen

Twilight was on the Caribbean. So magically did it blend all things that no one could mark the spot where sea and sky met. Sky and sea—they seemed to make up the whole world except one tiny speck of land that lay like a grain of sand on the rounded face of the ocean. There was no life on the island other than insects, unless a migrating bird chanced to rest there for an hour, or a turtle crawled up the rocks to bask in the sand. To find a man in such a place would have been startling. To find a boy there, alone, was amazing. Yet a boy was sleeping on the sand—a lad perhaps sixteen years old, curled up in the shadow of the rocks.

He slept as the evening deepened. Then at a sound he sat up suddenly, as one does who has been on the alert for days and nights together. He had a worn look, and his blue eyes were weary. His hair, worn in a short queue, was unkempt. His linen shirt, velvet breeches, silk hose, and silver-buckled shoes were stained with salt water and wrinkled.

Again came the sound, the crackling of a sail in the wind. He leaped to his feet and ran to the edge of the rocks. Yes, there was a ship—an English ship, by the build of her—standing off the island in the gloom. A weakness seized the boy, so that before he could hail the stranger he must lean against the rocks, giddy with joy. And then,

Courtesy of the author and BOYS' LIFE, published by the Boy Scouts of America.

as he filled his lungs to shout, he suddenly caught his breath and remained silent.

What he saw was a small boat on the beach. At the moment, two men were coming ashore from it, each carrying a heavy chest on his shoulder and a spade in his hand. Behind them walked a man bearing a ship's lantern. Its light played on the brass bindings of the chests. A pirate captain come to bury his treasure! Even in the year 1680, such a sight was enough to strike any boy dumb.

The three men came up the slope silently. They reached the top and descended into the little valley in the center of the island.

"Here!" The captain indicated a spot on the sand. "Sink a hole half a fathom and be quick, ye dogs."

The men put down the chests. As if driven by fear,
they fell to work with the spades. The captain set his
lantern on the ground as he watched. By its light, the
boy saw that he was short and powerfully built, with the
dress of a sailor except for a plumed hat which shaded his
face. He stood with his feet wide apart as though standing
on a deck, and when he folded his arms across his chest,
there was a pistol in each hand. The boy watched, spell-
bound.

"Lay off!" the captain snapped.

The men dropped their spades.

"Heave 'em in."

The men placed the chests in the hole.

"Bury 'em."

The two took up the spades again, the lantern-light
flickering on their naked, sweating backs. The captain
watched them silently as the dry sand whispered and slid
back into the hole. The boy was thinking feverishly. He
must make himself known, but to reveal himself as a witness of the planting of the treasure would be certain
death. Better to wait until the men were re-embarking,
and then shout as though just sighting them. After that,
events must guide him as they appeared.

This thought was shattered in a moment. The hole
was full. As the men stooped to smooth the sand above
it, the captain stepped close behind them. Fire leaped
from both of his hands at once, and the two slumped
upon the sand. Pocketing his pistols and picking up the
lantern, their master left them where they fell.

Shivering with horror, the boy watched the captain
climb the slope. On the crest, he stopped in his tracks.
A stream of curses rolled from his lips; he swung the

lantern around his head as if he were a madman.
Looking past him, the boy saw the cause. The ship that
had been standing by was now bearing away to sea, under
full sail! The captain dropped his lantern and went in
great leaps toward the beach. There he halted. The small
boat was gone.

"Ahoy, sir!" the boy shouted. There was now a bond
between himself and the man that made him throw away
caution.

"Who's that?" The captain wheeled and drew his
pistols.

"Don't shoot. I'm a castaway like yourself. I have a
boat. Shall we follow them?"

"A boat?"

"A small open craft with a sail."

"A fine match for my ship! The scoundrels have foxed
me, but I've not struck my flag yet. Who are ye, lad?" he
asked, walking slowly back from the water.

The boy picked up the lighted lantern and went to
meet him, boldly. "I'm Roger Wilkes from Port Royal,"
he said.

"What are ye doing on this beast's thumb o' rock?"

"Shipwrecked and drifting eight days in a boat. I
landed here at midday to feel the earth again."

"Alone?"

"Yes, sir. When our ship foundered we were making
ready the boats. We were too late and all went down
with her. When I came up I saw a boat floating and
climbed into it, but I never sighted one of our crew."

"Your boat was provisioned?"

"Partly. There is still some water and boucan left. And
the mate had put his navigating instruments aboard.

I don't know how to use them, but perhaps you might."

"Aye, I'm a navigator." The captain's small eyes glinted uneasily in the lantern light. "Show me the craft."

"She lies the other side of the island," Roger said, and led the way.

A Pirate's Way

The captain inspected the little boat with a glance that saw everything.

"Seaworthy if handled right," he muttered. "These instruments are good. I could circle the world with 'em."

"Then we can get away from here," Roger cried. "It is lucky for both of us."

"This all the water aboard?" The captain kicked a cask.

"Yes. And there is not a drop on the island. Are we far from fresh water?"

"No," said the captain, for he knew it was hundreds of leagues.

"Let's start now. This is a—a horrible place."

"Easy, lad. We'll give the ship leeway. If they sighted us at daylight they'd send us to the bottom to be rid o' me."

"They mutinied against you, sir?"

"The jellyfish lack the sand to mutiny." The captain
sat down on the cask and removed his hat, revealing an
egg-shaped skull set on a thick neck. "I reckon ye see'd
what happened here tonight," he added.

"I did," Roger answered evenly. "But circumstances
have made us shipmates and closed my mouth."

"Spoke like a gentleman! I reckon ye *be* a gentleman,"
the captain said. He was becoming more friendly all the
while. His tone was now that of a fisherman who wanted
to swap yarns for an idle hour. And Roger, who had been
alone on the ocean staring death in the eye for days,
found relief in talking.

"My father was captain of a ship running between Port
Royal and London," he explained. "She was a mail ship,
the *Rose of Jamaica*."

"That was her that went down with ye aboard?" The
captain replaced his hat so that its shadow masked his
face.

"Oh, no. I was on another one bound to trade with the Dutch at Darien. My father's ship has been missing a year past."

"Missing, ye say?"

"Strangely missing. She was a stout craft with a full crew, there were no great storms at the time, and no acts of warfare that we know of."

"Queer things happen at sea, lad."

"But I'll not believe what some say happened," Roger cried passionately.

"To the *Rose of Jamaica?*" The captain waited expectantly.

"Yes, sir. You see, she carried secret messages from the governor of Jamaica to the King about the Spaniards in Hispaniola. It's being whispered that she went over to the Dons and sold the papers for gold."

"They accuse your father of treason, eh?"

"No! Not him nor his officers. But they say the crew was bought in port and mutinied on the sea. It's a disgrace to a captain to be unable to handle his crew. My father's name is not as fair as it was. You know what gossip will do. I would give my life to clear my father's reputation."

The captain's teeth flashed in the starlight. "So it's a disgrace, eh, to let the crew get the upper hand?"

Roger went cold at his own clumsiness, but he would not retreat. "I've said it and I'll not deny it," he answered.

"Yours is a bold tongue, cockerel, and a bold heart, too. For that, I'll tell ye something. Shamed I may be for being left here like a puppy, but the joke is on the crew. For weeks past they've been a-muttering and I know'd

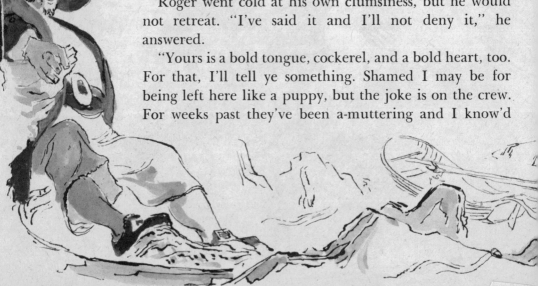

they was smelling the treasure in my cabin. My own treasure it was, too, my fair share of the purchases we'd made."

"And they wanted it?"

"Aye. They'd wasted their own and hankered for mine. So I hid it under my cabin floor, square in front o' the door where they don't expect it to be. I was a ship's carpenter once and I did the job myself. Then I filled them two chests with sand from the ballast and come ashore here to bury my treasure. 'Twas necessary to finish the two yonder to put the stamp o' truth on the business. Aye, lad, them chests yonder is full o' sand from the beach o' Tortuga." He threw back his head and laughed.

"But you have lost your treasure," Roger pointed out.

"I'll find it again. I'll find my ship, for I know this old Spanish Main as a merchant knows his pocket."

"You've no doubt we can escape from a place like this?"

"Didn't I say I could sail this craft round the world?"

"Then let's be going. The wind is favorable. Your ship will be far out of sight by morning and we'll be safe from it."

For a full minute the captain gazed at the stars, which blazed like diamonds on a velvet cloak. Then, "We'll waste no more time," he said. "Is all aboard?"

"Everything," Roger answered eagerly.

By the light of the lantern, the captain examined the oars, the sail—everything.

"She floats here?"

"Yes, sir. She's moored to that rock."

"Cast off and shove her out. I'll steer with an oar past the point."

Roger waded in, pushing the boat, until the water lapped as high as his armpits. Then he started to climb aboard.

"Stand off!" The captain's voice cut like a knife.

The boy looked past the lantern, which was on a seat, and saw a pistol pointed at his head.

"What are you doing?" His voice was high-pitched with fear.

"It's me or you," the captain said, unmoved. "And having the upper hand, it's me that gets away."

"You're going to leave me here!"

"Aye. There's water enough for only one. I'll leave ye here or shoot ye where ye stand. 'Twill help none to whimper."

"I'm not whimpering!" The boy's eyes blazed. "I'll not whimper for a coward like you."

"Lad," the captain said in a voice that was a bit less hard, "I've fancied the spirit o'ye from the start. I'd take ye if I could, but 'twould be death for the both o'us."

"I gave you all I had. I trusted you—you pirate!"

"I don't deny it, but I'm a man as wants to live. Ye may be took off."

"You know a ship never comes near this island. I'll die of thirst."

"Likely enough. But I'll give ye a crumb o'comfort. 'Twas I as sunk the *Rose of Jamaica*."

"You murdered my father!"

"He died fighting like a man."

"Thank you for that—if it is true."

"'Tis true. We needed supplies, so when we sighted a ship we ran up distress signals. When she hove to we boarded her."

"You brute! And now you taunt me with it."

The Price of a Boat

"Listen, lad. I took the captain's papers, for they might be handy in a pinch. Many a time I've saved my skin by knowing what was in a ship's papers. Among these was the secret dispatches ye spoke of. They meant nothing to me but I kept 'em, for it's things like that as saves a man's neck sometimes. They're in my cabin now and when I regain my ship—and I *will* regain her!—I'll send them papers to the governor o' Jamaica with a word that'll take the blot from yer father's name. That'll be the price o' this boat I'm taking from ye. Now, will ye take a bullet or will ye go ashore?"

Roger went ashore, for human nature fights for life to the last. Slowly the captain rowed away from land.

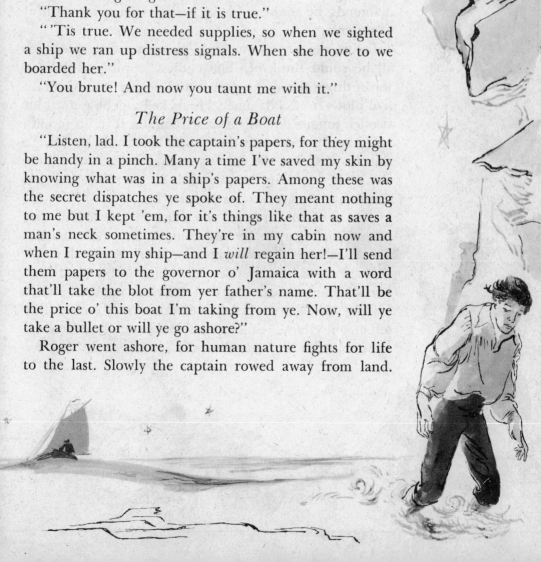

Then he raised the sail and disappeared in the darkness.

There was nothing to do. That was one of the terrible things about the situation. There was nothing to do but watch the horizon and wait. And in that out-of-the-way part of the ocean, there was nothing to wait for but death. When daylight came, Roger buried the two men. Poor wretches, he thought, but he knew that before it was finished, he would envy them the merciful suddenness of their going.

Toward night, in order to occupy his mind, he dug up the chests and found that truly they were full of sand. There was no disappointment in that. If they had held diamonds, he could not have bartered them for a tinful of water.

Before the second morning, his tormenting thirst was all he could think of. The endless lapping of the salt waves drove the agony deeper and deeper into his brain like blows from a hammer. He sucked a pebble until his swollen tongue no longer made room for it in his mouth. He prayed for a storm that might bring rain or drive a ship his way. But the sky was serene, and he knew there would be no rain for months. So overpowering was thirst that hunger was forgotten.

And gradually, toward the close of the fourth day, everything began to be forgotten. As in a daze, he had drunk sea water, knowing and not caring that such an act was the signal of surrender. Crawling on his hands and knees, fainting, reviving, and crawling on, he reached his lookout on the rocks. It was sunset, and, raising himself on one elbow, he took a final look around the horizon. It was action without thought, for his brain was too

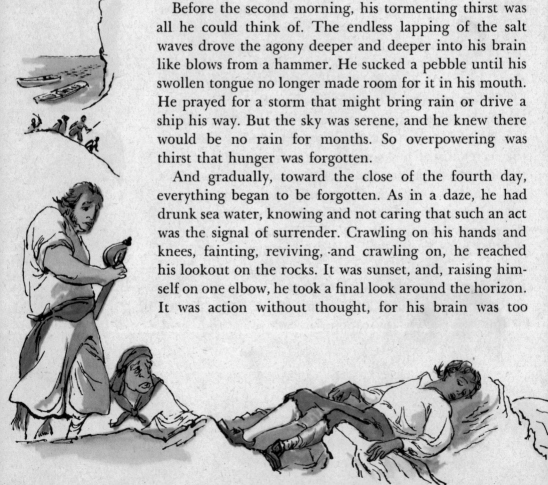

weak to tell him what his eyes saw. Whether that was a sail or a seabird in the southwest made no difference to him.

While he lay there, still breathing, the ship bore in and anchored off the island in the darkness. She knew the place well. She had left her commander there four days before, and was now returning for his treasure, which the crew had not dared to fight for then. By now, even if he were alive, the captain would be too weak to resist.

At dawn, they saw the form lying on the rocks and came ashore, jeering at the Old Man they had outwitted.

"Saint's blood!" cried the one who reached him first. "This is a lad!"

"The fiend's work!" another gasped. "The Old Man has changed his form!"

"Fools! He's some castaway," the mate said.

"Then where's the Old Man?"

"Search the island."

"We can see it all from here and he's not on it."

"I tell ye, he's changed hisself into a bird and flew away."

"There's the treasure chests!" They rushed upon them.

"Full o' sand!" They formed a ring and stared.

"He's changed the gold to sand," persisted the one who believed in miracles.

"The castaway done it. He's dug up the gold."

"But where's the Old Man?"

"Got away somehow."

"Then 'e took the gold. I knows 'im."

"I tell ye, it's the fiend's work. Git back to the ship."

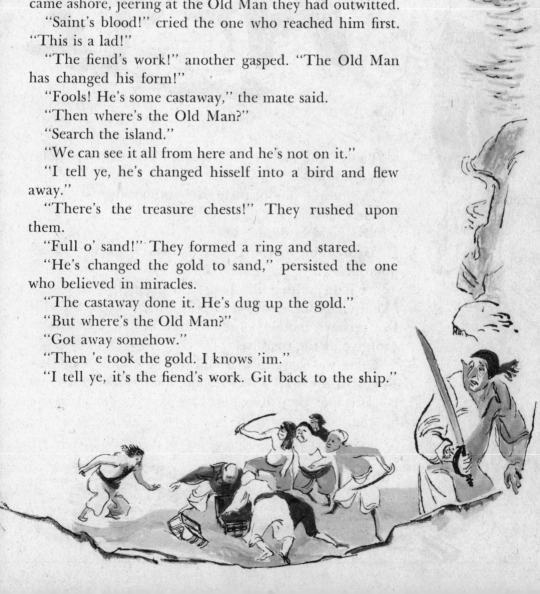

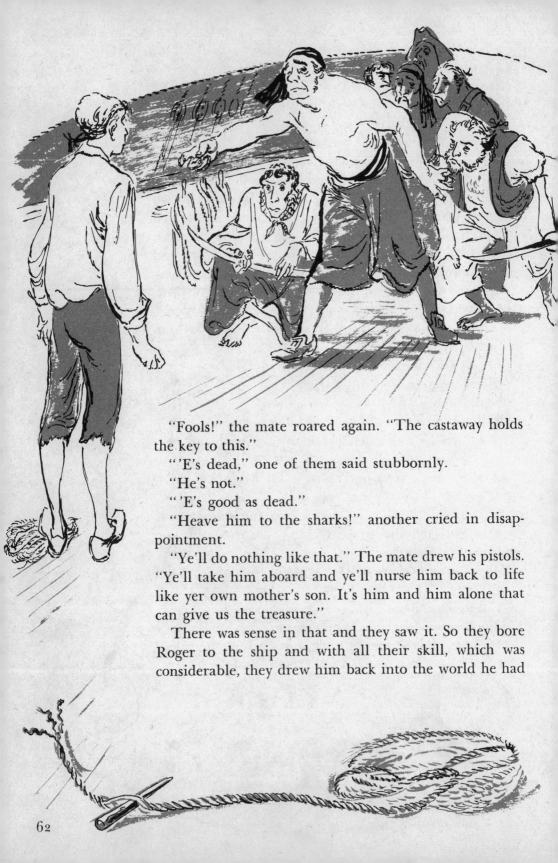

"Fools!" the mate roared again. "The castaway holds the key to this."

"'E's dead," one of them said stubbornly.

"He's not."

"'E's good as dead."

"Heave him to the sharks!" another cried in disappointment.

"Ye'll do nothing like that." The mate drew his pistols. "Ye'll take him aboard and ye'll nurse him back to life like yer own mother's son. It's him and him alone that can give us the treasure."

There was sense in that and they saw it. So they bore Roger to the ship and with all their skill, which was considerable, they drew him back into the world he had so nearly left. And when he was finally in the land of the living once more, with the deck of the old pirate craft rolling under his feet, he said wearily to the mate, "It was all done for treasure! The thought sickens me."

"But where is the treasure?" the mate asked, and the pirates pressed close for the answer.

"I know where it is." Roger felt a thrill at the power he had over them.

"We'll give ye a share," the mate promised.

"You will not." The boy shuddered. "It's blood money a thousand times over."

"Ye'd best tell us where it is." A threatening buzz arose.

"I'll bargain with you first. In the captain's cabin on this ship are papers taken from the *Rose of Jamaica*. When you set me ashore in Jamaica with those papers in my possession, I will tell you where the treasure is. I give you my word that every penny of it shall be yours. Kill me here and you will lose it all." He looked into the fierce eyes about him.

He had the cards, and his hand could not be forced. There were curses and threats, but eventually on a dark night he was rowed ashore at a point where the hills of Jamaica meet the sea. There he completed his story to the mate and told where the treasure lay under the cabin floor. Then he turned and ran toward the town, where the lights of home twinkled peacefully.

The Song of the Pirate King

Oh, better far to live and die
Under the brave black flag I fly,
Than play a sanctimonious part,
With a pirate head and a pirate heart.
Away to the cheating world go you,
Where pirates all are well-to-do;
But I'll be true to the song I sing,
And live and die a Pirate King.
  For I am a Pirate King,
    And it is, it is a glorious thing
    To be a Pirate King.

When I sally forth to seek my prey
I help myself in a royal way:
I sink a few more ships, it's true,
Than a well-bred monarch ought to do;
But many a king on a first-class throne,
If he wants to call his crown his own,
Must manage somehow to get through
More dirty work than ever *I* do,
  Though I am a Pirate King.
    And it is, it is a glorious thing
    To be a Pirate King!

—W. S. Gilbert

Tales Tall and Small

A tale so tall it tops the wall
    And climbs into the sky!
A taller one you cannot tell
    No matter how you try.

A tale so small you hold it all
    A trinket in your hand;
And yet its wisdom may be more
    Than you can understand.

                    —*Dorothy Hall*

Nail Soup

Retold by Christine M. Kowalski

When we were children, my grandfather often told us the story of the gypsy who claimed he could make soup from a nail—just a common ordinary nail. This is how the story went:

In the town where Grandfather lived, there was a market place. Here the peasants gathered to display the products of their own small farms. Tall, serious young farmers came with their talkative wives. Bright red, green, and yellow kerchiefs were everywhere. Tongues wagged while busy fingers pinched and tested before buying.

One market day, a lone gypsy settled himself in the center of the market place with a bundle of fagots and a large black bag. Untying the fagots, he laid them carefully on the ground and proceeded to light a fire. A few people stopped to watch, curious to see what was going on. Unconcerned, the gypsy pulled a blackened kettle from the bag, walked over to the town pump, and filled it half way. He set the kettle up over the fire.

"These fellows are getting bolder right along. Here's one cooking his dinner under our noses," said a farmer, as he and his wife pushed through the bystanders to have a look.

Just then, the gypsy reached into the lining of his coat and pulled out a white cloth packet, which he unwrapped with exceeding care. In the center lay a

nail. He held it up in the pale sunlight, squinting as he studied it, then rubbed hard at a spot, polishing it as though it were a precious jewel. The nail was ceremoniously dropped into the pot, where it clanked as it hit bottom. Then he took a battered spoon and stirred the water, a pleased smile on his face. Mystified, those who had been watching the strange performance moved closer. The gypsy leaned forward and tasted the brew. Then he smacked his lips.

"Say, old man, what are you cooking? There's nothing in that pot but a nail."

The gypsy looked at his questioner sympathetically. "This is a rare soup," he explained. "One I picked up in my travels. Wait until you have tasted it. There's nothing like soup from a nail," and he sighed happily. "It needs a little salt." Reaching into a pocket, he brought forth two small round boxes, one red, one black. "A pinch of this, and two of these peppercorns will bring out the flavor." He stirred again.

People looked at each other blankly. Either he was simple or up to some trickery, they whispered among themselves. The gypsy stirred again and tasted.

"If only I had a tiny onion." At the wistfulness in his voice, a young girl shyly held forth a bunch of small green onions. "Thank you, my dear," and he sliced several into the pot, returning the rest with a bow. His eyes wandered from one shopping basket to another, lighting on a bunch of bright green herbs. "Just a bit of that parsley would bring out the flavor. Of course, it isn't really necessary."

The good wife stepped forward and begged him to

take it, saying she could never bear soup without a bit of parsley. He thanked her also.

"I still don't see how he can do it," said another, leaning from her stall.

At this point the gypsy rose, stretched, and wandered around a bit from stall to stall, stopping at last before the doubter. "My, what beautiful large potatoes, and so free from spots! Can't tell if they are sound inside, though."

Heads turned to watch this little byplay.

"How dare you!" She grabbed a knife and cut open one potato after another. "See! How white and firm!" She pushed three or four cut potatoes into his hands. "Now are you convinced?"

"Thank you, madam. I am." And he bowed. He looked down thoughtfully at the cut pieces in his brown hands.

"Such perfect potatoes would make this not only a good soup but a superb soup."

"You couldn't find better," she said with satisfaction.

"Again you are right, madam." He edged his way back through the crowd to the fire. Several were sniffing the delicious aroma. The curious were peering into the pot.

There was muttering and unrest in the other stalls. "My vegetables are just as good as hers," sniffed a tall, thin woman. Armed with a bunch of carrots, she pushed her way through the crowd and made the gypsy accept them.

People were beginning to look a bit amused as a turnip was offered next, then a head of cabbage, a handful of peas, and so on. Anything more than he needed at the moment, the old gypsy stuffed into his bag. No one wanted to be left out. The aroma became more and more tantalizing.

Suddenly the church bells struck noon, and the villagers departed for their homes, leaving the gypsy to enjoy his well-earned meal. The last to go saw him fish out the nail, polish it up carefully, and, giving it a queer little salute, wrap it safely away again in the white cloth before he began to eat.

Pecos Bill and the Cyclone

A Tall Tale of the Southwest

Pecos Bill? Why, he was the rootingest, tootingest human being ever to come out of the State of Texas—if Bill *was* a human being, that is. Up to the time he was a man grown, he thought he was a full-blooded coyote.

It happened this way. When Bill was just a toddler, his family was migrating westward in a covered wagon through Texas. The wagon struck a bump, and little Bill went sailing through the air. When he came down, he was sitting in the middle of the trail, watching the wagon drive on, too surprised to cry. There were so many young ones in the wagon that his parents never knew Bill was missing until they happened to count the children a week later. Then it was too late to go back.

But Bill didn't fare so badly. Before he could get his mouth open to yell, back there in the trail, an old coyote came trotting up to him. Pretty soon the two of them made friends, and Bill grew up as a full member of the coyote pack. They were plenty smart, those coyotes, and Bill learned a lot from them that came in handy later.

Perhaps their greatest kindness, however, was keeping Bill from knowing he was a human being. When the time finally came that he had to find this out, it almost broke his heart.

However, there's no use crying over spilt milk. Since he was a man, Pecos Bill made up his mind to be a good one. So he became a cowpuncher at the IXL Ranch. And right away, he discovered that the cowpunching then being done in the State of Texas was hopelessly old-fashioned. It needed to be brought up to date.

Bill started out by inventing the lariat, to rope cattle, and teaching the cowboys how to use it. Used to be, the boys just put a noose down on the ground and waited for the critter to wander into it. When he had taught the cowboys how to throw a rope, Bill went on to invent cattle-brands and herding cattle and roundups. He finished by inventing rodeos, to give the cowboys some fun, and taught broncos how to buck.

Naturally, Bill became a very good rider. Not only could he ride any horse of the plains, including the famous horse Pegasus, later called Widow Maker; he also rode the Wouser, which is a cross between the mountain lion and the grizzly bear, and ten times larger than either one. But Pecos Bill's most famous ride was his ride on the cyclone.

Busting a Cyclone

Bill and his outfit had been having quite a little trouble with a drought on the plains. Things got so bad that every morning before breakfast, Bill had to go out and lasso a ten-mile stretch of the Rio Grande River and drag it to the ranch, just to keep things going.

The drought brought on a prairie fire, as everyone expected. And the prairie fire just sort of naturally brought on a cyclone.

Now Texas cyclones, as everybody knows, are the worst cyclones in the world; and this particular cyclone was probably the worst that Texas ever produced. The sky, a copper-colored gray from the smoke of the prairie fire, turned a blackish purple-green. The cattle stamped and snorted, and threatened to break into a stampede. Bill and his outfit had their hands full, breaking up the herd and keeping the critters moving to take their minds off the weather.

Then the men began to hear strange noises. And there was a great black funnel bearing down on them like an express train and purring like ten million wildcats! The cowboys tried to move the cattle to one side and get out of the cyclone's way. But that storm had its dander up. They could see it was out to get them and no mistake.

"Good night!" moaned Gun Smith, as pale as paper. "This is the granddaddy of all Texas twisters."

"It's all up with us for sure," said Mushmouth. "Look at the critter's eyes."

Then the boys heard a wild "Ee-yow!" and there was Pecos Bill on Widow Maker, riding straight at that black funnel and twirling his rope.

"Stop!" yelled Gun Smith, whipping off his hat and holding it in front of his eyes. He couldn't bear to see the end of Pecos Bill.

But Pecos Bill didn't stop. On he rode. Then at the last minute he let his rope fly out.

"Jumpin' catfish!" yelled Mushmouth. "He's ropin' that cyclone!"

The next moment, Bill was jerked high into the inky blackness and was gone. The horse Widow Maker dodged just in time. Even so, the storm scraped the saddle right off his back and got about an inch of his tail.

Then the cyclone was gone, too. The men saw it give a buck, like an outlaw horse. The next moment, it had disappeared.

"Did you see the way that twister tore out!" Gun Smith exclaimed. "Must of been when it felt Pecos Bill's rope tighten on its neck."

"Well, that's the end of that buckaroo," snarled Moon Hennessy. "This time, he tackled just one thing too many."

"Anybody can ride Widow Maker can ride anything," Gun Smith argued. "And I have a dime that says so."

"Make it two bits if you're so sure," Hennessy sneered. "I tell you, we'll never set eyes on Pecos Bill again."

A Wild Ride

In the meantime, Bill was having troubles of his own, sticking on the back of that crazy twister. It was still in a panic, stampeding from the first bite of the rope, and was sunfishing, skyscraping, and high-flying in handsome style. Holding his bowie knife between his teeth and a twenty-dollar gold piece in his hand, Bill waited for the twister to buck itself out.

But that storm was a deep one. When it saw it couldn't buck Bill off, it made up its mind to scare him to death. Reaching down, it pulled up half a dozen mountains by the roots and started throwing them at Pecos' head.

Bill ducked. He ducked so fast he made the cyclone dizzy, and it couldn't see where he was. Then the storm

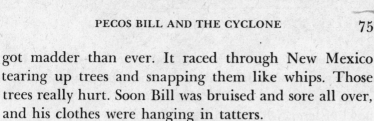

got madder than ever. It raced through New Mexico tearing up trees and snapping them like whips. Those trees really hurt. Soon Bill was bruised and sore all over, and his clothes were hanging in tatters.

When the storm hit Arizona, it cut a great gully through some of the dry mountains there. Now, besides the trees and mountains already whirling around inside the cyclone, the air was full of dust. Bill began to think he couldn't hold out much longer.

Apparently the storm was thinking the same thing. Just then it had its last bright idea. Since it couldn't get rid of Bill any other way, it would rain right out from under him!

Well, it started raining, in buckets, torrents, and waterspouts; and Bill, he saw he'd better be looking for someplace to jump. The rain had already filled the gully in the Arizona mountains and turned it into the Grand Canyon, and the clouds were getting mighty slippery and thin. So Pecos spotted what looked like a soft bed of sand, ahead and to the left, and he gave a tremendous heave, and over he went.

He fell for several hours, and when he hit he lost consciousness and didn't come to until the next morning. Then he saw he was in the bottom of a tremendous bowl of sand, which had been dug out by his fall. Down at the bottom were perfect prints of his hip bones, stamped in bed rock. Although he didn't realize it until later, Pecos Bill had just made Death Valley, the lowest point in the whole U. S. A.

Then Bill remembered something, and opened his hand. At first, he couldn't believe his eyes. That cyclone had blown his twenty-dollar gold piece into two half dollars and a plugged nickel! Quickly he opened his jaws. The bowie knife dropped out, blown into a dainty pearl-handled penknife.

Pecos Bill let out a whistle. "Without money and without a knife, looks like I'm going to have some trouble getting myself back home."

Months went by at the IXL, and Pecos Bill did not return. Gun Smith began to feel right mournful. Not only was Bill most likely dead, but there was his two bits wager with Moon Hennessy.

As for Moon, he began to act like the boss of the place. Secretly, he had always been jealous of Pecos Bill, and now he began to spread himself. One day, he was boasting right in front of Old Sol, the sheriff at Wichita Falls.

"Nope, the big show-off never turned up after the cyclone," Moon was saying. "Bit off more than he could chew, that time. Used to make me tired, all his bragging and blowing, and the rest of them eating out of his hand."

"You don't look for Bill back, then?" said the sheriff.

"No, and he'd better not come back," Moon bragged. "That buckaroo just naturally roped himself out of a job. There's a new boss at the IXL now and that's me."

The Mysterious Stranger

Now there was an odd-looking stranger near by, whittling and listening to this talk. He was dressed in rusty black, with a boiled collar and greasy black hair sticking out in a fringe underneath his hat. He came up to Moon Hennessy and stuck out his hand.

"Shake, mister. That's the way I like to hear a man talk. Happen you got a job on this IXL outfit for a feller like me?"

Moon Hennessy looked the stranger up and down. He was a queer one all right, and somehow looked familiar too. But Moon decided he was a tenderfoot.

"Where you from, stranger?" he finally asked. "Ever punch cows?"

"Yes, sir," said the stranger innocently. "Me and pop had twelve head, back in Missouri."

Well, Moon couldn't resist that. What fun the boys at the IXL would have with this greenhorn! So he took the stranger back to the ranch, and tipped the boys off.

After chuck, Gun Smith asked the stranger if he'd ever been on a horse. Why, yes, the stranger had, lots of times.

What kind of a horse, then?

"Oh, when I drove the cows down to water, back in Missouri, sometimes I rode Katie, our old gray mare, and sometimes I rode Robbie, the mule."

"Maybe you'd like to try one of our cayuses," Gun Smith suggested. Oh, yes, the stranger would like that.

"Bring on General Stonewall Jackson," said Smith, giving the boys the wink.

Now, next to Widow Maker, General Stonewall Jackson was the wildest horse on the place; and the only reason he didn't outbuck Widow Maker was that he just didn't have the talent. It seemed a mean trick to put an innocent stranger on a horse like this, only the boys never thought he'd get anywhere near him. So Moon and Mushmouth got their ropes and went after General Stonewall Jackson, and finally they lassoed him and saddled him and bridled him. Then they dragged him to where the tenderfoot stood.

"That's a mighty queer saddle," the stranger said, looking it over doubtfully. "Back in Missouri we never use a big saddle like that. I'd take it kindly if you'd peel that saddle off. I'd rather ride bareback than ride on a contraption like that."

So the boys worked and sweated and finally got the saddle off. Then the stranger scratched his chin and said, sort of doubtful-like, "I sure hate to put you fellers to any more trouble, but won't you please take off the bridle, too? Back in Missouri, my pop and me never

used anything except a halter on our old gray mare."

So Moon and Mushmouth worked and struggled to get that bridle off, with General Stonewall Jackson bucking and kicking and trying his best to kill them both.

The stranger still looked doubtful. "He looks a mite lively," he said. "Maybe I'll have some trouble getting on him."

"Do you want us to give you a hand?" Gun Smith said, sarcastically. "Or maybe bring a ladder?"

"No," said the stranger, sadly. "My pop always said a man should get onto his own horse."

And the next thing Gun Smith and the other boys knew, the stranger from Missouri had grabbed General Stonewall Jackson's mane and was sitting there on his back as pretty as you please.

What happened then was as good as a rodeo—better than most. General Jackson did every trick he knew to get rid of the stranger, and he knew plenty. He bucked forty ways for Sunday and a few extra for leap year. At last, the poor old cayuse gave up and just stood there,

his head hanging and a heart-broken expression in his eyes. In a flash, the stranger was off his back and feeding him lumps of sugar to cheer him up.

"Boys, we've been took!" Gun Smith shouted. "This feller's no greenhorn. Who be ye, stranger?"

At that, the stranger whipped off his black wig, and there stood Pecos Bill, grinning like a coyote. The boys just couldn't think of a thing to say.

"You don't look as if you were exactly pleased to see me back," Bill said mildly.

"We're not pleased; we're delighted!" Gun Smith whooped, finding his tongue. And then they were all shaking him by the hand, pounding him on the shoulder, and in general getting an eyeful of the glad sight.

All but Moon Hennessy, that is. Moon remembered he had business in another county, and was making tracks, fast.

"You, Moon, come back here!" Bill yelled. Moon came back, looking pretty small. But Bill just grabbed him by the hand.

"Why, you old hoss-face!" he cried affectionately. "Don't you know you and me is friends, no matter what? Let bygones be bygones, and say no more about it." And with that, he near wrung Moon's hand off.

Oddly enough, this episode cured Moon's jealousy. Never again did he hold a grudge against Pecos Bill. But, to his dying day, he could never understand it.

"Tain't human, him being so nice to a skunk like me," Moon used to sigh.

Which brings up the question we started with—*was* Pecos Bill human? Maybe he was a full-blooded coyote after all!

The Emperor's New Clothes

Hans Christian Andersen

Many years ago, there lived an emperor who was so exceedingly fond of new clothes that he spent all of his money on dress. He cared nothing for his army; he did not enjoy the theater, or a gallop through the woods. No, all he was interested in was showing himself off in his new clothes. He possessed a different suit for every hour of the day. And, while at other courts one would always be told, "The king is in his council-chamber," at *his* court the word was always, "The emperor is in his dressing-room."

In the great city where the emperor lived, life was very gay. Visitors from foreign lands arrived every day. Among them, one day, came two swindlers. These fellows pretended to be weavers who knew how to weave the handsomest cloth in the world. Not only were its colors and designs unusually gorgeous, but it had the wonderful property of being invisible to anyone who was not fit for the office he held or who was exceedingly stupid.

"Indeed, these would be wonderful clothes to possess!" thought the emperor. "By putting them on, I could easily detect those people in my empire who are not suited for the office they are holding. By myself, I can never tell a blockhead from a clever man. So I had better have those clothes woven for me at once." And he paid the two swindlers a considerable sum in advance to start them on their work.

The two rascals set up two real looms and pretended to start weaving. But of course, they put nothing on their looms that could possibly be woven into cloth. Every day, they demanded the finest silk and the most precious gold. But the gold and the silk went to line their own pockets, and they continued to work at the empty looms late into the night.

After some time, the emperor thought, "By now, those fellows have had quite a lot of gold and silk. I'd like to know how they are coming along with that cloth." Secretly, he was a little nervous at the idea that a person not fit for his office, or a dunce, could not see the fabric. Of course, he himself would have nothing to worry about. But all the same, he decided to send someone else to the weavers first, and find out how matters stood. Everybody in town, of course, knew the wonderful property the fabric possessed. And everybody was eager to see how bad, or how stupid, his neighbor was.

"My old, honest minister shall go to the weavers," thought the emperor. "He will be able to report on what the material is like. For he is undoubtedly very intelligent, and nobody could perform the duties of his office better than he."

So the good old minister went to the place where the two swindlers worked on the two empty looms. "Heaven forbid!" thought the old man, staring as he stepped into the room. "I can't see a thing!" But he did not say so.

The two swindlers begged him to come closer. They asked him whether he did not find the design exquisite, and the colors superb. They kept pointing at the empty looms and the poor old man kept on staring. But he couldn't see anything—for of course, nothing was there.

"Good heavens!" he thought. "Can it be that I am stupid? I would never have believed it. But not a soul must know. Am I really not fit for my office? I don't dare let on that I can't see that stuff."

"But you aren't saying a word!" exclaimed one of the swindlers, who pretended to be going on weaving.

"Oh, it is fine, wonderful—er, magnificent!" said the old minister. And he put on his spectacles to see all the better. "Such design! Such colors! Yes, yes, I shall tell the emperor that I like it exceedingly well!"

"We are deeply honored!" said the weavers, bowing. They told him the names of all the colors and explained the elaborate design. The old man listened attentively so that he would be able to repeat every word to the emperor. And that's just what he did.

The two swindlers now asked for still more money, for more silk and more gold. They must have it in order to finish the fabric, they said. But again, everything that they got went into their own pockets. Onto the looms went not a single thread. And they worked at the empty looms just as before.

Before long, the emperor sent another trusted courtier to the weavers, to find out how soon the cloth would be

done. With this man, things went just the same as with the old minister. The courtier looked and he looked, and for all his looking he saw nothing at all but the two empty looms.

"Is it not a gorgeous piece of material?" asked the two swindlers. They pretended to show and explain to the royal messenger the design that was not there.

"I *know* I'm not stupid!" thought the courtier. "It can only be that I am not fit for my office. This is very bad indeed. I must not betray it to anyone!"

And so he, too, praised the stuff, and exclaimed over the fine colors and the exquisite design. "Yes, it is truly wonderful, Your Majesty!" he said to the emperor when he returned.

Viewing the Invisible

Throughout the city, people could talk of nothing else but the marvelous material. And now, nothing would do but the emperor himself must go and see it while it was still on the loom. So, with a whole company of carefully selected courtiers—among them, to be sure, the two good officers who had been there before—the emperor paid a visit to the two clever swindlers. There they were at the two empty looms, weaving away with all their might, without a thread or a shred of cloth anywhere to be seen.

"Your Majesty, is it not *magnifique?*" asked the two good royal servants. (They tried, by speaking French, to pay the cloth the highest compliment in their power.) "Just see, what design, what colors!" And they pointed at the empty looms, sure that the others could all see what to them was invisible.

"What on earth!" thought the emperor, thunderstruck. "I can't see a thing! This is terrible. Am I stupid? Am I unfit to be emperor? This would be the most awful thing that could happen to me!"

"Yes, yes, it is very beautiful," the emperor said aloud. "I am entirely satisfied." And nodding royally, he looked at the empty looms. All his attendants looked likewise. And like the emperor, they said, "Yes, yes. It is very beautiful!" All the courtiers agreed that *they* were entirely pleased and satisfied also. And they begged the emperor to wear the clothes made from this wonderful fabric in the great procession soon to take place.

The emperor awarded each of the swindlers a medal to wear on his coat. He bestowed on each of them the title of Squire of the Loom.

The whole night long before the procession, the swindlers sat up working. Everybody could see that they were in a hurry to finish the emperor's new clothes. They pretended to take the fabric off the looms. With enormous scissors, they cut into the empty air. They sewed with needles that hadn't any thread in them. Finally, the rascals announced, "The emperor's new clothes are ready!"

The emperor approached, surrounded by his noblest courtiers. The swindlers pretended to hold the clothes up, piece by piece. "See, here are the pantaloons. Here is the tunic. Behold the robe!" And so on. "They are all as light as gossamer! One would think that one was not wearing clothes at all. But of course, that is the wonderful property these clothes possess."

"Yes, yes!" said the courtiers, staring admiringly at thin air.

"May it please Your Majesty to take off your present clothing now?" said the swindlers. "Then we shall put the new robes upon you before the tall mirror here."

So the emperor took off his clothes and the swindlers went through the motions of putting on him all the garments they had pretended to sew. They reached their arms around him as if to fasten on the long, sweeping train. And the emperor turned round and round before the mirror.

"Heavens, how perfectly they fit! How utterly becoming they are!" all the courtiers said. "What design! What color! *Magnifique!* These are indeed marvelous clothes!"

"The royal guard waits outside with the canopy that they are to carry above Your Majesty in the procession!" reported the lord master of ceremonies.

"I am ready!" said the emperor. He turned around once more before the mirror, as if he were viewing his splendor. "They certainly fit perfectly."

The chamberlains who were to carry his train felt with their hands along the floor as if they were gathering it up carefully. Then they fell into step with raised hands, as if they were carrying the train aloft.

The emperor strode along in the solemn procession, under the canopy. And all the people thronging the streets and crowding the windows exclaimed, "Heavens, how wonderful the emperor's new clothes are! What a gorgeous train! How perfectly they fit!" Every man was careful not to betray to his neighbors that he could see nothing. No one cared to let it be known that he was not fit for what he was doing, or else was stupid. Never before had any of the emperor's new clothes had such a success!

"But he doesn't have anything on!" said a little child.

"Goodness, just listen to the little innocent!" the father exclaimed. One onlooker began to whisper to another what the child had said.

"He hasn't anything on!" the child said again.

"No, he doesn't have anything on!" Everybody was saying it now.

The emperor was startled and shocked, for he saw that the people were right. But he thought, "I have to go through with this procession, all the same!" And so he drew himself up even more proudly; and the chamberlains walked behind him, carrying even higher the train that was not there.

The Wisdom of Solomon

Retold by Elizabeth Coatsworth

Now in the days of Solomon's might and glory, the Queen of Sheba heard of his fame and came from her kingdom beyond Egypt to put questions to him.

Their meeting was like the meeting of the sun and the moon; she was as beautiful as he was handsome. All about him stood youths chosen for their comeliness. About her were gathered maidens like stars shining in a cloudless sky. His crown blinded the eyes, and hers bewildered the mind. When the king arose from his throne to greet her, the attendants stood still with admiration. When the queen mounted the steps to sit beside him, her grace was such that a sigh of wonder rose from the throng.

Then before the eyes of the wise Solomon, the queen had displayed the treasures of her kingdom. Partly by art and partly by magic, her workmen had made things such as had never been seen before—a golden bird which could fly and speak, and animals so real that the mind could not believe that they were made by human hands.

Then, as the wise King Solomon gazed upon these things with admiration, the queen ordered her attendants to bring in two vases of flowers and to stand them at the foot of the throne.

"O Solomon, wisest of living men," said the queen, "I am but a woman and ruler of a weak little kingdom, unworthy of the thought of one so great as thou. So, only to amuse thee, and to make thee smile, I have ordered these playthings to be made for thee. Here, now, are two bouquets: one bouquet is made from living flowers and one is but a copy, which my craftsmen have fashioned of enamels and jewels. Stretch forth thy hand of wisdom, O Solomon the Wise, and say which is which."

Then the Queen of Sheba looked meekly at Solomon. But he knew well enough that this was no sport, but a test of his wisdom. If he failed, the world would ring with laughter and his glory would be lost to him.

But he smiled courteously at the queen and thanked her for her gifts. Then he turned his eyes upon the flowers. No words can tell you of the beauty of those blossoms. There were the lilies which he loved, and roses, and sweet-smelling jasmine, all with their leaves. At first, he looked for perfections, but lo, dew seemed to tremble upon the petals of both bouquets and he could not choose between them.

Then Solomon, the great king and wisest of men, searched for imperfections. At last he saw one wilted leaf, and he raised his head and was about to stretch forth his hand, when his eye, glancing at the other flowers, saw among them also one wilted leaf.

Then, having found no aid in perfections or in imperfections, the king sat in silence, and the queen's silence was equal to his, and to all their attendants'. And it was a day of late spring, and beyond the curtains drawn between the pillars of his courtyard Solomon, the great king, heard the bees in his gardens, and suddenly he smiled.

"Draw open the curtains there," he said to one of his attendants.

And when the curtains were drawn open, he waited. And the queen and all the court waited with him.

After a while, a bee entered and flew toward the throne and the flowers before it. And Solomon, the great king, smiled in his beard, for the bee had no hesitation. The bee was not deceived by beautiful workmanship, by jewels, or by enamels. Straight as an arrow, the creature flew to its flower, and Solomon turned to the queen and raised his hand to point to the true bouquet.

Now if you think that the Queen of Sheba respected Solomon, the wise king, less because he had been forced to call in a bee to instruct him, you are wrong. She, too, was wise. She saw that the great king understood the universe and knew to whom to go for instruction, if only to a bee. And this time she bowed her head before him, not in mockery, and gave him the treasure which she had brought with her.

Ali Baba
and the Forty Thieves

From *The Arabian Nights*

Once, in a city of Persia, there lived two brothers: by name, Cassim and Ali Baba. When their father died, they inherited a very modest fortune, which they divided equally.

But then Cassim married a rich wife, and was able to rise in the world and become a leading merchant in the city. Ali Baba had no such luck. He married a woman as poor as himself, and was forced to support his family by cutting wood in a forest near by, and bringing it into town to sell.

One day, Ali Baba had gone out to cut wood as usual, and was loading it, at the edge of the forest, onto his three small donkeys. Suddenly, he saw a thick cloud of dust on the plain, traveling toward him. Soon he was able to make out a crowd of horsemen, galloping swiftly. Frightened, Ali Baba drove his own beasts into the bushes and himself hastened to climb a thick tree which grew beside a large rock.

On swept the horsemen, until they reached the very rock beside which Ali Baba was hiding. He counted forty of them in all, and was sure from their costume and fierce appearance that they were robbers. Each man got down from his horse, tied the beast to a bush, took off the bridle, and slipped over its head a bag filled with barley. Then they untied the saddle bags, which appeared to be very heavy, as if laden with silver and gold.

The robber captain advanced up to the very face of the rock. "Open, sesame!" he commanded; and behold, a door in the rock opened, and all the robbers went in with their bags. The captain went in last of all, and the door closed behind him.

The robbers stayed inside the rock a long time, but Ali Baba dared not come down from his tree, lest they discover him. Finally the door opened again. The captain came out, and all his men after him. They untied and bridled their horses, and mounted. "Shut, sesame!" the captain said. The door in the rock closed, and the robbers rode off in the direction from which they had come.

After waiting some time, Ali Baba climbed down from his tree, and approached the rock. "Open, sesame!" he commanded. Instantly, the rock opened before him.

Stepping through the door, he found himself in a great room hewn out of the rock, with light coming in from an opening in the top. It was piled high on all sides with bales of rich silks and brocades, and heaps of gold and jewels. So great was the store of riches that Ali Baba thought not one, but several, generations of robbers must have used the cave as a treasure house.

Seeing some large leather bags, Ali Baba filled these with gold coins. The door of the cave had shut behind him, but it flew open when he pronounced the magic words, and shut again at his command when he was safely outside. He loaded the bags of gold on his three donkeys, concealing the bags under some of the wood he had cut. Then he took the road to town.

At home, Ali Baba shut the gate to the courtyard of his home with care. Then he carried in the bags of gold to show to his wife.

"Good heavens, husband, can it be possible you have become a thief?" she exclaimed.

"Do not fear, unless it is thieving to steal from thieves," Ali Baba reassured her. So he emptied the sacks before her and told her the whole story from beginning to end.

Now his wife was as joyful as she had been alarmed before. She started to count the gold, piece by piece.

"This is too slow," she cried, impatiently. "I shall borrow a measure from Cassim's household, and we can measure the money that way."

"Borrow the measure if you wish, my dear wife," Ali Baba said. "But do not let fall a single syllable concerning our good fortune."

Good Fortune Brings Evil

So Ali Baba's wife went to Cassim's wife, and asked to borrow a small measure, such as was used for measuring grain. Cassim and his wife were both of a curious and envious turn of mind, and Cassim's wife said to herself, "I wonder what kind of grain she wants to measure." So, secretly, she stuck some tallow on the bottom of the measure, and Ali Baba's wife took it home and measured the gold. And when she returned the measure, a small piece of gold that she did not notice was sticking to the tallow.

That night, when Cassim returned home, his wife had the gold piece ready to show him. "See, they are so wealthy they measure their gold instead of counting it!" she exclaimed. "You must find out at once how this came to pass."

Cassim needed no urging. He went directly to Ali Baba and demanded to know whence so much gold had come.

Ali Baba told him the whole story, and Cassim's envy and discontent knew no bounds. Early the next morning, he took ten stout donkeys and started out to visit the cave, alone.

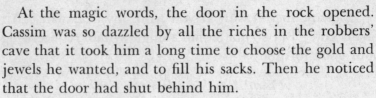

At the magic words, the door in the rock opened. Cassim was so dazzled by all the riches in the robbers' cave that it took him a long time to choose the gold and jewels he wanted, and to fill his sacks. Then he noticed that the door had shut behind him.

"Open, barley!" he said. But the door did not open. "Open, millet! Open, wheat!" In a panic, he said the name of every kind of grain he could remember, but "sesame" had gone clear out of his head. So, when the robbers came to the cave that day, they found Cassim and killed him immediately.

The robber captain was very uneasy. "In all these years, our cave has never been discovered," he said. "We must frighten these persons, if there are more of them." So he had Cassim's body cut into four pieces, in the most frightful manner, and hung just inside the door of the cave.

When Cassim did not return that night, his wife was sure that some misfortune had befallen him. So she went to Ali Baba, and begged him to seek his brother. Very early the next morning, Ali Baba set out for the cave. When he had opened the magic door, he perceived poor Cassim's body, and understood what had happened. He took down the pieces and wrapped them in sacks and loaded them onto his donkeys' backs. That night, under cover of darkness, he drove his beasts to Cassim's house. There he called Morgiana, a very intelligent female slave belonging to the household, and told her what had taken place.

"Cassim must appear to have died a natural death," Ali Baba said. "I fear the revenge of the robber band, if the smallest whisper of this should ever get about."

"Have no fear," said Morgiana. "I will manage every-thing."

So Morgiana kept her mistress within, where her weeping would not be heard. In the morning, she herself went to the druggist, where she bought a medicine used only in serious illness.

"Ah, my poor master!" Morgiana said, sighing. "For an entire day, he has neither spoken nor moved."

The following morning, Morgiana went to the druggist again, with her hair loose and tears in her eyes. She bought a medicine used only at the point of death. "Alas!" she said. "We do not think it possible that he can live through this day."

So that night, the neighbors were not surprised when great wailing announced Cassim's death.

The next morning very early, Morgiana went to a distant part of the city, where there dwelt an old cobbler. She promised him two gold pieces if he would let her blindfold him and take him to a certain house, there to do a piece of work she would set before him. So she brought him blindfolded to Cassim's house and he sewed up Cassim's body, and Morgiana blindfolded him and led him back, swearing him to secrecy. That day Cassim's

funeral was held, in the most proper manner; and no one suspected that there was anything strange about Cassim's death.

Soon, Ali Baba and his wife went to live in Cassim's fine house. Since Cassim had no children, Ali Baba's son took over Cassim's shop. And for some time, all went well.

The Robbers' Revenge

The robbers, however, were only biding their time. When Cassim's body disappeared, they knew that their secret was still at large. After much discussion, one of the robbers suggested a plan.

Disguising himself, he went to the city one morning, almost before it was light. By chance, he came to the very bazaar where the old cobbler plied his trade.

"Good morning!" said the robber, to make talk. "Is not this early light dim for your old eyesight?"

"Indeed, no!" boasted the cobbler. "It was not long ago I sewed a dead man together, in light much dimmer than this. But let that go—I promised not to speak of it."

The robber was overjoyed, but he tried not to show it. "By all means, let us not speak of it," he said politely. "Only I cannot help wondering, was it in the city or a place outside?"

"It was in the city, but at some distance away," said the cobbler. "I was blindfolded, but even so I could find the place."

The robber pulled out his purse and produced a gold coin. "What you say interests me," he replied. "I am a stranger in this city, and hence not interested in him who died. But I would like to know if a blindfolded man can truly find his way again. If you, blindfolded, can take me

over the same road you traveled before, this piece of gold
shall be yours."

The cobbler saw no harm in that. So he let the robber
blindfold him, and step by step the old man retraced the
way Morgiana had taken him. Finally, he stopped in front
of a door.

"I think it was here I stopped," he said.

"Good," said the robber. "I see you are an honest man,
and would not try to deceive me. Therefore take this gold
piece, and Allah be with you."

So the cobbler and the robber each departed. But first,
the robber secretly put a chalk mark on the door.

A little while later, the slave Morgiana returned from
the market. Her sharp eyes at once spied the chalk mark;
and getting a piece of chalk, she quietly marked with it
all the other doors on the street, in exactly the same way.

Later that day, when the robber proudly brought his captain to see the mark, he was horrified to find the same
mark on all the other doors. Nor could he tell which door
had been originally marked by himself. So he and the
captain returned to the cave, and the robber was put to
death for his failure.

Another fellow, however, thought he knew how to suc-
ceed where the first had failed. He approached the cobbler the same as the first robber, and was in turn taken to
the door. And he marked the door in another place,
almost unnoticeably, in red chalk. Again Morgiana saw
the mark and repeated it on the other doors. And so this
robber, too, was put to death.

The captain, fearing to lose his whole band profitlessly,
now went to the city himself, and was led by the cobbler
to the door. The captain did not mark the door, but only
looked at it until he could not possibly be mistaken. Then
he went away and laid his plans.

The Oil Merchant

A few evenings later, an oil merchant, leading thirty-
eight donkeys, came to Ali Baba's house and prayed room
for himself and his beasts during the night. Each beast
carried, slung at his side, an enormous leather jar. The
merchant opened the last jar, which was full of olive oil,
as he had said.

Ali Baba received him kindly. He ordered the donkeys
to be stabled in the courtyard, and fed hay and grain. To
the merchant himself he gave a room inside the house.

Pretending to see whether his beasts were comfortable
for the night, the merchant went out and approached the
jars, which had been unloaded from the donkeys.

"Harken," he muttered into the partially open mouth of each jar. "When the household is asleep, I shall throw pebbles against the jars from the window of my chamber. That is the signal for you to cut yourself out of the jar. Then I will steal down into the garden, and we shall complete our vengeance."

For instead of oil, thirty-seven of the jars contained each one a member of the robber band, and the false merchant was the captain!

Visitors were frequent in Ali Baba's household, and Morgiana was not alarmed. However, as she worked late at some household task that night, her light went out for lack of oil. And there was no more oil in the house.

"Do not be troubled," said the slave Abdullah. "There is the oil brought by the merchant. He will not mind if you take enough for your lamp."

So Morgiana went out into the garden, and approached the first jar. What was her horror to hear, from within, a man's voice saying, "Is it time, my captain?"

Morgiana understood the whole plot instantly. Assuming the oil merchant's voice, with the greatest presence of mind, she said softly, "Not now, but soon." She went from jar to jar, hearing the same question and giving the same answer, until she came to the last one. There she filled her lamp with oil, and hastily went in and prepared an enormous kettle over a hot fire.

Filling this kettle with the oil from the last jar, she heated it until it boiled. Then the brave woman went into the garden, and without alarming the robbers, poured into each jar enough boiling oil to smother instantly the man within it. That done, she put out her lamp and retired.

Presently the robber captain woke. Going to the window and seeing everything in darkness, he began to throw pebbles against the oil jars. Nothing moved. He threw more pebbles. Still, no figures appeared.

Hastily, the captain went down into the garden. When he opened the jars one after another, and smelled the scalding oil, he knew that his plan had failed. Climbing the wall, and making his way through the adjoining gardens, he escaped into the street and out of the city.

When Ali Baba arose the next morning, he was surprised to see the donkeys and the leather jars still in the courtyard.

"You will be even more surprised, master, when you look within the jars," Morgiana informed him. She accompanied him outside, and watched him start back after peering into the first of the jars.

"Each of them, except the last, contains the body of a man," she told him.

"And what is the meaning of this?" Ali Baba asked.

So Morgiana related the whole tale, beginning with the chalk marks on the door. "I did not feel it necessary to alarm you, my dear master," she said. "But I then became sure that vengeance was being planned. And last night, as I was seeking oil for my lamp, the whole scheme was suddenly revealed to me, as I have said. I took the only possible measures that would preserve you and our entire household."

"Excellent Morgiana!" exclaimed Ali Baba. "From this moment, accept your liberty at my hand. But now, how shall we get rid of these bodies?"

"Your garden is large," answered the wise Morgiana. "Tonight you and Abdullah can dig a trench near the palm trees. When you have buried the robbers, smooth the soil as though nothing had been disturbed. Abdullah can sell the beasts a few at a time, in the different bazaars of the city."

So the thing was done according to Morgiana's plan. But Morgiana feared further revenge on the part of the robber captain and the other two members of his band (she did not know they were dead). So, although free, she remained with the household, to guard them.

The Captain Tries Again

As for the robber captain, he was almost beside himself with rage and grief. At length, he hit upon another plan. Taking a store of rich goods from the cave, and assuming a disguise, the captain presented himself in the bazaar as one who wished to hire a shop. By chance, a shop was to let, just opposite the one formerly owned by Cassim, and now in charge of Ali Baba's son.

It was not long before the captain, who called himself Cogia Houssain, became aware of who the young man was, and his relation to Ali Baba. Craftily, over a period of time, Cogia Houssain set himself to win the young man's friendship. He gave him several presents, and several times invited the young man to his house, where he entertained him handsomely.

Ali Baba's son was delighted with his new friend, and wished to entertain him in return. But alas, his own home was small and modestly furnished. He spoke of the difficulty to his father, and at once Ali Baba invited his son to bring Cogia Houssain to his house, where more suitable entertainment might be provided. So it was arranged that on a certain day, the young man would

take Cogia Houssain walking, and they would pass Ali
Baba's house as it were by chance, and the merchant
would be invited to come in.

And thus it was done. At the door, Cogia Houssain
pretended to be reluctant, but let himself be forced to
enter. Ali Baba received him in the most friendly way.
"I beg you will do me the honor to share my humble
evening meal," he said.

"I thank you for your great kindness, but I may not,"
said the pretended merchant. "My physician has for-
bidden me to eat of any dish containing salt. For this
reason, I never presume on the kindness of my friends,
but dine always at my own table."

"Let that be no bar," said Ali Baba. "I shall myself
instruct that unsalted dishes be prepared for our repast."

But when Ali Baba went to the kitchen and told
Morgiana to prepare the food without salt, she felt that
something strange was afoot. When the supper was ready,
she herself assisted in serving it. Instantly she recognized
Cogia Houssain as the robber captain, in spite of his
disguise; and her sharp eyes noted also the dagger hidden
in his sash.

Retiring to her own quarters, she robed herself as a
dancing girl. For, in addition to her other gifts, Morgiana
was also young and beautiful, and an accomplished
dancer. Then, requesting Abdullah to bring his tabor,
she came before Ali Baba and asked if she might dance
for his guest.

Receiving permission, Morgiana began to dance in the
most beautiful and graceful way, till even Cogia Houssain
was moved to applaud. At the end, she whirled into a
wild dagger dance, in which she pretended to be about

to strike—now one of the guests, now her own breast. At the end, snatching the tabor from Abdullah, she held it out to Ali Baba, like a real dancing girl, the dagger still in her other hand.

Ali Baba threw a gold coin into the tabor. His son did likewise. Then Morgiana offered the tabor to Cogia Houssain, and while he was fumbling in his purse for a coin, Morgiana plunged her dagger into his heart.

Ali Baba and his son started up in horror. "Wretched woman, what have you done?" they exclaimed. "You have ruined us forever!"

"Nay, dear master, I have saved you," said Morgiana. "Look well at this man. He is no merchant, but the robber captain himself. See the dagger with which he was planning to stab you both!"

Then Ali Baba perceived that it was indeed his enemy, and could only wonder and exclaim, "But, Morgiana, how did you discover his disguise?"

"When he would not eat salt with you, I became suspicious," Morgiana said. "And when I saw who he was, I resolved to save you."

"Morgiana," said Ali Baba solemnly, "you are already free. Now it is my desire that you should become the wife of my son. Are you willing?" he asked, turning to the young man.

The young man was more than willing, for he had long admired Morgiana's beauty and her cleverness. So they were married, and with Morgiana's wisdom and the treasure in the cave, the family of Ali Baba remained for many years the wealthiest and most splendid in the city in which they lived.

The Pudding That Broke
up the Preaching

Retold by Ellis Credle

Talk about puddings! There never was a more astonishing pudding than the one Ma Tolliver beat up for the all-day preaching that went on down in Possum Holler Church on Thanksgiving Day. Folks came down to preachings from all over the countryside in those days—from Sandy Creek and Turkey Bottom and Huggin's Crossroads. They brought their dinners with 'em. Between sermons and singing morning and afternoon, they spread their victuals on the ground, picnic fashion, and had a real slapbang good dinner.

Everybody tried to out-do everybody else with their pies and cakes and roast turkey and what-not. And Ma Tolliver laid off, that Thanksgiving, to have a pudding that would top everything else at the preaching. She started on it early Wednesday morning, mixing up her meal and molasses, cutting up peaches and nuts and such fixings to make it extra fancy. After she'd had it on the fire a spell, it came to her that she'd forgot to put the salt in it.

Now every good cook knows a pudding's not right without a pinch of salt. So Ma, she called out to her oldest girl.

"Saphronie!" she says. "I forgot the salt in the pudding and I'm out here picking a turkey with my fingers all stuck full of feathers. Run in the kitchen for me and put in a good big pinch of salt."

"Lawsy, Ma, I'm a-ironing my dress for the big doings tomorrow. If I stop now, my iron'll get all cold." And she went on ironing as hard as she could.

"Hitty, you run in the kitchen and put some salt in the pudding for me," hollered Ma to the next oldest girl.

"I declare to goodness, Ma, I can't do it. I've just been to the witchwoman to get her to take the warts off my hands. She's smeared axle grease over both my hands and told me not to wash it off till I saw the evening star over my left shoulder. I can't pick up a pinch of salt with axle grease all over my hands."

By this time, Ma was mighty nigh wore out with hollering. But she decided to try once more. "You, Lucy!
Can't you run in the kitchen and put some salt in the
pudding for me?"

"Golly, Ma. I'm a-lying here in bed with cucumber
peelings all over my face a-trying to bleach off the freckles
before tomorrow. I can't get up now!"

"Sally!" Ma shouted to the youngest girl. "Hump yourself into the kitchen and throw some salt in the pudding
for me."

"Goodness sakes, Ma, I'm a-working like fire to get my
hair rolled up on old stockings, so's I'll have curls for the
doings tomorrow. I ain't got time to salt the pudding."

Since there weren't any more girls to ask, Ma hollered
at her son. "Rufus, go to the kitchen and throw a spoonful
of salt into the pudding." But Rufus was busy, too.

He was a young feller, just beginning to cotton to girls
and do a little courting. "I swan, Ma," he called back.
"I'm all full of bear-grease. Been slicking down my hair
with it. Now I'm a-greasing my Sunday-go-to-meeting
boots. I can't put any salt in the pudding now!"

By that time, all the children were used up. Ma began
to holler at her husband. "Lem, can't you stop whatever
you're doing and go put a spoonful of salt in the
pudding?"

"Shucks, Ma, I'm a-cleaning my gun for tomorrow.
S'posing a nice fat rabbit ran across the road whilst we're
a-going. If my gun wasn't ready, we'd miss a good rabbit
stew for supper. Got my hands full of gun-soot. I can't
take care of your pudding now."

"Oh, bother!" Ma said to herself, clear out of patience.
"I'll do it myself!" So she washed the feathers off

her hands. Into the kitchen she marched. She got a good big pinch of salt, went over to the hearth where the pudding was boiling away in a pot swung over the fire, and threw it in.

Well, after a while, Saphronie got her dress all done up. She got to feeling a little ashamed that she hadn't done what Ma had asked her to. So she went over to the salt box, got a big pinch, and threw it into the pudding.

Hitty got to feeling bad about refusing her Ma, too. "I reckon I could manage to get some salt in that pudding if I tried," she said. So she went into the kitchen, picked up a spoon with her black, greasy hands, dipped up a good, big dose of salt, and stirred it into the pudding.

Then Lucy, lying back on the bed with her face covered with cucumbers, got to thinking that she hadn't done right not to help her Ma when she was asked. So she got up, went to the hearth, and put some more salt in the pudding.

No sooner had she got out of the way, than Sally came into the kitchen with her hair done up in knobs all over her head. She got a good-sized pinch of salt and dropped it in the pudding.

Then Rufus got to thinking about it after he'd finished his boots. So into the kitchen he went and dipped up a good big tablespoonful. Being a man, he didn't know much about such things. He thought you had to put as much salt in a pudding as in a pot of stew.

Pa's conscience got to hurting him, too. As soon as his gun was all shined up and loaded, he clumped into the kitchen, dipped up a heaping spoonful of salt, and threw it over into the pudding.

At last the pudding was done. Ma took it off the fire. It turned out of the pot as pretty as you please.

"That's as fine a looking pudding as ever I saw!" Ma said. "With a pudding like that, I might even ask the preachers to have some tomorrow."

"Oh, yes, do, Ma!" the girls exclaimed.

The next day was sparkling and sunny. Everybody set off walking to the church. The preaching went fine. As soon as one preacher was winded, another one got up and took his place. By twelve o'clock, they were all worn out. So they called time out for Thanksgiving dinner.

Well sir, Ma was so proud of that pudding that sure enough, she invited all the preachers over to have some. There were four of 'em. So she cut off four huge hunks and told 'em to dig in.

The first one that took a bite looked at Ma with his eyes popping half out of his head.

"You never tasted anything like it, now, did you?" Ma said proudly.

"No, Sister, I never did, and that's a fact," the preacher said.

"Go on, don't be bashful. Finish it up!" Ma urged. The poor fellow, not to hurt her feelings, took another bite and gulped it down.

Those four preachers sure proved their Christian feelings that day. All four of 'em choked down the pudding without saying a word against it.

After they'd staggered off toward the church, Ma cut some off for herself and passed each of her family a piece. Everybody took a bite and looked up horrified. Then it came out how each of 'em had gone into the kitchen and salted the pudding.

Ma was mortified. "Too many cooks sure spoilt this pudding!" she said.

They spoilt the preaching, too—you can be sure of that. As soon as one preacher got started, he'd have to stop and whisper for a glass of water. There was so much water hauled up to the pulpit that day that folks stopped thinking about the preaching. They began to wonder what the trouble was. Some took to counting the glasses.

What with preachers tormented with thirst and everybody whispering to each other asking questions, the meeting broke up way ahead of time. The tale about the pudding finally got around. Ever since that time, folks around Possum Hollow tell about Ma's pudding that broke up the big Thanksgiving all-day preaching.

Wings and Four Feet

To swoop and dare the flowing air
   With strong, unwearied wing;
To float at one with cloud and sun—
   How glorious a thing!

To roam at will the field and hill
   On swift, untiring feet;
Then safe to den, and rest again—
   How good the earth, and sweet!

           —Dorothy Hall

The Peddler

Eric Knight

Lassie, a fine gold-black-and-white collie, belonged to Sam Carraclough, a Yorkshire miner. The mine shut down, and Sam, to help his family, had to sell Lassie to the Duke of Rudling. The dog was taken to the Duke's estate in northern Scotland, four hundred miles away. But Lassie could not be happy away from Sam's son Joe. One day she ran away and started on the heartbreaking journey home. One of her adventures on the way was with a peddler named Rowlie.

Rowlie Palmer finished shaving and cleaned off his old-fashioned straight razor. He was a little, cheery man with a red face that somehow seemed full of buttons. His eyes were like buttons, his weather-beaten lips were like buttons, there were odd bumps and warts on his forehead and chin that were like buttons.

Rowlie's face and form were well known throughout the North of England, for he was a traveling potter. He lived in the horse-drawn wagon-caravan which carried his goods, and traveled slowly along the roads. When he came to a village or town, he would take out a stout staff and begin to beat one of his largest pottery bowls—an enormous thing of brown and yellow glaze. The result would be a sound like the rich-toned chiming of a great bell.

And Rowlie would lift up his voice and chant: "Here comes Peddler Palmer, the Potter. Bowls and pots, I've got lots! Bowls and pots!"

Once a year he covered his route, traveling by day, at night pulling his horse Bess over to the side of the road by a good camping place. It was a comfortable, happy life.

On this particular morning, Rowlie's cot was made, his breakfast finished, his dishes put away. Bess was harnessed, her oat-bag slung beneath the cart. Rowlie got to the seat. "Hi, up, Bess!" he cried.

Once out on the road, Rowlie jumped down from the seat of his moving van and began walking alongside it, singing a story of a hapless village maiden. It was a sad song, but Rowlie did not mind that. In his lonesome life, his own voice kept him company from town to town. He had no other company but Bess and Toots. And Toots—she was a one, as Rowlie would put it. She sat on the seat now, a tiny white dog, which might have been poodle, fox terrier, Pomeranian, or Skye terrier; but was all of them.

Toots was almost as well known as Rowlie. She could stand on her hind legs on an inverted bowl and balance another smaller bowl on her nose. She could jump on a ball of wood and roll it by walking along, still balancing. She could pick up pennies from the ground. She could jump through hoops.

Whenever Rowlie reached a good village, he would put on a show with Toots—not for the pennies, but because he enjoyed the laughter and happiness of the children.

This morning, Rowlie's mind was not on the words of his song. Instead, as always, his senses were alert to

the world about him. His eyes flicked over a field, and his song halted.

He walked over beside his moving cart and stood on the step beside the shafts. As he went, he watched. It was a dog, coming steadily across the field, curving toward the road.

She came without halting—as if a horse-drawn van was a thing of nature, like a tree or a deer. Rowlie knew that and so kept his body out of sight. Only he muttered to himself, "Now what are you up to, eh?"

Nearer the dog came, until it slipped to the road, just as the cart passed.

"Well, and what do you want?" Rowlie said out loud.

The dog looked up and recrossed the ditch into the empty fields.

"Don't like my company, eh?" Rowlie said.

He got down from the step and began walking again. His eyes followed the dog, now going ahead and to his left, yet traveling almost parallel. But its passage was stopped by a stream. It began moving back to the road again, where it could cross on the bridge.

Rowlie clambered into his cart. When he came out, he had in his hand a few small pieces of liver. Toots lifted her nose and wagged her stub of a tail.

"It's not for thee, my lass," Rowlie said.

He kept his eye on the dog. It would arrive at the bridge just as his wagon did.

"Well, we'll pretend not to notice thee this time," he said aloud. He began singing again, with vigor.

"Ah-gee-way, there Bess. No, not right into th' ditch. Ah-gee-whoa a bit. That's it!" And he fell to singing again.

Lassie Shows Her Breeding

So singing, timing the speed of his horse, Rowlie arrived at the bridge as the dog drew near. He went on, pretending not to notice it. The dog halted, as if to let him pass first. Rowlie did not turn his head. Instead, he waved the pieces of liver in his hand, so that the scent scattered in the air. Unconcernedly he dropped one. Then he passed over the bridge. Half turning his head, he looked to see what the dog would do.

Behind, by the bridge, Lassie walked slowly to the piece of meat. Her hunger drove the saliva glands to work and her mouth filled with wetness. She walked nearer. She bent her nose to touch the meat.

But training of years was there, too. How carefully had Sam Carraclough taught her not to pick up strange food!

He had done that by dropping small pieces of meat at various places—and in the meat had been put cores of burning red pepper. As a pup, Lassie had started to eat those bits and had soon discovered that they contained what seemed to be balls of living flame. Moreover, as her mouth burned, she had been scolded by the voice of her master.

"It's a cruel hard thing to do," Sam Carraclough had told his son Joe. "But it's t'only way I know that can teach 'em—and I'd sooner have a pup taste hot pepper than have a raised dog dying o' poisoned meat some madman has thrown to it."

And that lesson had stayed with Lassie. A dog must not eat stray bits of food! Her nose trembled. She nuzzled the piece of liver. Then suddenly she wheeled. She left the meat and crossed the bridge.

Ahead of her Rowlie Palmer, by his wagon, nodded his head. "A good tyke and a well-brought-up one," he said. "But we'll see . . ."

He walked on singing, but still waving liver in the air. And in that smell of desired food, Lassie now traveled. Once over the bridge, her impulse was to leave the road again. But she did not want to leave the trail of this sweet-smelling food. She trotted along and began traveling slightly to the rear.

Rowlie Palmer sang merrily to Toots on the seat:

> *"There's a tyke that's shy and canny,*
> *But I think she's coming near.*
> *Aye, she may be fearfu' canny,*
> *But we'll overcome her fear.*

How's that for a rhyme, Toots? Eh, you'd like a companion. Well, we'll see."

So Rowlie Palmer traveled along his road. Sometimes, when he turned his head, he could see the collie in the fields behind him. Sometimes she was lost to view. But always she would be back again, drawn to the scent of meat, following it steadily. And each time she would come a bit nearer the wagon and the man who seemed to pay not the slightest heed to her.

When the sun was high, Rowlie Palmer pulled off the road. He saw the dog halt behind him.

"Time for a bite, Toots," he said.

Quickly he set up a small brazier and built a fire. He boiled water and made tea. He warmed over a pot of stew. He cut up liver and put it down in a bowl for Toots. He ate. All the time he watched the collie, drawing nearer and nearer.

He made a show of feeding bits of food to his little dog. He saw the collie, now sitting only twenty feet away, following with its eyes every move that his hand made. Toots barked at her, shrilly, once or twice, but Rowlie quieted his pet promptly.

When at last his meal was done, he rose. "Now," he said, "we know a trick or two, don't we, Toots? And we'll see whether you'll eat or not."

He took from his stock a flat bowl. He filled it with bits of liver. As unconcerned as if it were something he had done every day for years, he walked halfway to the collie and set the bowl down.

"There's your dinner," he said. "Eat it up."

Lassie watched him go back to the brazier. Then, as he seemed to be taking no notice of her, she rose from her sitting position. Slowly she walked to the bowl.

A dog must not eat stray bits of food! But this was different. It was set out in a bowl. That was it. It was in a bowl. And when a bowl or plate was set out by man, that meant a dog could eat without fear. There would be no living fire inside the food.

Gently Lassie dropped her head. With her front teeth, she lifted a piece of meat. She snapped it upwards. Then in the joy of eating again, she tore into the food. She cleaned up the bowl. She licked the bowl itself. Then she sat, looking at the man, as if to say, "Well, for an appetizer that was all right. Now where's the real meal?"

Rowlie shook his head and spoke out loud. "Ah, no. Ye'll come along wi' me if ye want any more. Didn't I say we knew a thing or two about tykes, Toots? Well, up we get and on our way!"

He took off Bess's nosebag. He tipped his brazier and stamped out the fire carefully. Snugly he stowed everything away. All the time from the corner of his eye, he saw the collie, sitting as if waiting. And when at last he was on the road again, Rowlie Palmer grunted happily. For the collie was traveling with him—not in the field now, but close behind the van. It was not too close. But Rowlie didn't mind that. That would come later, he very well knew.

Days later, Lassie was still with Rowlie Palmer. She trotted by the road, always a few feet behind the pottery van.

She never liked the banging and shouting as they came into villages. But it was as if she put up with it, knowing it could not last long. She was content as long as Rowlie went south. Once, at a fork in the road, Rowlie turned his van east. Some sense told him that part of his animal family was missing. He looked back. Lassie was sitting at the road junction.

Every time he called to her, she came a few steps. Then she circled, went back, and sat down.

Finally, Rowlie threw up his hands. He climbed to the seat of the van, turned Bess round, and started south on the other fork. "Eigh, I can just as well go round Godsey way as by Menlip," he said affably.

It was a good life, traveling along the quiet, empty lanes of the North country, far from the main highways where the trucks and lorries and motorcars went racing along. And Rowlie sang as the miles passed.

Command Performance

"Well, Your Majesty. Shall us common folks do a little vulgar business?" Rowlie addressed the words to

Lassie behind the wagon. She walked along, giving no sign of having heard.

"I know, Your Majesty," Rowlie said humbly. "It does hurt your royal ears to hear me speak of such things as money, but us humbler folks has got to live. So if you don't mind—*if* you don't mind—me and Toots will earn a little money."

Delighted with his own make-believe, Rowlie lifted his cap to Lassie and bowed low. Then he turned to his wagon and took down the largest bowl and his staff. He banged loudly as he approached the first house. The bell-like din echoed in the village.

> *"Bowls and pots, I've got lots,*
> > *Bring your penny or ye won't get any!*
> > *Bowls and pots!"*

The women flocked to the doors, and Rowlie greeted them. He halted his wagon by the village center, as the housewives fingered his wares and argued and joked about prices.

"They're so strong ye can't break 'em!" Rowlie chanted.

"I broke the one I got fro' ye last year," a woman cried.

"Well, I have to have 'em break once in a while," Rowlie said, his eyes gleaming. "If I made 'em absolutely unbreakable, ye'd never want any new ones and I'd do myself out of a job."

He winked broadly, and the women screamed with laughter.

"Now," Rowlie said, when the buying was done. "Who wants to see the tyke do a few tricks?"

The children yelled and clapped their hands. Rowlie got out the equipment from the wagon and set it up. Toots scrambled nimbly from the seat. Rowlie clapped

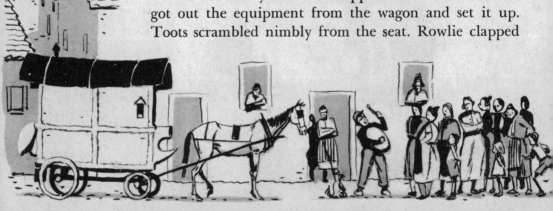

his hands. But nothing happened. The little dog sat waiting.

"What's the matter?" Rowlie said. "Ye're waiting for someone? Eigh, I see. Her Majesty hasn't arrived for the command performance. Why, here she comes now."

Carefully trained by Rowlie, Lassie strolled before the crowd and sat down. Rowlie gave her a little bit of liver as her reward.

"Well, now Her Majesty's here at last, we can begin, can't we?" Rowlie pattered on.

At the signal with his hand, Toots barked excitedly and began her tricks. She jumped through the hoops. She told how old she was by barking. She played "dead dog." She picked out the prettiest girl in the crowd—all

by Rowlie's hidden signals. Then she ended with her best
trick, walking on the ball of wood while she carried in
her mouth a tiny national flag.

"Doesn't the collie do aught?" a child cried.

"Why, ye wouldn't expect royalty to perform, would
ye?" Rowlie answered. "But it does seem like she's on a
sit-down strike."

Rowlie advanced to Lassie, carrying Toots in his arms.

"Would ye like to do some work?" he asked. Lassie sat
unblinking.

"Would ye like to pick up the things after the star's
finished?" Lassie still sat.

"Pick up those things!" Rowlie ordered in a thunderous
tone.

Lassie did not move, and the children screamed happily.
Rowlie scratched his head in mock dismay. Then his eyes
brightened. He held up his finger to the children. Then
he turned to Lassie.

"May it please Your Majesty, but as a favor to me,
would you *please* pick up the things?"

This time he gave the signal with his hand—for the
words had no bearing on the trick—and Lassie rose
proudly. She pushed the wooden ball with her slim muz-
zle to the van. She picked up the hoops one by one and
set them in a pile by the door. Rowlie bowed to her. Lassie
curtsied, stretching her front legs forward stiffly as a dog
does after it has been sleeping.

"Ye see," Rowlie said to the children. "Always remember to say please, and ye'll get more in this world. Well.
Off we go. Don't forget Peddler Palmer the Potter. I'll
be back next year. Good-bye."

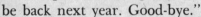

The Mother Teal and the Overland Route

Ernest Thompson Seton

A green-winged Teal had made her nest in the sedge by one of the grass-edged pools that fleck the sunny slope of the Riding Mountain. The passing farmer, driving his creaking ox-wagon, saw only a pond with the usual fringe of coarse grass, beyond which was a belt of low willow and an old poplar tree. But the little Teal in the rushes, and her neighbors, the Flickers, on the near-by poplar, saw in the pool a kingdom, a perfect paradise. For this was home. The little Flickers had almost chipped their glassy shells; and the eggs, the ten treasures of the Teal, had lost the look of mere interesting things, and were putting on, each, an air of sleeping personality, warm and almost vocal.

The little Teal had lost her mate early in the season. At least, he had disappeared, and it was fair to suppose him dead. But her attention was fully taken up with her nest and her brood.

All through the latter part of June, she tended them carefully. A little while each day, she left to seek food. Then she covered them carefully with a dummy foster-mother that she had made of down from her own breast.

One morning, as she flew away, leaving the dummy in charge, she heard an ominous crackling in the thick willows near at hand, but she wisely went on. When she returned, her neighbor, the Flicker, was still uttering a note of alarm. Down by her own nest were the fresh tracks of a man. The dummy mother had been disturbed, but, strange to tell, the eggs were all there and unharmed.

As the days went by, the little Greenwing felt the mother love growing in her heart to be ready for the ten little prisoners that were to be set free. They were no longer mere eggs, she felt. Sometimes she would talk to them in low raucous tones, and they would seem to answer from within in whispered "peepings," or perhaps in sounds too fine for human ear. So there is small wonder that when they do come out, baby Teal have already learned many of the few simple words that make up Teal-talk.

The many dangers of the early nesting-time were rapidly passed. But then a new one came. The growing springtime had turned into a drought. No rain had fallen for many, many days, and the pond was shrinking, quickly shrinking. Already, it was rimmed about by a great stretch of bare mud. Unless the rains came soon, the first experience of the little ones would be a perilous overland journey.

It was just as impossible to hurry up the hatching as it was to bring rain. The last few days of the mother's task were in view of a wide mud-flat where once had been the pond.

They all came out at last. The little china tombs were broken one by one, disclosing each a little Teal; ten little balls of mottled down, ten little cushions of yellow plush, ten little golden caskets with jewel eyes, enshrining each a spark of life.

But fate had been so harsh. It was now a matter of life and death to reach a pond. The mother must face the problem and face it now, or lose them all.

The Ducklings do not need to eat for several hours after they are hatched. But then they must eat. The nearest pond was half a mile away. And the great questions were: Could these baby Ducks hold out that long? Could they escape the countless dangers of the road?

All this the mother felt instinctively; and as soon as the ten were warmed and lively, she led them into the grass. Such a scrambling and peeping and tumbling about, as they tried to get through and over the grass-stalks that, like a bamboo forest, barred their way! Their mother had to watch the ten with one eye and the whole world with the other, for not a friend had she or they outside of themselves. The countless living things about were either foes or neutral.

The Marsh Hawk

After a long scramble through the grass, they climbed a bank and got among the bushes. Here they sat down to rest. One little fellow that had struggled along bravely with the others was so weak that there seemed no chance of his reaching that far-away Happyland, the pond.

When they were rested, their mother gave a low, gentle *quack* that doubtless meant, "Come along, children." And they set off again, scrambling over and around the twigs, each peeping softly when he was getting along nicely, or plaintively when he found himself caught in some thicket.

At last, they came to a wide open place. It was easy to travel here, but there was great danger of Hawks. The mother rested long in the edge of the thicket, examining the sky in every direction before she ventured into the open. Then, when all was clear, she gathered her little army for a dash over this great desert of nearly one hundred yards. The little fellows bravely struggled after her, their small yellow bodies raised at an angle, and their tiny wings held out like arms.

She was anxious to finish it all at one dash. But she soon

saw that that was hopeless. The strongest of her brood could keep up with her, but the others dragged in order of weakness. The brood now formed a little procession over twenty feet long, and the weakling was nearly ten feet behind that again.

A dangerous rest in the open was now enforced. The peepers came panting up to their mother. Full of anxiety, she lay there beside them till they were able to go on. Then she led them as before, quacking gently, "Courage, my darlings!"

They were not half-way to the pond yet, and the journey was telling on them. The brood strung out into another procession, with a wide gap to the runtie in the rear, when a great Marsh Hawk suddenly appeared, skimming low over the ground.

"Squat!" gasped Mother Greenwing, and the little things all lay flat, except the last one. Too far off to hear the low warning, he struggled on. The great Hawk swooped, seized him in his claws, and bore him peeping away over the bushes. All the poor mother could do was gaze in dumb sorrow as the bloodthirsty pirate bore off the downling. Yet, as he flew straight to the bank of the pond where lodged his crew of young, the Hawk heedlessly passed over the home bush of a Kingbird. That fearless little warrior screamed out his battle-cry as he gave chase. Away went the pirate, and away went the King, the one huge, heavy, and cowardly, the other small, swift, and fearless as a hero—away and away, out of sight, the Kingbird gaining at every stroke, till his voice was lost in the distance.

The sorrow of the Mother Greenwing, if less deep than that of the human mother, was yet very real. But she had now the nine to guard. She led them as quickly as possible into the bushes, and for a time they breathed more freely.

Thenceforth, she managed to have the journey lie through the cover. An hour or more passed by in slight alarms and in many rests. The pond was very near. And well it was, for the Ducklings were almost worn out. Their little paddles were scratched and bleeding, and their strength was all but gone. For a time they gasped under shadow of the last tall bush before again setting out in a compact flock to cross the next bare place, a rough opening through the poplars.

And they never knew that death in another form had lurked upon their track. A Red Fox crossed the trail of the little Duck army. His keen nose told him at once that here was a feast awaiting, and that all he had to do was follow it up and eat. So he sneaked softly and swiftly along their well-marked trail. He was already in sight of them. He was near enough to count the little marchers, if count he could, when the wind brought something which made him stop and crouch low. Then, at a surer whiff, he slunk away, fled as swiftly as he could without being seen. And the realest danger, surest death of all that had threatened, was overcome by an unseen power. Not even the Mother Duck had the slightest hint of it.

Rescue

The little ones now toddled along quickly again after their mother. To her delight, a long arm of the pond was quite close, just across that treeless lane. She made straight for it, joyfully calling, "Come, my darlings!"

But alas! The treeless opening was one of the man-made things called a "cart-trail." On each side of it were the deep-worn, endless canyons that man calls "wheel-ruts." Into the first of these fell four of her brood. Five managed to scramble across, but the other rut was yet deeper and wider, and the five were there engulfed.

Oh, dear, this was terrible! The little ones were too weak now to climb out. The ruts seemed endless in both directions, and the mother did not know how to help them. She and they were in despair. As she ran about calling and urging them to put forth all their strength, there came up suddenly the very thing she most feared—the deadliest enemy of Ducks—a great, tall man.

Mother Greenwing flung herself at his feet and flopped on the grass. Not begging for mercy! Oh, no! She was only trying to trick the man into thinking she was wounded, so that he would follow her, and she could lead him away.

But this man knew the trick, and he would not follow. Instead of that, he looked about. He found the nine little downlings deep in the ruts, vainly trying to hide.

He stooped gently, and gathered them all into his hat.

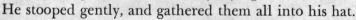

Poor little things, how they did *peep!* Poor little mother, how she did cry! Now she knew that they were all to be destroyed before her very eyes, and she beat her breast on the ground before the terrible giant in agony of sorrow.

Then the heartless monster went to the edge of the pond, no doubt for a drink to wash the Ducklings down his throat. He bent down, and a moment later the Ducklings were spattering free over the water! The mother flew out on the glassy surface. She called, and they all came scurrying to her. She did not know that this man was really her friend. She never knew that he was the divinity whose mere presence had been enough to drive the Fox away, and she went on hating him to the end.

She tried to lead her brood far away from him. She took them right across the open pond. This was a mistake, for it exposed them to other, to real, enemies. That great Marsh Hawk saw them, and he came swooping along, sure of getting one in each claw.

"Run for the rushes!" called out the Mother Green-wing. And run they all did, pattering over the surface as fast as their tired little legs could go.

"Run! Run!" cried the mother. But the Hawk was close at hand now. In spite of all their running, he would be upon them in another second. They were too young to dive. There seemed no escape. Just as he pounced, the bright little mother gave a great splash with all her strength, and using both feet and wings, dashed the water all over the Hawk. He was astonished. He sprang back into the air to shake himself dry. The mother urged the little ones to "keep on." Keep on they did. Down came the Hawk again, again to be driven off with a shower of spray. Three times did he pounce, three times did she drench him. At last, all the downlings were safe in the friendly rushes. The angry Hawk now made a lunge at the mother. But she could dive, and giving a good-by splash, she easily disappeared.

Far in the rushes she came up, and called a gentle *quack, quack!* The nine tired little ones came to her, and safely they rested at last.

But that was not all. Just as they began to feast on the plentiful insect life, a far-away faint peep was heard. Mother Greenwing called again her mothering *qu-a-a-a-a-c-c—k*. And through the sedge demurely paddling, like an old-timer, came their missing one that the Hawk had carried off.

He had not been hurt by the claws. The valiant King-bird had overtaken the Hawk over the pond. At the first blow of his bill, the Hawk had shrieked and dropped his prey. The little Duck fell unharmed into the water, and escaped into the rushes till his mother and brothers came. Then he rejoined them, and they lived happily in the great pond till they all grew up and flew away on wings of their own.

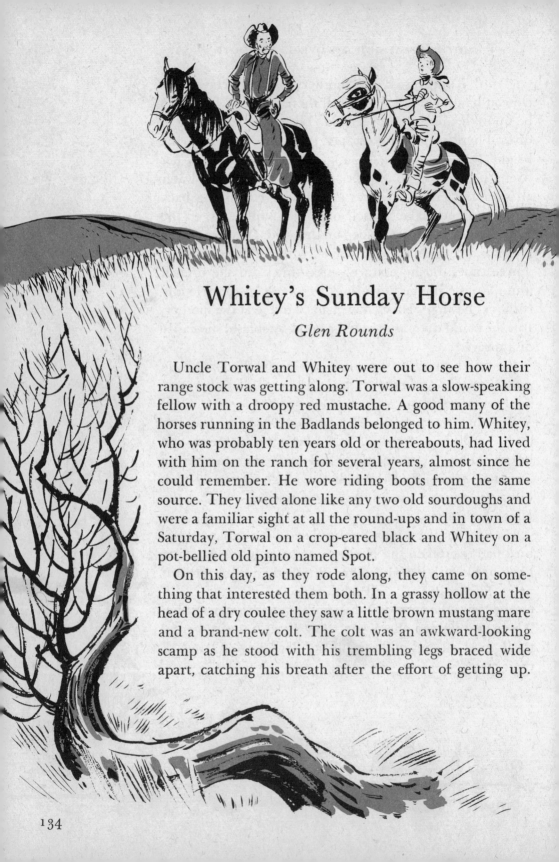

Whitey's Sunday Horse

Glen Rounds

Uncle Torwal and Whitey were out to see how their range stock was getting along. Torwal was a slow-speaking fellow with a droopy red mustache. A good many of the horses running in the Badlands belonged to him. Whitey, who was probably ten years old or thereabouts, had lived with him on the ranch for several years, almost since he could remember. He wore riding boots from the same source. They lived alone like any two old sourdoughs and were a familiar sight at all the round-ups and in town of a Saturday, Torwal on a crop-eared black and Whitey on a pot-bellied old pinto named Spot.

On this day, as they rode along, they came on something that interested them both. In a grassy hollow at the head of a dry coulee they saw a little brown mustang mare and a brand-new colt. The colt was an awkward-looking scamp as he stood with his trembling legs braced wide apart, catching his breath after the effort of getting up.

His body was close knit and compact, and his back was strong and flat, but his legs were so long and slender he appeared to be walking on stilts.

The mare whirled to face them, keeping the colt behind her. With her teeth bared and her ears laid back, she looked half wolf for sure.

"Spunky critter, that mare," Whitey said to Torwal as they rode carefully around, trying to get a good look at the colt.

"She's a wolf, all right," Torwal agreed. "Better not crowd her."

They sat on their horses and admired the colt. "Reckon we better take him home," asked Whitey, "so the wolves won't get him?"

"Don't reckon we'll take him anywhere," Torwal told him. "Looks like I'm a-going to have to shoot him!"

"Shoot him! Why?" squalled Whitey. "Why, he's the purtiest colt on the ranch!"

"Better look him over closer, Bub," said Torwal.

"I don't see anything wrong, myself," Whitey told him, after he'd walked Spot in a circle around the mare and colt again. "He looks to me just like the kind of critter I'd like to have for a 'Sunday' horse."

"Look at his eyes! They're white," Torwal growled. "That colt's blind as a bat!"

"Aw, they're just china eyes, Uncle Torwal," Whitey said. "Lots of horses have china eyes. Even old Spot has one."

They're not china eyes, not by a long shot," said Torwal. "If you look close, you'll see that they're pure white. He's blind, and we gotta shoot him. Otherwise he'll fall in a hole or get wolf et."

"Well, even if he is blind, do we *hafta* shoot him?" Whitey asked. "Couldn't I take him home and keep him at the ranch?"

"All he'd be is a mess of trouble even if you got him home. I doubt that he'd get that far," Torwal told him.

"Couldn't we just let him go loose?" Whitey said.

"Now quit your squalling," Torwal told him patiently. "I don't like it any more than you do. But if we leave him, he'll either fall in a hole and starve or else get wolf et."

While Whitey sat with his lip hanging down almost to his collar, Torwal got out the rifle hanging at his saddle. But whenever he tried to get near the colt the little mare was there, lashing out with her heels and baring her teeth to bite either man or horse that got too near.

After this had gone on a little while, Whitey spoke up again. "Listen, Uncle Torwal," he said, "I don't believe any wolf could get to that colt, the way the mare uses her heels. If you'll let him go, I'll watch mighty close to see if he falls in anything. I'll ride out every day. And if he does fall in, I—I—I'll shoot him myself!"

Uncle Torwal thought the matter over a while. "You want that colt mighty bad, don't you?" he said at last.

"I sure do! He's the purtiest thing I've ever seen!" said Whitey. "I don't think anything will happen to him, really, Uncle Torwal! He's too smart!"

"Well," Torwal said doubtfully, "since you feel like that about it, we'll let him go this time. We'll be riding over here every day for a while, so we can always shoot him later. But don't go getting your hopes up," he added. "The chances are he won't last a week."

"Nothing is going to happen to him," Whitey exclaimed. "You'll see."

"Maybe," said Uncle Torwal. Whitey could see that he was glad to have an excuse for not shooting the colt. They sat watching a while longer, and then rode off.

The little mare stood guard until they were out of sight. When she could no longer hear them, she started down the trail toward the place she'd left the mustang band, with the blind colt following close against her flank.

Lessons for the Colt

Off and on all summer and fall, Whitey saw the mustangs and the blind colt with them. He seemed to have learned how to take care of himself as well as the colts that could see. Then late in the winter—March it was—there came a great blizzard. One morning, Whitey went out to

the horse pasture and saw the blind colt in the open-faced
shed with the saddle horses. He could only guess what had
happened. Probably the blind colt had gotten separated
from the wild horses as they drifted ahead of the storm
and had stumbled on until he found shelter. Ordinarily,
the ranch horses would have chased him out because he
was strange to them. But old pot-bellied Spot took a fancy
to the lost and lonely youngster, as old horses will sometimes do, and let him have a place between him and the
wall of the shed.

When Whitey first saw them, the colt was sticking to
the old horse as if it were his mother. Then Spot saw the
boy and trotted up to meet him, but the colt galloped off
to a safe distance, where he stood cocking his ears forward
and back and snorting softly.

Whitey's excitement can be imagined, when he saw
that it was the blind colt that was following Old Spot. He
rubbed Spot's head and talked softly to the colt, which
was still standing some distance off. Spot seemed to be as
proud of the colt as if it belonged to him. Confusion,
the dog, sat on the snow with his tongue hanging out and
didn't express an opinion.

Whitey didn't mean to let Uncle Torwal find out that
the blind colt was there if he could help it. He might
start talking about shooting the poor blind critter.
Whitey thought the matter over as he threw hay over the
fence and scattered it out on the snow.

After he'd thrown the hay out, Whitey hung around as
long as he dared. But after a while he had to leave, for
fear Torwal would get to wondering what had happened
to him and come out to look.

That afternoon, he came back again. He still didn't

have a plan, but he brought a pan of oats. When he rattled them in the pan, Spot threw up his head and came trotting up. He knew what the sound meant. The colt followed at a distance as he had in the morning. Tolling Spot along with the pan of oats, Whitey walked away from the rest of the horses. When he'd got him off by himself, he scattered some of the oats on the snow and walked off some distance and stood still.

Spot got busy right away eating the oats. The colt listened to find what Whitey was doing. Not hearing anything, he moved cautiously forward a few steps at a time, snorting and bowing his neck. By the time he got to where Spot was, most of the oats were gone. But he did manage to get a taste.

When Spot finished, Whitey rattled the pan again, and poured out some more oats on the snow where he stood. Spot trotted to him while the colt whirled away, only to come slowly back as Whitey stood still. He repeated the performance several times that afternoon, and the first thing next morning he was back again. He was trying to teach the colt to come to the rattle of the oats pan.

Gradually, the colt lost some of his fear. After a time, he would come up within a few feet and eat the spilled oats greedily. But before he got so he'd let Whitey touch him, the snow was gone. Something had to be done about him if Uncle Torwal wasn't to find out.

So, one afternoon, Whitey brought the oats and a rope halter and caught Old Spot and climbed up on his back. Then he rattled the oats pan and rode slowly off towards the far end of the pasture. He'd remembered a little box canyon over in the far corner that had a small unused corral.

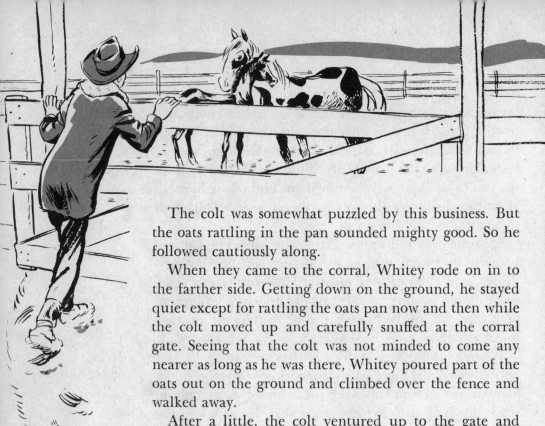

The colt was somewhat puzzled by this business. But the oats rattling in the pan sounded mighty good. So he followed cautiously along.

When they came to the corral, Whitey rode on in to the farther side. Getting down on the ground, he stayed quiet except for rattling the oats pan now and then while the colt moved up and carefully snuffed at the corral gate. Seeing that the colt was not minded to come any nearer as long as he was there, Whitey poured part of the oats out on the ground and climbed over the fence and walked away.

After a little, the colt ventured up to the gate and snorted around until he was convinced that Old Spot was alone inside. After that, he walked up to get his share of the oats. While he was busy with them, Whitey moved around and shut the gate.

Then he pushed his second-hand Stetson to the back of his head and looked through the bars of the corral at his new horse. The colt was his now. He was so full of pride that his chest hurt him considerably. He felt as if he might swell and bust any minute.

Now all he had to do was keep Uncle Torwal from finding out anything until he had the colt gentled and perhaps taught him some tricks. He figured that once he got him trained, Uncle Torwal would see what a smart horse he was and wouldn't say anything more about turning him loose.

It took plenty of patience to gentle that wild colt. But finally Whitey had him so he would come and eat out of his hand. Then, gradually, the colt lost his fear of the boy and would let himself be curried all over, have his feet picked up, and would even lead. Next, Whitey taught him to come to his whistle.

The Showdown

One afternoon, Whitey was sitting on top of the old corral fence watching Spot and the colt busy grazing some distance off and thinking how lucky he was that Uncle Torwal hadn't found out what he was doing.

He was just in the middle of deciding that he'd show the blind colt at the county fair in the fall, and was in the middle of listening to the crowds in the grandstand hollering with excitement at seeing the blind colt jump through a flaming hoop, when he was interrupted.

"What's that little 'Crow-bait' doing here, Bub?"

Whitey nearly fell off the fence, he was so surprised. Uncle Torwal had ridden up from the other side, and he'd been so busy with his county fair imaginings that he hadn't heard him.

"Oh, he's just grazing with Old Spot," Whitey said after he had pulled himself together. "Isn't he a purty scamp, though?"

Uncle Torwal got off his horse and climbed up on the fence beside Whitey before he answered. Then he took his jackknife out of his pocket and settled down to whittling like he was going to spend the afternoon horse trading or something.

"He is a right likely looking piece of horseflesh, for a fact," he said after a while. "Too bad he's blind."

"You bet he's purty!" Whitey said. He wondered what he should say next. He knew that the time had come for a showdown, but he also knew that Uncle Torwal had his horse-trading mood on and that there was no use coming straight out and asking him anything. So he decided to horse trade too, and he took out his jackknife so he could wait for Uncle Torwal to make the next move.

"Him and Old Spot act like they was old friends. Kinda looks like the colt musta been in here some time," Torwal said after a while.

"Yessir, it does kinda look that way for a fact," Whitey agreed, and whittled busily.

"Wouldn't be surprised if maybe he drifted in during the blizzard," Uncle Torwal went on after a time.

Whitey knew that all this had nothing to do with whether he could keep the colt or not. Uncle Torwal was just playing cat and mouse with him. He'd have a lot better chance of keeping the colt if he could keep on acting like a horse trader. So he tipped his old hat a little further back on his head and whittled some more.

"Yessir, that's probably just about what happened," Whitey said, as if he weren't worried at all.

"Now that he's made up to Old Spot the way he has, it's kinda too bad we gotta shag him out on the range again," Uncle Torwal said.

"Yeah, it does seem kinda too bad," said Whitey.

"Of course, if he was gentle and knowed anything, it'd be different," Torwal went on. "But you take a critter raised wild like he was, and being blind too, I doubt that a feller would ever be able to do anything with him."

"But you figure that if he could be gentled, he might make a good Sunday horse?" Whitey asked, grinning to himself.

"Well, I dunno," Torwal said. "But when I was a kid I had a blind saddle mare and she was a dandy. Sure footed as a goat, she was. But she was extra smart," he added.

"This colt is mighty smart!" Whitey exclaimed.

"Well, he did manage not to get wolf et," Torwal

agreed. "But that was probably just luck. It doesn't mean he could learn anything else."

Whitey saw that now was the time to get busy if he wanted to keep the colt. So he slid down off the fence.

"Watch this, Uncle Torwal," he said, and whistled shrilly.

The colt stopped grazing and came trotting up. When he got close, he smelled Torwal and snorted and stopped. Whitey called him and the colt came on, keeping his ears pointed at Torwal, however, and snorting a little. Whitey fed the colt a handful of oats and put the halter on him. He rubbed his hands all over the colt and picked up his feet, one by one, to show that he was gentle. He'd seen horse traders do that. Then Whitey called Confusion. The dog came running and jumped up on the blind colt's back.

"How do you like this, Uncle Torwal?" Whitey asked as he led the colt up with Confusion still on his back.

"Well, now!" Torwal exclaimed. "Don't know as I've ever seen anything like it before."

"Oh, he's a smart feller all right," Whitey said, grinning fit to split his face.

"Hmm," Torwal said, cautiously. "Can he do anything else?"

Whitey had hoped Uncle Torwal would ask that, because he had spent a lot of time teaching the colt a special trick.

He turned to the colt. "Do you think you could learn to be a fancy saddle horse?" he asked him. He scratched him lightly between the forelegs. The colt nodded his head up and down.

"You're never going to be any trouble to anybody, are you?" he asked him again. At the same time he scratched the colt's shoulder. The colt nodded his head sidewise.

"See that, Uncle Torwal!" Whitey said. "He can even talk!"

Torwal grinned. "Reckon he's smarter than I figured!"

"Yessir!" said Whitey. "And he'll learn to do a lot of other things, too!"

Uncle Torwal climbed down off the fence and walked over to his horse.

"Well, you better bring him home and put him in the calf pasture if you figure on keeping him," he said, as he climbed into the saddle.

"Yessir! I'll bring him right over!" Whitey said.

Bambi and The Enemy

Felix Salten

*Bambi was a young deer. All his life he had lived in the
forest. From his earliest days, he had been taught to watch
for danger—above all, from Man.*

*But now Bambi's cousin Gobo had just come back to
the forest. Gobo had been captured by hunters when he
was only a fawn, and he did not fear Man at all.*

All the deer soon saw that Gobo had habits which
seemed strange and suspicious to the rest of them. He
slept at night when the others were awake. But in the
daytime, when the rest of them were looking for places to
sleep in, he was wide awake and went walking. When he
felt like it, he would even go out of the thicket and stand
with perfect peace of mind in the bright sunshine on the
meadow.

Bambi found it impossible to keep silent any longer.
"Don't you ever think of the danger?" he asked.

"No," Gobo said simply, "there isn't any for me."

"You forget, my dear Bambi," Gobo's mother broke in,
"you forget that He's a friend of Gobo's. Gobo can take
chances that the rest of you cannot take." She was very
proud.

Bambi did not say anything more.

One day Gobo said to him, "You know, it seems strange
to me to eat when and where I like."

Bambi did not understand. "Why is it strange? We all do it," he said.

"Oh, you do," said Gobo in a superior way, "but I'm different. I'm accustomed to having my food brought to me or to being called when it's ready."

Bambi stared pityingly at Gobo. He looked at Faline and Marena and Aunt Ena. But they were all smiling and admiring Gobo.

"I think it will be hard for you to get accustomed to the winter, Gobo," Faline began. "We don't have hay or turnips or potatoes in the winter time."

"That's true," answered Gobo, considering it. "I hadn't thought about that yet. I can't even imagine how it would feel. It must be dreadful."

Bambi said quietly, "It isn't dreadful. It's only hard."

"Well," Gobo declared grandly, "if it gets too hard for me I'll simply go back to Him. Why should I go hungry? There's no need for that."

Bambi turned away without a word and walked off.

When Gobo was alone again with Marena he began to talk about Bambi. "He doesn't understand me," he said. "Poor old Bambi thinks I'm still the silly little Gobo that I once was. He can never get used to the fact that I've become something unusual. Danger! . . . Danger is something for him and the likes of him, not for me."

Marena agreed with him. She loved him and Gobo loved her and they were both very happy.

A few weeks passed, and one morning Bambi and Faline, Gobo and Marena were standing together again in the old familiar hazel thicket. Bambi and Faline were just returning from their wanderings, intending to look for their hiding place, when they met Gobo and Marena. Gobo was about to go out on the meadow.

"Stay with us instead," said Bambi. "The sun will soon be rising and then nobody will go out in the open."

"Nonsense," said Gobo, scornfully. "If nobody else will go, I will."

He went on, Marena following him.

Bambi and Faline had stopped. "Come along," said Bambi angrily to Faline, "come along. Let him do what he pleases."

They were going on, but suddenly the jay screamed loudly from the far side of the meadow. With a bound, Bambi had turned and was running after Gobo. Right by the oak, he caught up with him and Marena.

"Did you hear that?" he cried to him.

"What?" asked Gobo, puzzled.

Again the jay screamed. "Did you hear that?" Bambi repeated.

"No," said Gobo calmly.

"That means danger," Bambi persisted.

A magpie began to chatter loudly and, immediately after her, another and then a third. Then the jay screamed again and far overhead the crows gave warning.

Faline began to plead. "Don't go out there, Gobo! It's dangerous."

Even Marena begged, "Stay here. Stay here today. It's dangerous."

Gobo stood there, smiling in his superior way. "Dangerous! Dangerous! What has that to do with me?" he asked.

Bambi had an idea. "At least let Marena go first," he said, "so we can find out. . . ."

He hadn't finished before Marena had slipped out. All three stood and looked at her, Bambi and Faline breathlessly, Gobo with obvious patience, as if to let the others enjoy their foolish notions.

They saw how Marena walked across the meadow step by step, with hesitant feet, her head up. She peered and snuffed in all directions. Suddenly she turned like a flash, with one high bound, and rushed back into the thicket.

"It's He, He," she whispered, her voice choking with terror. She was trembling in every limb. "I, I saw Him," she stammered. "It's He. He's standing over by the alders."

"Come," cried Bambi, "come quickly."

"Come," Faline pleaded. And Marena, who could hardly speak, whispered, "Please come now, Gobo, please."

But Gobo remained unmoved. "Run as much as you like," he said. "I won't stop you. If He's there, I want to talk with Him."

Gobo could not be dissuaded. They stood and watched

how he went out. They stayed there, moved by his great confidence, while at the same time a terrible fear for him gripped them.

Gobo was standing boldly on the meadow looking around for the alders. Then he seemed to see them and to have discovered Him. Then the thunder crashed.

Gobo leaped into the air at the report. He suddenly turned around and fled back to the thicket, staggering as he came.

They still stood there, petrified with terror, while he came on. They heard him gasping for breath. And as he did not stop but bounded wildly forward, they turned and surrounded him and all took flight.

But poor Gobo dropped to the ground. Marena stopped close to him, Bambi and Faline a little farther off, ready to flee. Gobo lifted his head with a feeble twisting motion.

"Marena," he said with an effort, "Marena . . ." His voice failed.

There was a loud, careless rustling in the bushes by the meadow. Marena bent her head towards Gobo. "He's coming," she whispered frantically. "Gobo, He's coming! Can't you get up and come with me?"

Gobo lifted his head again feebly with a writhing motion, beat convulsively with his hoofs, and then lay still. With a crackling, snapping, and rustling, He parted the bushes and stepped out.

Marena saw Him from quite near. She slunk slowly back, disappearing through the nearest bushes, and hastened to Bambi and Faline. She looked back once again and saw how He was bending over and seizing the wounded deer.

The Snare

Bambi was alone. He walked beside the water that ran swiftly among the reeds and swamp-willows. He went there more and more often now. There were few trails there, and he hardly ever met any of his friends. That was just what he wanted. For his thoughts had grown serious and his heart heavy.

One day, Bambi wandered through a whole sea of goldenrod, passed through a grove of young beeches, crossed through old hazel thickets until he reached the edge of the deep ditch. He roamed around it, hoping to meet his friend, the old stag. He had not seen the old fellow for a long while.

Then he caught a glimpse of the stag from afar, and ran to meet him. For a while they walked together in silence. Then the old stag asked, "Well, do they still talk about him the way they used to?"

Bambi understood that he referred to Gobo and replied, "I don't know. I'm nearly alone now." He hesitated. "But I think of him very often."

They went on. Suddenly the old stag stopped. "Don't you hear anything?" he asked.

Bambi listened. He didn't hear anything.

"Come," cried the old stag and hurried forward. Bambi followed him. The stag stopped again. "Don't you hear anything yet?" he asked.

Then Bambi heard a rustling that he did not understand. It sounded like branches being bent down and repeatedly springing up again. Something was beating the earth dully and irregularly.

Bambi wanted to flee. But the old stag cried, "Come with me," and ran in the direction of the noise. Bambi at his side ventured to ask, "Isn't it dangerous?"

"It's terribly dangerous," the old stag answered mysteriously.

Soon they saw branches being pulled and tugged at from below and shaken violently. They went nearer and saw that a little trail ran through the middle of the bushes.

Friend Hare was lying on the ground. He flung himself from side to side and writhed. Then he lay still and writhed again. Each of his motions pulled at the branches over him.

Bambi noticed a dark threadlike leash. It ran right from the branch to Friend Hare and was twisted around his neck.

Friend Hare must have heard someone coming, for he flung himself wildly into the air and fell to the ground. He tried to escape and rolled, jerking and writhing in the grass.

"Lie still," the old stag commanded. Then, with a gentle voice that went to Bambi's heart, he repeated in his ear, "Be easy, Friend Hare, it's I. Don't move now. Lie perfectly still."

The Hare lay motionless, flat on the ground. His breath rattled softly in his throat.

The old stag took the branch between his teeth, and twisted it. He bent down. Then he walked around, putting his weight cunningly against it. He held it to the earth with his hoof and snapped it with a single blow of his antlers.

Then he nodded encouragingly to the Hare. "Lie still," he said. "Even if I hurt you."

Holding his head on one side, he laid one prong of his antlers close to the Hare's neck and pressed into the fur behind his ear. The Hare began to writhe.

The old stag immediately drew back. "Lie still," he commanded. "It's a question of life and death for you." The Hare lay still, gasping. Bambi stood close by, speechless with amazement.

One of the old stag's antlers, pressing against the Hare's fur, had slipped under the noose. The old stag was almost kneeling. He twisted his head as though he were charging. He drove his antlers deeper and deeper under the noose, which gave at last and began to loosen.

The Hare could breathe again, and his terror and pain burst from him instantly. "E-e-eh!" he cried bitterly.

The old stag stopped. "Keep quiet!" he cried. "How can you be so stupid as to cry at this time? Do you want the fox to come? Do you? I thought not. Keep quiet then."

He continued to work away, slowly exerting all his strength. Suddenly the noose broke with a loud snap. The Hare slipped out and was free. He took a step and sat down again dazed. Then he hopped away, slowly and timidly at first, then faster and faster. Presently he was running with wild leaps.

Bambi looked after him. "Without so much as a thank you!" he exclaimed in surprise.

"He's still terrified," said the old stag.

The noose lay on the ground. Bambi touched it gently. It creaked, terrifying Bambi. That was a sound such as he had never heard in the woods.

"He?" asked Bambi softly.

The old stag nodded. They walked on together in silence. "Take care when you're going along a trail," said the old stag. "Test all the branches. Prod them on all sides of you with your antlers. And turn back at once if you hear that creak. I never use trails any more."

Bambi sank into troubled thought. "He isn't here," he whispered to himself in the deepest astonishment.

"No, He's not in the forest now," the old stag answered.

"And yet He is here," said Bambi, shaking his head.

The old stag said slowly, "We must learn to live and be cautious."

Smoky

Marion Holland

The whole family was getting ready to leave for the cottage in New Hampshire where they spent their summers. "Then that's the way we'll do it," said Father to Mother. "You take the plane to Boston tomorrow morning, and catch the afternoon train to the lake. That will give you time to get the cottage opened and everything ready while I drive up in the car with the children and the heavy luggage."

"But, Father," argued Andy, "why can't I go on the plane, too, with Mother? Gee, I've never been in a plane in my whole life!"

"Because you can just as well go in the car. It costs too much to send you in the plane just for the fun of it. And one more thing—I will *not* drive all the way to New Hampshire again with that awful cat in the car."

"But, Father," wailed Anne, who was sitting on the floor cuddling the big Persian cat, "we've got to take Smoky! Why can't he go in the car with us?"

"Maybe you've forgotten what happened last year, but I haven't," said Father grimly. "We stopped for gas in Baltimore, and Smoky got out and climbed on the filling station roof. It took forty minutes to find a ladder and get him down again. And in Philadelphia, he jumped out the window and ran down the middle of the street in all that traffic—and it took two policemen and the whole

family an hour to round him up again. Not to mention the way he yowled all the way, and dug that big hole in the upholstery—"

"Yes, I remember," said Anne hastily. "But he's a whole year older, now, and he'll behave better. Won't you, Smoky?"

Smoky opened one green eye, and shut it again. Sharp curved claws crept out from an enormous paw and hooked quietly into the best rug.

"Scat!" shouted Father. "Get off that rug! I wouldn't mind that cat's being such a complete nuisance," he went on in a reasonable tone of voice, "if he were the slightest use in the world. But what good is he? Won't eat this, won't eat that. Sleeps in the best chair. Won't catch mice— why, there are mice in the pantry right now, dying peacefully of old age—"

Smoky lifted his superb plume of a tail and stalked majestically from the room. "Oh, Father," cried Anne. "Now you've hurt his feelings again!"

"All right, all right, he can go. But not with me. That's final."

"Maybe we could ship him by freight," suggested Mother mildly. "Of course, it would take several days—"

"Smoky would hate that. Couldn't he go on the plane with you?" asked Anne.

"I don't know whether planes take cats as passengers," said Mother doubtfully.

"Call up and see," urged Andy.

They called up. Yes, the plane would take a cat, but not as a passenger. He would have to be crated and weighed in, and travel with the rest of Mother's luggage. "Say—why couldn't I go as luggage, too?" shouted Andy.

"You," said Father, "can march down to the basement, right now, and fix up a crate for Smoky. A good strong one."

Anne and Andy found a box in the basement and bored a few holes in it for air and fixed a lid with hinges and a latch. "The lucky dog—cat, I mean," grumbled Andy. "Getting to ride in a plane."

"Look, what about Smoky if there should be an accident or something?" asked Anne anxiously. "You know how it always is in the movies, people jumping out of planes with parachutes. Are there cat parachutes?"

"Say, that's an idea. Have we still got that big hunk of parachute stuff that Uncle Jim brought back from the Pacific?"

By dinner time, the cat parachute was finished. The large, circular piece of nylon was attached by strings to

a fancy leather harness that Smoky had once gotten for Christmas but never cared much about. Andy wanted to test it on the cat, but Smoky took one good look at the contraption, dug four sets of claws into Andy's arm, and departed rapidly over the back fence. So they found a piece of oak in the woodpile that weighed about as much as Smoky. They fastened the harness around this and dropped it out of the attic window. At first it fell like a stone; then the chute billowed out and the piece of wood checked and descended more slowly, swaying gently from side to side.

"Let's not bother Mother and Father about this," said Andy thoughtfully. "I'll leave it in the crate for tonight, and we'll put it on him in the morning before we start."

Next morning, while their parents were loading the car for the trip, they found a small can of sardines looking forlorn and forgotten on the pantry shelves. They lured Smoky into the basement with this, and quickly buckled on the harness while he was happily eating. The parachute, folded neatly, fitted into the bottom of the box, and they bundled the cat in on it. Andy slammed and latched the lid and waited for the explosion. But Smoky was full of sardines, and besides, he had been out all night. He curled up and went to sleep.

He woke up, though, when the crate was put in the car. You could tell that by the noise coming out of the crate. "That cat," said Father.

At the airport, there were quite a number of people standing around where the luggage was being weighed in, and they were all interested when Smoky's crate was set on the scales. It suddenly rose up in the air an inch or two, all by itself, and came down again with a crash that jiggled the weights on the bar. The noise was really something to hear—not exactly a howl, and not exactly a growl, but something about midway between the two. The whole scales quivered.

Smoky's crate was loaded aboard with Mother's suitcase, and Mother got on with the other passengers. Andy, waving as the big plane taxied down the runway, could not help feeling that an airplane ride was wasted on a crated cat and a lady who, even if she was his mother, couldn't tell a P-51 from a C-54.

Smoky Bails Out

"When do the passengers put on their parachutes?" asked Anne, watching the plane grow smaller.

"Parachutes?" said Father. "Why, they don't bother with parachutes in these big passenger planes. They're as safe as trains. Safer, maybe."

"Oh," said Anne. "All that work and we needn't have bothered. Poor Smoky."

"What about Smoky?" asked Father, starting the car.

Anne and Andy looked at each other, feeling foolish. "Nothing," they said.

"That's fine," said Father. "I would be just as glad to hear nothing about that cat for the rest of this trip. When I think about the way he ate the biggest fish I caught all last summer—it wasn't so much that I grudged him the fish, but he might at least have waited until I had taken a picture of it."

They found plenty to talk about without mentioning Smoky again. Late on the second day, the car turned into the dirt road leading to the cottage, and Andy leaned out the window, yelling, "I see the lake!"

"I see the dock!" shouted Anne.

"I see Mother!" shouted Andy. "Hi, Mother! How was the plane ride?"

"Did Smoky just hate it?" asked Anne, jumping from the car.

"The plane ride was fine," answered Mother. "But—
oh, dear, I hardly know how to tell you. Such a day as
I had yesterday. The man at the airport office in Boston
kept talking about whether it should be our loss or the
company's. And there was a reporter who kept asking
questions and *asking* questions—why, he seemed to think
the whole thing was funny! It's a wonder I didn't miss
my train!"

"What *is* this all about?" demanded Father.

"Smoky," said Mother.

"Yes, where *is* Smoky?" asked Anne, looking around.

"Gone," said Mother.

"Gone where?" asked Andy.

"Oh, dear. Well, sit down and I'll get it over with.
You see, just before we came in at Philadelphia—we
stopped at Philadelphia and New York on the way—anyway, somebody opened the door to the little place up
front where the hand luggage goes—and everything happened all at once. Smoky must have gotten out of his
crate somehow. Andy, are you sure you had it fastened
properly? Anyway, he just shot between the man's legs
and came flying down the aisle. Such confusion, with

everybody dodging and yelling! But Smoky doubled back into the luggage place and the man had him cornered against the far door, and then—oh, dear—"

"And then—what?" demanded Anne breathlessly.

"And then—that door opened, the co-pilot it must have been. And Smoky simply sailed past him, right up to where the pilots sit, and shot out that little side window and disappeared into a cloud—"

"Oh no!" cried Anne. "You don't mean Smoky jumped out the window, and he's—"

"Well, yes, dear. You know how Smoky is—was, I should say."

Anne burst into tears.

"And the strangest thing about it," went on Mother, "was that he must have gotten tangled up in someone's scarf, because he was dragging this long white thing behind him. Only it was bigger than a scarf, really, more like a nightgown. Though I can't imagine where he would have gotten hold of a nightgown, and nobody complained about missing one—"

"But that was his parachute!" cried Andy excitedly. "Did it open all right?"

"His *what?*" exclaimed Father and Mother.

"Parachute. We made him one. He had it on in the crate."

"If you wrapped something around Smoky, no wonder he clawed his way out of the crate," said Father severely. "He probably thrashed around and got so tangled up in it he could hardly move."

"Well, I wouldn't say that," said Mother thoughtfully. "He was moving, all right. I don't think I ever saw anything move any faster."

"But don't you see?" cried Andy. "Stop crying, Anne. If it opened all right, he probably made a perfect four-point landing. All we have to do is find out where the plane was when he jumped, and go back and get him."

"We can *not,*" said Father, in a very final sort of voice. "Just make up your mind that Smoky is gone. It's too bad, of course, but that cat has just jumped out of one window too many. When we get home again, we'll see about getting you another cat. One that will eat table scraps and be glad to get them. One that will catch mice," said Father.

The Mysterious Prowler

At about this time, a farmer named Paxon in Pennsylvania was saying to his son, "Bill, I want you to keep your eyes open around the chicken house. Something is after those baby chicks. There are four missing today, and I found tracks in the mud near the water pan."

"Tracks? Gee, what kind of tracks?"

"Well, that's the funny thing about it. Big tracks. Bobcat, I'd say, but I never heard of any bobcats around here."

"Bobcat? Golly!" Bill raced down to the chicken house. There were the tracks, all right, and they certainly looked enormous. When he returned to the house, he had something in his hand. "Look, Dad, what I found stuck on a nail by the chicken house door. Like a piece off a handkerchief, or something. Maybe it was a tramp that took the chicks."

His father looked closely at the piece and shook his head. "A tramp would go for frying chickens—or old hens. But I never heard of a bobcat carrying a silk pocket-handkerchief."

Mrs. Paxon ran her fingers over the scrap. "Why, this is real fine material."

"Say!" cried Bill. "We got a fine first-class mystery to solve!"

"Fine or not," grumbled his father, "if any more chicks turn up missing, I'm going to solve it with a shotgun."

The next day there were more chicks gone, and fresh tracks. "It's a bobcat, all right," said Mr. Paxon, loading his shotgun. But that afternoon, Bill dashed in from the pasture with another and much larger piece of cloth. "Found it caught in that mess of blackberry bushes," he explained. "Looks like your bobcat is a mighty fancy feller." His father scratched his head. But his mother took the piece of material, exclaiming, "Why, that will make a real nice handkerchief. Find me a bigger piece, son, and I'll have a new Sunday dress."

The next morning, there were more chicks missing, and that night something tipped over a can of pig scraps on the back porch. The can rolled down the steps with a clatter that woke Mr. Paxon. He jumped to the window,

and stared out across the moonlit farmyard. "Well, I'll be dad-blamed," he muttered in a shaken voice.

"What is it? The bobcat?" asked his wife sleepily.

"Blamed if I know," he replied. "But I'd be willing to go into court and swear it's got a white tail over a yard long!"

The next morning, Bill hurried through his chores. He intended to take his dog and go bobcat hunting. He dumped wood into the box by the kitchen stove, and piled old newspapers beside it. A headline over a little item at the bottom of a column caught his eye. "Cat Leaps From Plane," he read. While he was reading the short story under the headline, a plane zoomed overhead, already losing altitude for its stop at Philadelphia. Day in and day out, as regular as clockwork, the big passenger planes swept over the farm. Bill ran to the door and watched the plane out of sight. Then he reread the piece in the paper. He looked at the date on it, then tore it out and put it in his pocket.

"Why not?" he argued with himself. Anyway, he could find out, maybe—quietly, without getting laughed at. "Think I'll go bobcat hunting, Dad," he announced. "What'll you give me if I catch it for you?"

"If it is a bobcat," replied his father cautiously, "there might be a bounty on it. But go easy—better take the dog with you."

Bill did not answer. The dog was the last thing he wanted to take along, now. He made a quiet visit to the pantry and set off, with a large hunk of cold fried fish in his pocket.

The Bobcat Hunt

It was a strange bobcat hunt. Bill walked back and forth across the pasture, calling in a soft, coaxing voice, "Here kitty, kitty, kitty. Come, puss, puss." He thought he heard a rustle under the tangle of blackberry bushes where he had found the second piece of mysterious cloth. Of course, it might be rabbits. Or the wind. But he sat down close to the bushes and laid the piece of fish on the ground beside him. He kept very quiet, except to go on calling gently, "Kitty—kitty—kitty—"

The stealthy rustle in the bushes commenced again. Soon Bill could make out two glowing eyes. Inch by inch, an enormous cat worked his way out. A couple of times Bill thought he was stuck on something, but he pulled himself free. As soon as he could reach the fish, he began eating hungrily. Bill reached out and touched him. He growled, but went right on eating.

"Poor puss, nice kitty," said Bill, stroking the long fur. It was all matted with mud and burrs. "Why, kitty," he exclaimed. "You're all tangled up in something." With his pocket knife he cut the cat free. Then he held up the tangle of dirty strings and shredded cloth and whistled. "So that's where the stuff came from. Cat, did you *parachute* out of that plane?"

"Prrraow," said the cat, licking the last of the fish flavor off its chops.

Bill's hands parted the fur over the harness. "Smoky," he read on the little metal plate. "Well, come along, Smoky." The big cat allowed himself to be picked up and carried. "Mother! Dad!" shouted Bill, running back to the house. "Come and see your chicken thief! And you're wrong about bobcats, Dad—they *do* carry silk pocket handkerchiefs!"

"Oh, the poor thing," cried his mother. "I wonder if he's hungry."

"Hungry!" retorted her husband. "*Hungry?* With all those chickens in him?"

"But where did he come from?" asked Mrs. Paxon. "Why, he's a beauty!"

Bill showed them the clipping, and what was left of the parachute. "It doesn't say anything about a parachute," he admitted. "But look, it says, 'Valuable Persian cat, property of—' Gosh, there wouldn't be *two* of them!"

His mother said, "It gives the address. Why don't you write to the people? Maybe there's a reward."

"That's right," laughed Bill. "A bounty on bobcats! Shall I write, Dad?"

"Never mind the bounty," said his father. "But some-body ought to pay for all those chickens. Go ahead and write."

When the letter arrived in New Hampshire, Andy shouted, "I told you so!" Anne was so happy that she burst into tears all over again.

"I suppose it really is Smoky," said Mother cautiously.

"I'm afraid so," said Father. "The letter describes the harness and everything. But what are we going to do about it?"

There was quite a long pause, and Mother said gently, "I'm afraid the only thing to do is to drive down, and thank the people, and bring Smoky back."

"That cat," said Father, but in a defeated tone of voice.

The day Smoky arrived home, Anne and Andy washed and brushed and fed and petted him within an inch of his life. "That cat," said Father to Mother as they were going to bed. "But apparently he had to hunt for himself while he was gone. He must have learned to catch mice. That's something, anyway."

In the dark living room of the cottage, Smoky stalked over to the largest chair. He sharpened his claws on it for a while, then he leaped lightly onto the seat. He kneaded a hollow place in the cushion, turning around and around, and settled down with a contented purring. After a while, a very small mouse crept in from the kitchen. It paused in the middle of the floor. Smoky opened one green eye and looked at it. Then he closed the eye and settled down more comfortably into the curve of his fluffy tail.

Smoky was home again.

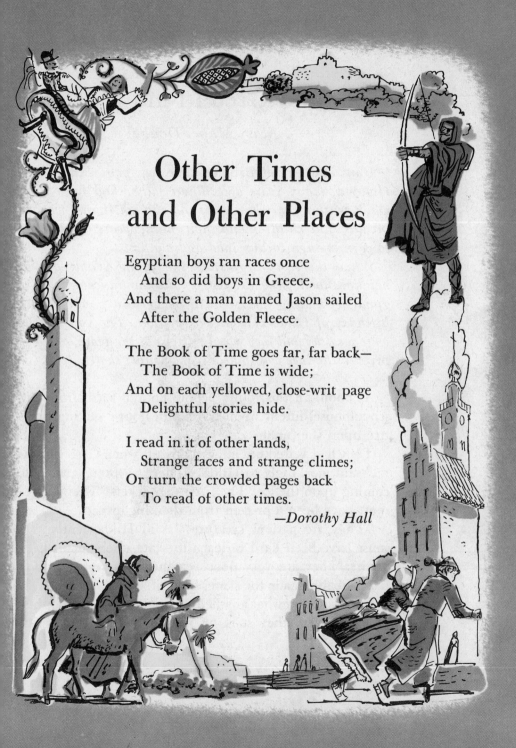

Other Times
and Other Places

Egyptian boys ran races once
  And so did boys in Greece,
And there a man named Jason sailed
  After the Golden Fleece.

The Book of Time goes far, far back—
  The Book of Time is wide;
And on each yellowed, close-writ page
  Delightful stories hide.

I read in it of other lands,
  Strange faces and strange climes;
Or turn the crowded pages back
  To read of other times.
                    —Dorothy Hall

Hans and Gretel Find a Friend

Mary Mapes Dodge

Hans and Gretel Brinker were two poor children of Holland, many years ago. Their father had been hurt while working on the dikes, and though living, was an invalid. The children and their mother were barely able to earn enough to buy food and clothes.

When the story begins, all the young people of the neighborhood were excited by the announcement of a grand ice-skating race soon to be held in honor of the birthday of Hilda van Gleck's mother. The van Glecks were wealthy and important citizens of the place, and the prize in the race was to be a pair of silver skates.

At noon, all the young people poured forth from the schoolhouse, intent upon having an hour's skating practice upon the canal.

They had skated but a few moments when Carl Schummel said mockingly to Hilda, "There's a pretty pair just coming upon the ice! The little rag-pickers! Their skates must have been a present from the king direct."

"They are patient creatures," said Hilda gently. "It must have been hard to learn to skate upon such queer affairs. They are very poor peasants, you see. The boy has probably made the skates himself."

Carl was somewhat abashed. "Patient they may be; but as for skating, they start off pretty well, only to finish

with a jerk. They could move well to your new *staccato* piece on the piano, I think."

Hilda laughed pleasantly, and left him. After joining a small group of the racers, and sailing easily past every one of them, she halted beside Gretel, who, with eager eyes, had been watching the sport.

"What is your name, little girl?"

"Gretel, my lady," answered the child, somewhat awed by Hilda's rank, though they were nearly of the same age. "And my brother is called Hans."

"Hans is a stout fellow," said Hilda cheerily, "and seems to have a warm stove somewhere within him. But *you* look cold. You should wear more clothing, little one."

Gretel, who had nothing else to wear, tried to laugh as she answered, "I am not so very little. I am past twelve years old."

"Oh, I beg your pardon! You see, I am nearly fourteen, and so large of my age that other girls seem small to me. But that is nothing. Perhaps you will shoot up far above me yet. Not unless you dress more warmly, though— shivering girls never grow."

Hans flushed as he saw tears rising in Gretel's eyes. "My sister has not complained of the cold, but this is bitter weather, they say." He looked sadly upon Gretel.

"It is nothing," said Gretel. "I am often warm, too warm, when I am skating. You are good, *jufvrouw* (Miss), to think of it."

"No, no!" answered Hilda, quite angry at herself. "I am careless, cruel; but I meant no harm. I wanted to ask you—I mean—if—" And here Hilda, coming to the point of her errand, grew embarrassed before the children she wished to serve.

"What is it, young lady?" exclaimed Hans eagerly. "If there is any service I can do, any—"

"Oh, no, no!" laughed Hilda, shaking off her embarrassment. "I only wished to speak to you about the grand race. Why do you not join it? You can both skate well. Any one may enter for the prize."

Gretel looked wistfully at Hans, who, tugging at his cap, answered respectfully, "Ah, *jufvrouw*, even if we could enter, we could skate only a few strokes with the rest. Our skates are hard wood, you see." (He held up the sole of his foot.) "They soon become damp, and then they stick, and trip us."

Gretel blushed as she stammered timidly, "Oh, no! We can't join. But may we be there, my lady, on the great day, to look on?"

"Certainly," answered Hilda, looking kindly into the two earnest faces, and wishing from her heart that she had not spent so much of her monthly allowance. She had but eight *kwartjes* (small silver coins) left; and they would buy but one pair of skates, at the furthest.

Looking down with a sigh at the two pairs of feet so

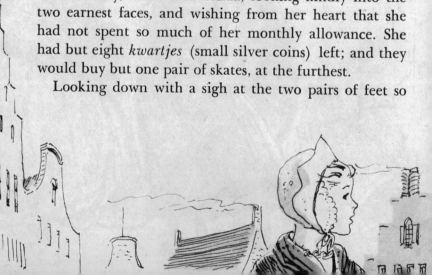

very different in size, she asked, "Which of you is the better skater?"

"Gretel," replied Hans promptly.

"Hans," answered Gretel in the same breath.

Hilda smiled. "I cannot buy you each a pair of skates, or even one good pair, but here are eight *kwartjes*. Decide between you which stands the best chance of winning the race and buy the skates accordingly. I wish I had enough to buy better ones. Good-by!" And with a nod and a smile, Hilda, after handing the money to the electrified Hans, glided swiftly away to rejoin her companions.

"Jufvrouw, jufvrouw van Gleck!" called Hans in a loud tone, stumbling after her as well as he could, for one of his skate-strings was untied. Hilda turned.

"We cannot take this money," panted Hans, "though we know your goodness in giving it."

"Why not, indeed?" asked Hilda, flushing.

"Because," replied Hans, "we have not earned it."

Hilda was quick-witted. She had noticed a pretty wooden chain upon Gretel's neck.

"Carve me a chain, Hans, like the one your sister wears."

"That I will, lady, with all my heart. We have white-wood in the house, fine as ivory. You shall have one tomorrow." Hans hastily tried to return the money.

"No, no!" said Hilda, decidedly. "That sum will be but a poor price for the chain." Off she darted. Hans sent a long, bewildered gaze after her. It was useless, he felt, to make any further resistance.

"It is right," he muttered, half to himself, half to his faithful shadow, Gretel. "I must work hard every minute, and sit up half the night, if mother will let me burn

a candle. The chain shall be finished. We may keep the money, Gretel."

"What a good young lady!" cried Gretel, clapping her hands with delight. "O Hans! was it for nothing the stork settled on our roof last summer? The luck has come to us at last. Now, Hans, if mother sends us to town tomorrow, you can buy the skates in the market-place."

Hans shook his head. "The young lady would have given us the money to buy the skates. But, if I *earn* it, Gretel, it shall be spent for wool. You must have a warm jacket."

Which Shall Have the Skates?

"Oh!" cried Gretel in real dismay. "Not buy the skates! Why, I am not often cold. Mother says the blood runs up and down in poor children's veins humming, 'I must keep 'em warm, I must keep 'em warm!' O Hans!" she continued, with something like a sob, "don't say you won't buy the skates. It makes me feel just like crying. Besides, I want to be cold—I mean I'm real, awful warm—so, now!"

Hans looked up hurriedly. He had a true Dutch horror of tears, or emotion of any kind. Most of all, he dreaded to see his sister's blue eyes overflowing.

"Now mind," cried Gretel, seeing her advantage, "I'll feel awful if you give up the skates. *I* don't want them: I'm not such a stingy as that. But I want *you* to have them. And then, when I get bigger, they'll do for me. Oh-h! count the pieces, Hans. Did you ever see so many?"

Hans turned the money thoughtfully in his palm. Never in all his life had he longed so intensely for a pair of skates. He had known of the race and had, boylike, fairly ached for a chance to test his powers with the others. He felt confident that, with a good pair of steel runners, he could readily distance most of the boys on the canal. Then, too, Gretel's argument was so tempting. On the other hand, he knew that she, with her strong, graceful little frame, needed but a week's practice on good runners to make her a better skater than Rychit Korbes, or even Katrinka Flack. As soon as this last thought flashed upon him, his resolve was made. If Gretel would not have the jacket, she should have the skates.

"No, Gretel," he answered at last. "I can wait. Some day I may have money enough saved to buy a fine pair. You shall have these."

Gretel's eyes sparkled. But, in another instant, she insisted rather faintly, "The young lady gave the money to *you*, Hans. I'd be real bad to take it."

Hans shook his head resolutely as he trudged on. His sister had to half skip and half walk in her effort to keep beside him. By this time, they had taken off their wooden skates and were hastening home to tell their mother the good news.

"Oh, *I* know!" cried Gretel, in a sprightly tone. "You can do this. You can get a pair a little too small for you, and too big for me. We can take turns and use them. Won't that be fine?" And Gretel clapped her hands.

Poor Hans! This was a strong temptation, but he pushed it away from him. "Nonsense, Gretel! You could never get on with a big pair. You stumbled about with these like a blind chicken, before I curved off the ends. No—you must have a pair to fit exactly. You must practice every chance you can get until the 20th comes. My little Gretel shall win the silver skates."

Gretel could not help laughing with delight at the very idea.

"Hans, Gretel!" called out a familiar voice.

"Coming, mother." And they hastened toward the cottage, Hans still shaking the pieces of silver in his hand.

On the following day, there was not a prouder or a happier boy in all Holland than Hans Brinker, as he watched his sister, with many a skillful sweep, flying in and out among the skaters who at sundown thronged the canal. A warm jacket had been given her through the

kindness of Hilda and the burst-out shoes cobbled into decency by Dame Brinker. As the little creature darted backward and forward, flushed with enjoyment, and quite unconscious of the many wondering glances bent upon her, she felt that the shining runners beneath her feet had suddenly turned earth into fairyland. "Hans, dear, good Hans!" echoed itself over and over again in her grateful heart.

"By den donder!" exclaimed Peter van Holp to Carl Schummel, "but that little one in the red jacket and patched petticoat skates well. Gunst! she has toes on her heels, and eyes in the back of her head. See her! It will be a joke if she gets in the race, and beats Katrinka Flack, after all."

"Hush! not so loud!" returned Carl, rather sneeringly. "That little lady in rags is the special pet of Hilda van Gleck. Those shining skates are her gift, if I make no mistake."

"So, so!" exclaimed Peter, with a happy smile, for Hilda was his best friend. "She has been at her good work there too!" And Peter, after cutting a double 8 on the ice, to say nothing of a huge P, then a jump, and an H, glided onward until he found himself beside Hilda. They skated together, laughingly at first, and then sedately talking in a low tone.

Strange to say, Peter van Holp soon arrived at a sudden conviction that his little sister needed a wooden chain just like Hilda's.

And two days afterward, on St. Nicholas Eve, Hans, having burned three candle-ends, and cut his thumb into the bargain, stood in the market-place at Amsterdam, buying another pair of skates.

Dark Danny

Dark Danny has eyes
As black as the sloe,
And his freckles tell
Where the sunbeams go!

Dark Danny has hair
Like a raven's wing,
And his voice is gay
As the thrush in Spring.

Dark Danny will show
You the first wild rose;
Where the earliest violet
Blooms—he knows!

Where the red fox hides,
Why the nightingale sings . . .
Dark Danny knows all
These lovely things.

—*Ivy O. Eastwick*

A Red-Gold Terrier from Lhasa

Louise Rankin

Momo, a girl of far-away Tibet, had one desire in life. She wanted a red-gold Lhasa terrier, such as the head lama of the monastery had. Such dogs were very expensive, and Momo and her family were poor. But a lama promised Momo that her great wish would surely be granted by Heaven.

"How does the dog come to you?" Pasang, Momo's brother, asked. The children's best guess was that the dog would somehow come by one of the great wool caravans on their way to India.

Through the summer, herdsmen high in the mountains and plains of Tibet cut the thick wool from their flocks. Then, when the heavy rains of the Indian monsoon season are over, they send this thick, fine wool into the wool-trading towns. Here the muleteers, men of Khamba province, tall and immensely strong, are waiting to load it onto the backs of their mules. And then the caravans begin their long march across the lofty Tibetan plateau, the Roof of the World, over the mountains of the Himalayas, the highest in the world, down into the plains of India.

All the caravans stopped in Momo's village to rest their mules. And while the mules rested, the men would come into Momo's house to drink tea. Because of the caravans, Momo loved the winter. As soon as the skies cleared in autumn and the sun shone on woods turning yellow and scarlet, she would listen eagerly for the first silvery tinkle of the mule trains.

To give warning to oncoming travelers over the mountain passes, every mule in a train is belled. Every train has a leader who wears a whole collar of bells. Whether they are of brass or bell metal, or only of iron, the bells are always clear in tone, and their mingled notes float through the air like sweet music. Long before Momo's sharp eyes could see a mule train moving up through the forested mountainside, she would hear these bells chiming. Now, even while she and Pasang were laughing, Momo was listening. Suddenly above their laughter she heard a different sound, and caught her breath. It was— yes, it *was* the music of the mule bells—faint, still far away, but clearly ringing.

Jumping to her feet, she rushed up the path to her home, shouting as she went.

"Mother! Here they come — they are coming!" Her mother smiled at her and said, "Then come quickly to churn the tea, while I get some cheese and curds ready."

So Momo ran over to the churn, which was so high that she had to stand on a stool to reach its plunger. Her mother poured in the strong, black tea which had been brewing on the stove, added some salt and soda, some butter, and some boiling water. Then Momo pushed the plunger up and down as hard and fast as she could.

Meanwhile her mother took one of the strings of smoked cheese off the peg and pushed the dried pieces, like brown beads, off the string into a pan of warm water to soften them. These cheese-beads are of yak milk and are called *tsampa*. Next, Momo's mother turned out a dish of curds and whey that had been standing on the back of the stove, and set it on the table.

"Good!" she said, taking the plunger from Momo. "I'll finish this and pour it into the pots. Go and see them come." And Momo ran to the door to watch the lead mule climb into sight.

"Ah!" she murmured, her eyes shining with joy. "Ah!" Outside of the monasteries and the dances of the lamas, there was nothing so fine to hear and to see as this coming on of a mule train. The leader-mule carried his pack lightly, proud of his great responsibility of keeping to the trail, and picking the easiest and safest way over boulders or snow drifts. With every step, his embroidered bell collar jingled, and its great tassel of red yak hair bobbed gently against his strong shoulders.

One by one, scrambling up the stony way, the other

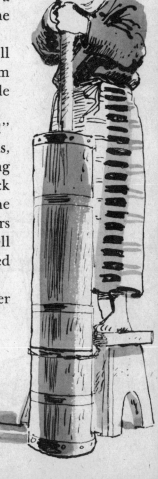

mules followed their leader. For every eight or ten mules there was a muleteer, watching to see that the packs did not come loose. They wore high red felt boots and turquoise earrings, and walked with a spring. Momo smiled to see them. Though the men of Khamba are known to be hot-tempered, like all Tibetans they are cheerful and fond of children.

The mules knew exactly where they were going, and what to do. They gathered in the mule yard by the house, stamping their little feet. "Seventy-nine, eighty," said Momo, counting the mules as they came up. "Eighty mules and eight muleteers," she called to her mother.

"Not very big," she thought. Sometimes there would be hundreds of mules in a caravan. "But *the first!*" She watched the muleteers examine their animals to make sure the wooden packs were not cutting sores into their backs. Then she smiled as they came stamping into the house, calling out greetings.

"You are the first caravan to come over the pass. Oh, lucky ones!" cried Momo's mother, as she welcomed them. The men laughed and sat down, pulling their tea-cups out of the fold in their blouses. They were in high spirits. To be first going out of Tibet over the narrow mountain passes meant that they would not meet any returning caravans, coming back into Tibet laden with bricks of tea and brocaded silks, after having sold their wool.

"Lucky indeed, if we escape late rains or early snow!" their leader replied. "We shall certainly not have to fight our way over the mountains." For when two long mule caravans meet on the mountain trails, so narrow that only one mule may pass, the hot-tempered men of Khamba fight fiercely for the right of way. This leader was himself a peaceful man, and hated to bring violence and bloodshed into the quiet mountains.

They waited eagerly for Momo's mother to fill their cups with the steaming hot tea, and dipped into the bowl of *tsampa* that Momo brought.

"Why, here is Momo," cried the leader, who remembered this little girl, the same age as his own. "How you have grown! You are taller now than my Dolma." He laughed again.

"What do you think my Dolma wanted me to bring her back from the big bazaar at Kalimpong?" he asked them all. " 'Shall I bring you a coral bead, or a turquoise nose drop?' I asked." And in a high, thin falsetto he copied a child's voice. " 'No, no—bring me *momo*. I want *momo*.' " He turned to Momo. "Will you come?" he asked.

They all roared with laughter at this. For "Momo" was only a pet name that her father had begun to call

her when she was a baby. *Momo* is really a sweet little dumpling, which the Tibetans like to eat better than anything.

"This child cares nothing for sweets," her mother said. "She wants only one thing in all the world — a Lhasa terrier"—

"A red-gold Lhasa terrier, Mother," Momo interrupted. Her mother nodded, and sighed.

"Yes, even the color must be as she wishes," she said.

A Wish Comes True

At this, Urtken, the leader, looked thoughtfully at Momo.

"How came you, child," he asked, "to set your heart on a red-gold terrier from Lhasa?" And Momo answered simply, "Because the head lama at Kargayu has one such, and I saw it there—oh so many years ago! And I have wanted one like it ever since."

Urtken scratched his chin, and fingered the turquoise in his ear, and sat thinking, like a man trying to make up his mind. Finally, he struck his hand upon the table and beckoned Momo to him.

"See what I have here," he said. So Momo went and stood beside him, watching curiously as he fumbled around in the fold of his heavy robe. Both men and women in Tibet wear long, heavy woolen robes, which they tie with a cord about their waists, and pull into a big blouse. And in the big pouch made by this folding of the robe they carry everything they own—which is not much.

"See here!" Urtken repeated, drawing his hand out of the fold. And when she saw what he held, Momo caught her breath and clasped her hands. For in the hollow of his big hand, Urtken held a golden puppy! It was fat and sleepy, and so young that its eyes were still blue, and it looked like a ball of golden fuzz.

"See!" said Urtken dramatically. "A red-gold terrier from Lhasa!"

"Ah! A-ah!" Momo sighed, as the mule leader put the warm little puppy into her outstretched hands. She held it close, and laughed when the puppy licked at her brown cheek, his eyes, so softly blue, close to her own.

"Is he for me?" asked Momo. She looked pleadingly at her mother.

"What is his price?" asked her mother, coming over from the stove to look carefully at the puppy.

"It should be much," replied Urtken. "There are no Lhasa terriers in all our land more finely bred. His mother was one of those belonging formerly to our Grand Lama himself. But the mother has died on this journey, and I cannot feed and care for this little one on the long way into India. Let us make this bargain: the puppy is yours, Momo. When he is grown, he shall be the father of other fine dogs for me."

Her mother nodded, and Momo gasped for joy, hugging the little creature to her.

"But mind you feed him well," the muleteer said to her mother. "He is worth all the milk and *tsampa* he can eat."

"He shall be fed as well as if he were a child," Momo's mother promised. And Momo added, "Yes, yes, certainly he shall have all the yak milk and *tsampa* he can eat."

Then, just as politely as if he were concluding the sale of all the wool in his caravan, Urtken smiled and said, "May good come upon you. May no sickness happen in your home." And Momo and her mother bowed and said, "Thanks, thanks. Great mercy."

Then Momo forgot everything in the world but this wonderful puppy of hers. All day she was busy making a bed, feeding it warmed yak milk, watching it totter about, or lie quietly asleep near the stove. When her father came in, he rejoiced at her happiness.

"What do you call him?" he asked.

Momo was thunderstruck. She had never thought of a name to give the dog she wanted, and names are very important in Tibet. They bring luck. When a child is born, the parents call in an astrologer. He studies the position of the stars at the time the child is born. And

from those stars which are highest in the heavens at that time, he draws up a horoscope, which is a plan of the child's life—telling what will happen, and what its nature will be. Then he advises the parents on names that will be good and suitable. Momo's own name was Pempa, which means "Saturday," the day she was born, and Tsering, which means "May she have long life."

"I have no name for the puppy," Momo replied to her father. "Let us call in the astrologer."

Her father began to laugh. First he leaned against the door. Then he sat down and rocked back and forth. He laughed and laughed till the tears ran down his face, and his cheeks and stomach muscles were stiff.

"Oh, oh!" he said to her mother, holding his sides, "was there ever such a child? She wants a horoscope for her *dog*." And he laughed again, "Ho! Ho! Ho!" throwing back his head and crinkling his eyes till they were little slits, and the tears ran down his cheeks and into his mouth.

"No, father, not a horoscope—only a name. It's very important, his name," persisted Momo.

At this moment, a man came in the open door. Momo rushed forward with a squeal of joy.

"Oh, come in, Dawa, come in!" she cried. "See, father, here is the astrologer himself. We want a name for my new dog," she said quickly to Dawa. "My father laughs at me, and says I am silly. But you don't think I am, do you? My dog should have an auspicious name, shouldn't he?" She dragged Dawa to see the sleeping puppy. He looked thoughtfully from the puppy to Momo.

"Get me the plan of the child's life," he said. So Momo's mother fetched it from the chest where they kept

their few precious belongings, and gave it into Dawa's hands. All three looked with awe at the paper whose lines foretold the life of little Momo. Dawa studied it in silence. Finally he nodded, pursing up his mouth, rolled the paper up, and gave it back to be put away.

"Yes," he said. "He merits a good name indeed." To the astonished father, he added, "You will live to see this dog the bearer of good fortune." Then he turned briskly to Momo. "You got the dog today, you say?" She nodded.

"This is Saturday—Pempa. It is, moreover, the day of the full moon—a most auspicious day. Why not call him Pempa?"

"Oh, yes, of course. It is my name too," said Momo. "That is right."

"It is indeed right," Dawa told her, "that you two be given the same name. For you two will go through many adventures, and this dog will bring fortune to you all."

"What's that you say?" cried Momo's father. "Fortune to come to us through him? How will he do it? Dig us a treasure?" He laughed at the impossibility of the idea.

"I did not say treasure," replied Dawa severely. "But mark well my words, Nema Tundoop. Today adventure and good fortune have come into your house with the dog."

Nema, who intended no disbelief of Dawa's words, was abashed. "May you grow rich," he said thankfully to the astrologer. "Adventure! Fortune! Coming to *us!* When, Dawa?"

But Dawa merely smiled and said, "Wait and see."

The Wedding

Kate Seredy

Jancsi, a boy of Old Hungary, was the son of a rancher on the great Hungarian plains. His city cousin Kate had come to live with them. Today Kate was very excited. The whole family had been invited to go to a wedding in the village—a real Hungarian wedding.

Sunday began like any other day on the ranch. The family was up with the first crow of the roosters. When the sun pushed its round, red face over the horizon, they were almost through with the morning meal.

Father, Jancsi, and Uncle Sandor were talking placidly about some fences and new buildings. Kate, who had rushed through her morning chores and gulped down her breakfast, began to squirm in her chair.

Finally, she whispered to her aunt, "The wedding! Aren't we going to get dressed for the wedding?"

"I should say not," said Mother.

"Auntie! Aren't we . . . aren't we going?" This was a wail, loud enough to make the men look up and take notice.

"Of course we are going. But we can't get dressed until we have been called. It would not be seemly," explained Mother calmly.

"Called? You mean invited? But we *have* been invited. Everybody has been invited. Why . . . Why, Auntie!"

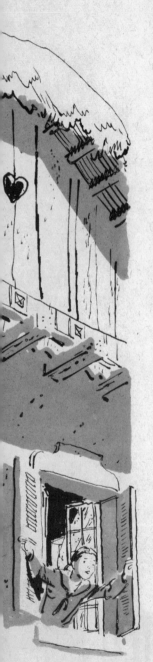

Father smiled. "In a little while you will see an ancient ceremony, the 'wedding call,'" he explained to Kate. "The words in that ceremony are almost as old as the Magyar race. Every word the callers will say, every word we will say, has been said in just that way at every Hungarian wedding for hundreds of years."

"They should be here any minute now," said Jancsi.

"Yes, and we had better get to work. It won't do at all to let them find us waiting," said Father, rising from the table.

To Kate's consternation, everybody got very busy, chopping wood, carrying water, brushing the already shiny horses. Mother insisted that Kate help her with the dishes, a task she usually didn't want any help with. After the last dish had been polished, she said, "Open the windows in the 'clean' room, Kate, and dust the chairs."

The 'clean' room was very seldom opened. It was a kind of parlor reserved for the most festive occasions. Any visitor who was led into the clean room was an honored guest indeed.

"Hurry!" cried Mother. "Here they come."

Opening the windows and shutters of the clean room, Kate saw two wagons drive into the yard. They had been freshly painted and each was pulled by four white horses. Wagons and horses were all but covered with wreaths of flowers and ribbons. Men, young and old, came piling off. The wide sleeves of their shirts and their pleated, full trousers were dazzlingly white, their vests were a colorful riot of appliqué work and embroidery, their boots were so glossy — Kate giggled as she thought — "a fly would break its neck on them."

Father was walking toward them, followed by Jancsi.

The men stood in an orderly line. Their leader, carrying a flower-laden staff, stepped forward.

Mother and Kate hurried out just when Father began to speak. "May Heaven give a good day to all you men. What happy event has brought you such a long way to our modest home?"

"A very good day to you, our host," spoke the leader. "It is a great honor for us to be received in your good home."

Father stepped aside, indicating the door with an outstretched arm. "Please enter and accept our hospitality."

"We thank you," said the leader. Slowly they walked in, through the kitchen, into the clean room, followed by the family. There the men stood in a line again. The leader stepped forward, and knocked with his staff on the floor.

"Our kind host," he began. "We have come to ask for your help and the help of all your dear family."

"We are at your service," said Father seriously. "We are," repeated Mother and Jancsi. Kate, to whom all this was like a play, piped up a moment later, "Me, too."

"Thank you." The leader bowed his head. "There is a little white dove back home where we came from. She has been kept in a cage all her life. But this spring the door of her cage has been opened. She has flown off to the woods and there heard the call of her mate."

"That is as it should be," Father said.

"That is as it should be," nodded the leader. "Now, the little white dove and her mate are ready to build their nest. We have come to ask you, dear host, to help."

"We will," said Father.

The leader lifted his staff high, then knocked with it on the floor three times. "And so we call you to the wedding of the maid Mari Vidor and the lad Peter Hódi, to the feast and the rejoicing at the house of János Vidor, and to the 'Lead Me Home' procession tonight." He paused for a moment. Then he added, "You have been called."

"We have been called," said Father. "We shall come gladly."

With Father's last words, the ceremony was over. The men relaxed and began to talk about everyday things. Father and Mother brought in refreshments and invited the callers to sit down. This, however, was politely refused. They each took a bite and a sip, then shook hands with everybody and left.

The moment the wagons turned down the lane, Mother closed the windows and shutters of the clean room. "Now hurry, all of you, and get dressed!" she cried. "I don't want to be late for the wedding. Hurry!"

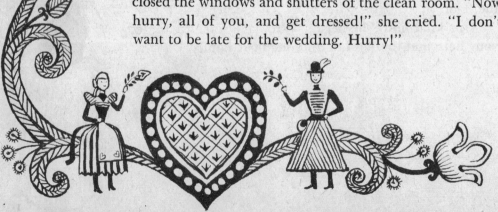

"Auntie," mumbled Kate, struggling into her petti-coats, "why couldn't we have dressed before? We knew we were going!"

"It would have seemed forward to take it for granted. Let me see you now. Bonnet, blouse, bodice, petticoats, skirt, apron, boots . . . yes, you'll do. Get the prayerbooks and the lace kerchiefs. Don't wrinkle them, now! Here we go."

The men eased Mother and Kate into the wagon, carefully, as if they were baskets of eggs.

"Want to drive, Son?" asked Father.

"No, sir. I am riding Bársony," declared Jancsi. "If we are going to stay for the 'Lead Me Home,' we won't be back until late. Somebody has got to milk the cows because . . ."

"A cow isn't interested in excuses. All a cow wants is to be milked!" chanted the whole family, laughing. They remembered the time Father had said those words to Jancsi, when he was late for milking.

The "Seeking"

Once on the main road, they became part of the long line of wagons, carriages, and riders, all headed for the village. People were singing, shouting to one another. One wagon carried a whole gypsy band, playing lively tunes.

By the time Father found a place for the wagon and horses, the small church was packed to overflowing. So, to Mother's disappointment, they had to stand on the steps. From the sound of murmuring voices broken by moments of stillness inside the church, they could follow the service. They all joined in the singing of hymns. When the organ rang out triumphantly, pronouncing the end of the ceremony, the singing and shouting mingled with the booming bells in the steeple.

There was a stir in the wide doorway of the church. The crowd parted, and the bridal procession began to move slowly down the steps. The bride, Mari Vidor, dressed in foaming, glistening white, seemed to float on the crest of a wave of color. As she reached the lowest step, she was whisked off, back to her father's house. The girls and women scattered into groups, each group taking up its post in a different house along the main street.

The men and boys stayed with Peter and began the traditional game, the "Seeking." Led by the "callers" and followed by the softly playing gypsies, they went from house to house. At every door they stopped and Peter knocked.

"Good people in this house, I have lost my white dove.

My white dove has flown away. Help me find her, good people."

The door was opened and the women, who had arrived there only a short while before, came out. "We have not seen your white dove, but help you we will."

This was repeated over and over again, and the procession grew. The whole village was behind Peter when finally they reached the Vidor farm. Here Peter repeated his call and Mari's mother opened the door.

"I have seen your white dove, and find her you will." A great shouting and cheering broke out at these words. The gypsies crashed into a wild tune. The crowd formed a large half-circle around the door. János Vidor appeared, leading a bent old woman by the hand. "May this be the white dove you are seeking?"

Peter walked around the old woman solemnly. Then he stepped back and shook his head. "This one is too old to be my white dove."

Now Mari's mother came, leading a small girl. "May this be the white dove you are seeking?"

Again Peter shook his head. "This one is too young to be my white dove."

One by one they led out tall girls, short girls, fat girls, thin girls. To each one Peter objected, to the immense amusement of the crowd. The game went on and on. Then suddenly the bride appeared in the doorway and everybody shouted, "May this be the white dove you are seeking?"

Peter threw his hat into the air and cried, "This is my white dove I have been seeking!"

The crowd cheered, the band swung into a czardas, and Peter swept Mari into the dance. This was the sign for the real festivities to begin. Young and old danced, faster and faster. The bride flew from hand to hand, around and around, until she had danced with every man. Then she was led back to Peter, who had danced with every girl and woman. Together, they led the cheering guests back of the house to the garden and orchard. Long, sturdy tables had been piled high with food. The food visible on the tables was only a beginning. More came every minute, brought from the wagons of the guests and the neighbors' kitchens. There were roast pigs and lambs, chickens, geese, and ducks by the dozens, mountains of sausages, pastries, cakes, baskets of bread, buns, and rolls.

Eat and dance, dance and eat—that's what everybody did all afternoon. Holidays like this were few and far between for these hardworking people. When one came, they threw themselves into the gaiety with the complete abandon of children.

Late in the afternoon the tired gypsies were given a

rest. People separated into groups, talking, singing, playing games. Some of the men, like Jancsi, went home to tend their animals before dark so they could take part in the "Lead Me Home" procession.

At last, dusk began to fall. Here and there, torches were lighted—first two, then three, then more and more, in readiness for the procession.

"Look, there's Jancsi!" Mother cried. "How big he is!"

"He must have been riding like the wind!" exclaimed Kate. "Here comes the first wagon with the gypsies. Come, Auntie. I want to see everything. Look, they're bringing the furniture. Come on!"

The climax of all Hungarian country weddings, the "Lead Me Home," had begun. Men loaded all the bride's belongings into wagons. First came the freshly painted, gay new furniture. Then came homespun linens, sheets, pillowcases, curtains, tablecloths—dozens and dozens of everything, the product of twenty years of spinning, weaving, and sewing. Dishes, cooking utensils, wooden implements came next, filling another wagon to the brim. The next one was loaded with food, bags and barrels of it.

After all Mari's belongings had been packed into wagons, the guests piled into their own vehicles and the long procession began. The gypsies went ahead, playing favorite old songs and marches all the way. Each following wagon was lighted by six torches. In the last one, Mari and Peter were riding.

Peter's farm was quite a distance from the village, and by the time he and Mari arrived, the house was ready for them. Furniture had been placed, and the table set for two. The guests had even fed the chickens, pigs, and the cow. When Mari and Peter alighted, the first "caller"

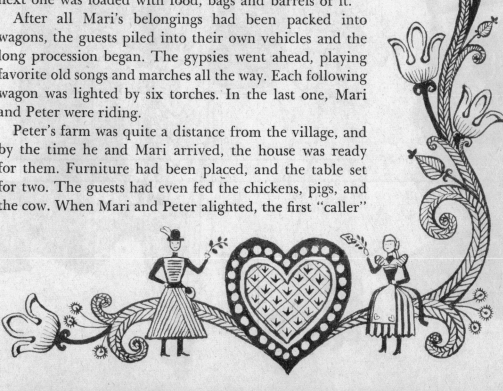

took them by the hand and led them over the threshold.
They stood there, inside their home, waiting for the
parting words of the caller—words without which no
wedding was complete. Again the guests stood in a half-
circle and the caller began to speak.

"Peter and Mari Hódi, may Heaven bless you and your
home. May Heaven give you good health and happiness,
long life, peace, and prosperity." He reached for the
doorknob, and as he closed the door he said, "May this
door keep all worry, all sadness and strife out of your
house forever and after. Good night."

"I liked that part best of all, what he said about the
door," spoke Kate sleepily out of a long silence when
they were driving away. "I always like to close the door
at night . . ."

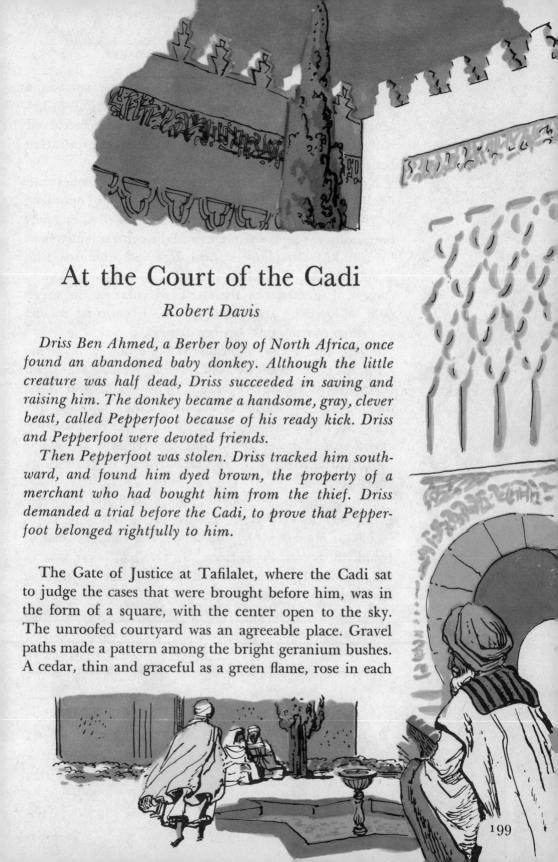

At the Court of the Cadi

Robert Davis

Driss Ben Ahmed, a Berber boy of North Africa, once found an abandoned baby donkey. Although the little creature was half dead, Driss succeeded in saving and raising him. The donkey became a handsome, gray, clever beast, called Pepperfoot because of his ready kick. Driss and Pepperfoot were devoted friends.

Then Pepperfoot was stolen. Driss tracked him southward, and found him dyed brown, the property of a merchant who had bought him from the thief. Driss demanded a trial before the Cadi, to prove that Pepperfoot belonged rightfully to him.

The Gate of Justice at Tafilalet, where the Cadi sat to judge the cases that were brought before him, was in the form of a square, with the center open to the sky. The unroofed courtyard was an agreeable place. Gravel paths made a pattern among the bright geranium bushes. A cedar, thin and graceful as a green flame, rose in each

corner. A blue enameled fountain, no bigger than a goldfish bowl, played where the paths met. The pillars of white marble, and the horseshoe arches, were carved with curly designs of Arab writing. Around the wall were benches for the witnesses and lawyers.

No one was in a hurry. Men in flowing robes and rimless hats shook hands, kissed each other's shoulders, or rubbed cheeks, depending upon how well they knew one another. The law students and the court servants bent low and kissed the fingers of the dignified professors, who swept majestically to their seats. They were the great and successful members of their tribe, owners of the green oasis of gardens and palm groves. Everything moved according to rules that were centuries old.

In the courtroom, everyone rose and bowed when the Cadi, his beard as snowy as his turban, took his seat upon the platform. He waved genially to his friends and to the older lawyers, with an especially friendly salute to the rich and important merchant, Ben Mansour. The merchant, seated in the front row, was tapping his fingers impatiently, like a man who feels that he is wasting precious minutes.

In this dignified company, one small figure was completely overlooked. With the first ray of daylight, Driss, inside the hood of his *jellaba* (coat), had thought what he could do to save Pepperfoot. No one had been astir in the *fondouk* (inn), and he had plenty of time. Munching his bread, he rehearsed what he would say before the Cadi—that is, what he would like to say, if he were allowed to say anything.

Without question, the stout merchant would have a paper, stamped and in order, showing that the animal

had been bought of a man whose business it was to fur-
nish donkeys. The policeman had warned Driss to bring
witnesses. But whom did he know in this foreign city?
Who could speak for his character?

There were two points, and only two, which he must
make clear to the Cadi—the color of the donkey, and the
fact that he, Driss Ben Ahmed, was his rightful owner.
He studied these two matters until the caravan men had
loaded their camels, and with much groaning and moaning, had punched and pried them to a standing position.

Driss had two hours to wait before the booth of the
druggist opened. His purchase was two cents' worth of
alcohol and a small sponge.

At the Gate of Justice he had an equally long wait,
for the janitor had not finished washing down the tiled
steps when the boy arrived. He walked around the courtyard, sniffed the flowers, and finally made himself small,
on the lowest step of the platform, near where the judge
would sit. He dozed a bit, chewed more of his bread,
watched the people who were filling the room, but understood very little of what was going on. But when the Cadi
mentioned the word "donkey," he jumped to his feet,
listening hard.

"Due to the importance of our good friend, Ben Mansour," said the Cadi, "and the smallness of the matter,
I will hear that case first, so that the Telek may lose none
of his valuable time. The Telek Mansour is defendant
in the case of a stolen donkey. Is the boy, Driss Ben
Ahmed, of the Ait Affane people, present?"

Driss's mouth was dry, but he remembered the words
that he had practiced in the *fondouk* yard. "I am here,
Honorable Judge, and I kiss your hand. It is my *behime*

(donkey) that the honorable merchant was riding yesterday in the market. He was stolen from our *douar* (tents) four days before the full moon. May I have my donkey back, please."

The Cadi leaned back in his chair, smiling broadly. At any rate, this boy had not wasted the court's time, as so many lawyers did. "Have you upright men who can witness for you?" asked the Cadi. "In the matter of donkeys and sheep, as they all look alike, we need to be very careful. Have you men here who can prove this donkey to be yours?"

Driss shook his head, feeling more helpless and small than ever. The judge turned his head toward the Telek Mansour. "You have some paper, I believe, to prove your lawful possession of this animal?"

The merchant rose and cleared his throat. "I ask your

permission, excellent Judge, to read this receipt, for the payment of thirty silver pieces, for the animal in question. The seller is Dillal Ben Abbes, and it covers the sale of a brown donkey, sound in wind and limb, and of a smooth pacing gait. I made this purchase in the public *souk* (market), before witnesses. As a business man, it is my opinion that this young mischief-maker from the country is nothing but a rascal. I would ask Your Honor not only to dismiss this trifling case but to have the boy soundly whipped, for making busy people like myself waste their time."

The Cadi nodded to the merchant. There did not seem much more to be said. He was about to ask the clerk to call the next case, when he noticed Driss, eagerly raising his hand to be heard.

"But I do have a witness, even if he is not a man. I have a witness who is better than a man, if Your Honor will have him called in. He is tied in front of the building." In his anxiety to be heard, Driss was almost shouting. "It is the donkey himself who is my witness. The receipt says that the Telek Mansour bought a brown donkey, but this is a silver-gray donkey. Please, Your Honor, have the donkey before you, and you will see the truth. This is not a brown donkey."

The Cadi laughed aloud. "What do you think this court is, you young savage from the backwoods—a circus or a marketplace? But you are in your right. Under our law, a person who claims to have suffered a wrong has the right to call any witness whatsoever, whether living or dead, man or beast, if he thinks that it will aid the judge to decide justly. We must waste no time. Will the doorkeeper bring in the animal which the Telek Mansour

purchased. If it is stolen property, it must be returned to its owner. Bring in the animal. Make haste."

Pepperfoot Testifies

The merchant was instantly on his feet. "Honorable Judge, I object to this nonsense. This miserable little brown animal is mine. I bought him in the regular way that all business is done. My time is very valuable. Yours, too, is worth something. Shall we spend the whole morning watching this beggar boy play his tricks? I request you to settle this case without further folly." The stout Telek Mansour was very angry. His pink face had become purple.

More and more, Driss was remembering what the village council had said. Every tribesman had the right, the unquestionable right, to produce a witness who might establish the truth.

"Excuse me for speaking again, Your Honor. But I am a full member of the Ait Affane tribe. Among the men of the Northern Mountains, the name of the Cadi of Tafilalet is everywhere held in reverence, as a ruby that

shines in the crown of the Prophet—Blessed be His Name. But if you refuse to have my witness called, it will be told in every *souk*, beside every bakeoven, in every village council of the four tribes. Before the wool that is now growing upon our sheep is next clipped, men will be saying the name of the Cadi of Tafilalet, not with reverence, but with the spitting that soils the name of an enemy. It will cost nothing. It will be done with speed. I beg you to have my witness brought before you."

The Cadi looked puzzled. He beckoned to the clerk, who, in turn, beckoned to Ben Mansour. The three heads wagged gravely together. "They are our neighbors on the north, you understand. These tribes are rough men, handy with their rifles. They are like a stack of straw, easily set afire. We must treat them with especial tenderness, for they are proud of their long history and independence. They are fierce, these highlanders, and you must forgive us, Telek Mansour, if we Chleus treat them with softness. It may seem a little irregular, but we must have the animal in." The merchant reluctantly accepted the Cadi's decision.

Pepperfoot walked gingerly upon the slippery tiled

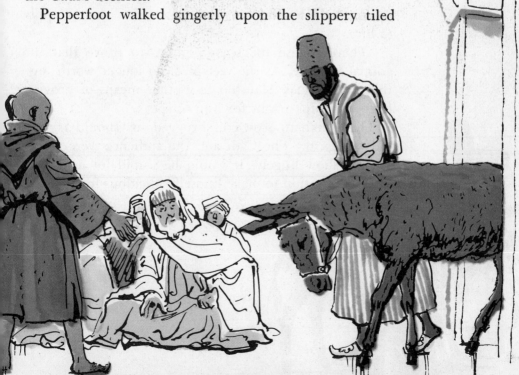

floor as the court janitor led him through the side door.
Driss stood beside him.

"I will not abuse your kindness, Honorable Cadi. The
first fact which I should like to make plain is that this
is not a brown donkey, and therefore cannot be the one
mentioned in the receipt of the horse-seller. Here in my
hand is a sponge, which I moisten with alcohol from
this bottle. As I rub the animal with alcohol, the walnut
stain comes off. We see that this is a gray donkey, and
so cannot be the one belonging to the honorable merchant."

The people of Africa, Berber and Arab alike, love a
pantomime, an illustrated speech. As the sponge left the
donkey's flank, the sponge was a dark brown, and the
animal's hair was nearly white. The audience clapped.
This was as good as a story-teller of the *souks*. It was quite
evident that the donkey had been washed with boiled
walnut stain.

"That is the first point, Your Honor," announced
Driss, more confident now, since the crowd was favoring
him. "This is not a brown, but a dyed, donkey. The
receipt held by the honorable merchant cannot apply
to him.

"There is also the second point—to prove that the
animal is mine. As the receipt is no longer worth anything, has Telek Mansour any other means of proving
his ownership? I wait for him to speak."

The merchant scowled, shrugged his shoulders, but
did not speak. The Cadi and the audience were enjoy-
ing the show hugely. It would be stupid for a man of
his high position to make himself ridiculous for the sake
of a donkey.

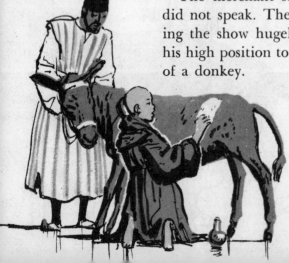

Driss, more sure of himself, had adopted a showman's manner. He addressed the judge as though he were a friend. "I must next prove that this donkey comes from our *douar*. When he was three days old, I began to feed him with goats' milk. He took the habit of coming when I called that word. Will Your Honor kindly watch him now?"

In a soft whine, the boy said, "Melek, Melek, Melek." The donkey broke away from the janitor who was holding him and trotted expectantly to Driss. The rows of lawyers, who were leaning forward, laughed with delight. This case would become famous.

"When he was weak and small," continued Driss, "he slept under the same rug with me, for warmth. I used to say to him, 'Lie flat, lie flat,' so that the cold air should not enter by the edges. Will the Honorable Cadi regard him as I say those words?"

The boy hissed the sounds. One could conjure up the

picture—the tent, the narrow place, the chill darkness, the forlorn little animal crawling in beside his protector for comfort. "Lie flat, lie flat and be still." The donkey laid back his ears, folded his legs under him, and seemed to become as flat as the floor. Everyone applauded again, and the Cadi himself laughed. Telek Ben Mansour, seeing that his cause was lost, rose and stalked from the hall, looking neither to right nor left.

"If that is not enough to show that he and I belong together, Honorable Judge," said Driss, the thrill of success in his voice, "he will roll over, and shake hands, and sit down. Shall I have him do that, too?"

"No, no, you have proved your two points," admitted the Cadi. "He is gray, he is yours. Take your animal and return to the Berber mountains. I only wish that every case that comes before me were as well proved."

Even in the wave of thankfulness that flowed over him, Driss did not forget his manners. With a single leap, he cleared the steps to the Cadi's platform and kissed the gold ring upon his finger.

On their way out of Tafilalet, the donkey and boy stopped but once, to buy four pennies' worth of bread. After half an hour's walk, they reached high ground. As they looked back, the oasis made an attractive picture, the emerald foliage between the whitewashed houses, the glancing reflections from the lake formed by the great spring. Driss and Pepperfoot were dividing a piece of bread.

"Do you know why it looks so pretty to our eyes?" asked Driss. "I will tell you the answer, stupid. It is because we are on our way home. When your eyes are turned toward home, everything looks beautiful."

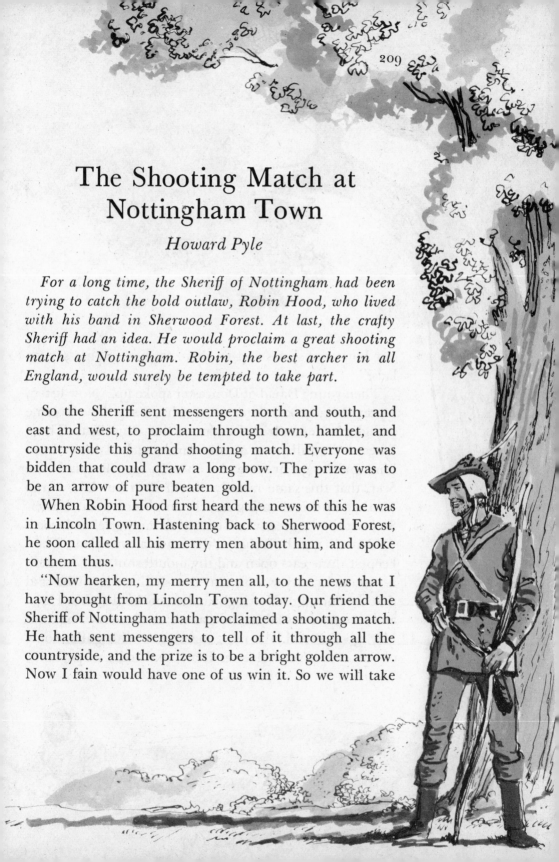

The Shooting Match at Nottingham Town

Howard Pyle

For a long time, the Sheriff of Nottingham had been trying to catch the bold outlaw, Robin Hood, who lived with his band in Sherwood Forest. At last, the crafty Sheriff had an idea. He would proclaim a great shooting match at Nottingham. Robin, the best archer in all England, would surely be tempted to take part.

So the Sheriff sent messengers north and south, and east and west, to proclaim through town, hamlet, and countryside this grand shooting match. Everyone was bidden that could draw a long bow. The prize was to be an arrow of pure beaten gold.

When Robin Hood first heard the news of this he was in Lincoln Town. Hastening back to Sherwood Forest, he soon called all his merry men about him, and spoke to them thus.

"Now hearken, my merry men all, to the news that I have brought from Lincoln Town today. Our friend the Sheriff of Nottingham hath proclaimed a shooting match. He hath sent messengers to tell of it through all the countryside, and the prize is to be a bright golden arrow. Now I fain would have one of us win it. So we will take

our bows and shafts and go there to shoot. What say ye, lads?"

Then young David of Doncaster spoke up. "Now listen, I pray thee, good master, unto what I say. I have come straight from our friend Eadom o' the Blue Boar. There I heard the full news of this same match. I know from him, and he got it from the Sheriff's man Ralph o' the Scar, that this same rascally Sheriff hath but laid a trap for thee in this shooting match. So go not, good master. Stay within the greenwood lest we all meet grief and woe."

"Now," quoth Robin, "thou art a wise lad. Thou keepest thine ears open and thy mouth shut, as becometh a wise and crafty woodsman. But shall we let it be said that the Sheriff of Nottingham did cow bold Robin Hood and sevenscore as fair archers as are in all merry England? Nay, good David. We must meet guile with guile. Some of you clothe yourselves as friars, and some as peasants,

and some as beggars. But see that each man taketh a
good bow or broadsword, in case need should arise. As
for myself, I will shoot for this same golden arrow. Should
I win it, we will hang it to the branches of our good
greenwood tree, for the joy of all the band. How like
you the plan, my merry men all?"

Then, "Good, good!" cried all the band right heartily.

A fair sight was Nottingham Town on the day of the
shooting match. All along upon the green meadow
beneath the town wall stretched a row of benches. These
were for knight and lady, squire and dame, and rich
burghers and their wives. At the end of the range, near
the target, was a raised seat bedecked with ribbons and
scarfs and garlands of flowers, for the Sheriff of Nottingham and his dame.

The range was two score paces broad. At one end stood
the target, at the other a tent of striped canvas, for the
archers. Across the range from the seats for the better
folk was a railing to keep the poorer people from crowding in front of the target.

Now all the benches were filled with guests. At last,
the Sheriff himself came with his lady, he upon his milk-
white horse and she upon her brown mare. Upon his head
he wore a purple velvet cap. Purple velvet was his robe,
all trimmed about with rich ermine. His jerkin and hose
were of sea-green silk, and his shoes of black velvet, the
pointed toes fastened to his garters with golden chains.
His lady was dressed in blue velvet, all trimmed with
swan's down. They made a gallant sight as they rode along
side by side, and all the people shouted.

Then when the Sheriff and his dame had sat down, he
bade his herald sound upon his silver horn. The man
sounded three blasts that came echoing cheerily back
from the gray walls of Nottingham. Then the archers
stepped forth to their places. All the folk shouted with
a mighty voice, each man calling upon his favorite. "Red
Cap!" cried some. "Cruickshank!" cried others. "Hey for
William o' Leslie!" shouted others yet again. Ladies
waved silken scarfs to urge each to do his best.

Then the herald proclaimed the rules of the game.
"Shoot each man from yon mark, which is sevenscore
yards and ten from the target. One arrow shooteth each
man first. From all the archers shall the ten that shooteth
the fairest shafts be chosen for to shoot again. Two arrows
shooteth each man of these ten. Then shall the three
that shoot the fairest shafts be chosen for to shoot again.
Three arrows shooteth each man of those three. To him
that shooteth the fairest shafts, shall the prize be given."

But Where Is Robin Hood?

The Sheriff leaned forward, looking keenly among the
many archers. No one was there clad in Lincoln green,

such as was worn by Robin and his band. "Nevertheless," said the Sheriff to himself, "he may still be there, and I miss him. But let me see when but ten men shoot. For I wot he will be among the ten."

And now the archers shot, each man in turn. The good folk never saw such archery as was done that day. Six arrows were within the clout, four within the black. Only two lodged within the outer ring.

And now but ten men were left of all those that had shot before. Of these ten, six were famous throughout the land. These six men were Gilbert o' the Red Cap, Adam o' the Dell, Diccon Cruickshank, William o' Leslie, Hubert o' Cloud, and Swithin o' Hertford. Two others were yeomen of Merry Yorkshire. Another was a tall stranger in blue, who said he came from London Town. And the last was a tattered stranger in scarlet, who wore a patch over one eye.

"Now," quoth the Sheriff to a man-at-arms who stood near him, "seest thou Robin Hood among those ten?"

"Nay, that do I not, your worship," answered the man. "Of those Yorkshire yeomen, one is too tall and the other too short for that bold knave. Robin's beard is as yellow as gold, while yon tattered beggar in scarlet hath a beard of brown, besides being blind of one eye. As for the stranger in blue, Robin's shoulders are three inches broader than his."

"Then," quoth the Sheriff, smiting his thigh angrily, "yon knave is a coward as well as a rogue. He dares not show his face among good men and true."

Then, after they had rested a short time, those ten stout men stepped forth to shoot again. Each man shot two arrows. And as they shot, not a word was spoken.

All the crowd watched with scarce a breath of sound. But when the last had shot his arrow, another great shout arose. Many cast their caps aloft for joy of such marvelous shooting.

"Now," quoth old Sir Amyas o' the Dell, who sat near the Sheriff, "ne'er saw I such archery in all my life before. Yet have I seen the best hands at the long bow for three-score years and more."

And now, but three men were left of all those that had shot before. One was Gill o' the Red Cap, one the tattered stranger in scarlet, and one Adam o' the Dell of Tamworth Town. Then all the people called aloud, some on Red Cap, some on Adam. But not a single man in the crowd called upon the stranger in scarlet.

"Now, shoot thou well, Gilbert!" cried the Sheriff. "If thine be the best shaft, fivescore broad silver pennies will I give to thee beside the prize."

"Truly I will do my best," quoth Gilbert right sturdily. He drew forth a fair smooth arrow with a broad feather,

and fitted it skillfully to the string. Drawing his bow
with care, he sped the shaft. Straight flew the arrow and
lit fairly in the clout, a finger breadth from the center.
"A Gilbert, a Gilbert!" shouted all the crowd. "Now, by
my faith," cried the Sheriff, smiting his hands together,
"that is a shrewd shot."

Then the tattered stranger stepped forth. All the
people laughed as they saw a yellow patch that showed
beneath his arm when he raised his elbow to shoot, and
also to see him aim with but one eye. He drew the good
yew bow quickly. Quickly he loosed a shaft. So short was
the time that no man could draw a breath betwixt the
drawing and the shooting. Yet his arrow lodged nearer
the center than the other by twice the length of a barley-
corn.

"Now by all the saints in Paradise!" cried the Sheriff.
"That is a lovely shaft, in very truth!"

Then Adam o' the Dell shot, carefully and cautiously.
His arrow lodged close beside the stranger's. Then, after
a short space, they all three shot again. Once more, each
arrow lodged within the clout. But this time Adam o' the
Dell's was farthest from the center, and again the tattered
stranger's shot was the best.

After another time of rest, they all shot for the third
time. This time, Gilbert took great heed to his aim, keenly
measuring the distance and shooting with shrewdest care.
Straight flew the arrow, and all shouted till the very flags
that waved in the breeze shook with the sound. The shaft
had lodged close beside the spot that marked the very
center!

"Well done, Gilbert!" cried the Sheriff, right joyously.
"Fain am I to believe the prize is thine, and right fairly

won. Now, thou ragged knave, let me see thee shoot a
better shaft than that.''

The One-Eyed Stranger

Naught spake the stranger but took his place. All was
hushed. No one spoke or even seemed to breathe. Meanwhile, also, quite still stood the stranger, holding his bow
in his hand, while one could count five. He drew his
trusty yew, holding it drawn but a moment, then loosed
the string. Straight flew the arrow, and so true that it
smote a gray goose feather from off Gilbert's shaft, which
fell fluttering through the sunlit air. The stranger's arrow

lodged close beside his of the red cap, and in the very center. No one spoke a word for a while, but each man looked into his neighbor's face amazedly.

"Nay," quoth Adam o' the Dell presently, drawing a long breath and shaking his head. "Twoscore years and more have I shot shaft, and maybe not all times bad. But I shoot no more this day. No man can match with yon stranger, whosoe'er he may be." Then he thrust his shaft into his quiver, rattling, and unstrung his bow without another word.

Then the Sheriff came down from his dais and drew near to where the tattered stranger stood leaning upon his stout bow. The good folk crowded around to see the man who shot so wondrously well. "Here, good fellow," quoth the Sheriff. "Take thou the prize. Well and fairly hast thou won it. What may be thy name, and whence comest thou?"

"Men do call me Jock o' Teviotdale. Thence am I come," said the stranger.

"Then, Jock, thou art the fairest archer that e'er mine eyes beheld. If thou wilt join my service, I will clothe thee with a better coat than that thou hast upon thy back. Thou shalt eat and drink of the best. At every Christmastide, fourscore marks shall be thy wage. I trow thou drawest better bow than that same coward knave, Robin Hood, that dared not show his face here this day. Say, good fellow, wilt thou join my service?"

"Nay, that will I not," quoth the stranger, roughly. "I will be mine own. No man in all merry England shall be my master."

"Then get thee gone, and a plague seize thee!" cried the Sheriff. His voice trembled with anger. "And by my

faith and troth, I have a good part of a mind to have thee beaten for thine insolence!" Then he turned upon his heel and strode away.

It was a right motley company that gathered about the noble greenwood tree in Sherwood's depths that same day. A score and more of barefoot friars were there, and some that seemed to be beggars and peasants. Seated upon a mossy couch was one all clad in tattered scarlet, with a patch over one eye. In his hand, he held the golden arrow that was the prize of the great shooting match. Then, amidst a noise of talking and laughter, he took the patch from off his eye and stripped away the scarlet rags from off his body and showed himself all clothed in fair Lincoln green. Quoth he, "Easy come these things away, but walnut stain cometh not so speedily from yellow hair."

Then all laughed louder than before. For it was Robin Hood himself that had won the prize from the Sheriff's very hands. Then all sat down to the woodland feast, and talked of the merry jest that had been played upon the Sheriff, and of the adventures that had befallen each member of the band in his disguise.

But when the feast was done, Robin Hood took Little John apart. "Truly am I vexed in my blood," said he. "I heard the Sheriff say today, 'Thou shootest better than that coward knave, Robin Hood.' I would fain let him know who it was who won the golden arrow from out his hand, and also that I am no coward such as he takes me to be."

Then Little John said, "Good master, take thou me and Will Stutely. We will send yon fat Sheriff news of all this by a messenger such as he doth not expect."

That day, the Sheriff sat at meat in the great hall of his house at Nottingham Town. Long tables stood down the hall, at which sat men-at-arms and household servants. There they talked of the day's shooting as they ate their meat. The Sheriff sat at the head of the table upon a raised seat under a canopy, and beside him sat his dame.

"By my truth," said he, "I did reckon full roundly that that knave, Robin Hood, would be at the game today. I did not think that he was such a coward. But who could that saucy knave be who answered me to my beard so bravely? I wonder that I did not have him beaten. But there was something about him that spoke of other things than rags and tatters."

Even as he finished speaking, something fell rattling among the dishes on the table. Those that sat near started up, wondering what it might be. After a while, one of

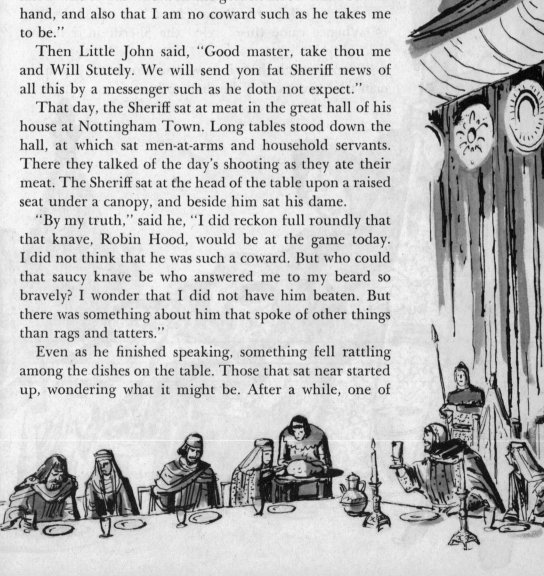

the men-at-arms gathered courage enough to pick it up
and bring it to the Sheriff.

Then every one saw that it was a blunted gray goose
shaft, with a fine scroll, about the thickness of a goose
quill, tied near to its head. The Sheriff opened the scroll
and glanced at it. The veins upon his forehead swelled
and his cheeks grew purple with rage as he read. This
was what he saw:

> *"Now Heaven bless thy grace this day,*
> *Say all in sweet Sherwood,*
> *For thou didst give the prize away*
> *To merry Robin Hood."*

"Whence came this?" cried the Sheriff in a mighty
voice.

"Even through the window, your worship," quoth the
man who had handed the shaft to him.

Sing High, Sing Low

Sing high, sing low in winter snow,
Sing loud in April weather,
Sing free and clear now summer's here,
Chanting all together.

Carol plain in autumn rain
A secret to remember:
A song's blithe rhyme is summertime,
Even in November!

—*Dorothy Hall*

If I Were a One-Legged Pirate

If I were a one-legged pirate
  Galumping around on a peg,
I'd flourish my pistol and fire it;
  Then, sure as my right wooden leg,
I'd buy me a three-decker galleon
  With cannon to port and to lee,
And wearing the king's medallion,
  I'd head for a tropical sea!
Roaring a rough Ha-ha! Ha-ho!
  Roving the routes of old,
Over the billows we would go
  Sweeping the seas for gold!
    Plying the lane
    Of the Spanish Main
      For Gold!
        Gold!
        Gold!

If I were a one-legged pirate
  Galumping around after loot,
I'd flourish my pistol and fire it:
  Then, sure as my red leather boot,
I'd buy me a three-decker galleon
  With cannon to thunder a mile,
And bucking the sea like a stallion
  I'd head for a tropical isle!

Roaring a rough Ha-ha! Ha-ho!
　　Chanting a chantey bold,
Over the billows we would blow,
　　Sweeping the seas for gold!
　　　Plying the lane
　　　Of the Spanish Main
　　　　For Gold!
　　　　Gold!
　　　　　Gold!

But since I was not born a pirate
　　Galumping around on a stick,
And since my toy gun when I fire it
　　Gives out but a little toy click;
Pretending my boat is a galleon,
　　My pond is a tropical sea,
I'll play I'm an old rapscallion,
　　But really I won't hurt a flea.
Roaring my small Ha-ha! Ha-ho!
　　Saying I'm someone bold,
Over the duck pond I will go
　　Roving the routes of old;
　　　Plying the pond
　　　And the stream beyond
　　　　For Gold!
　　　　Gold!
　　　　　Gold!

　　　　　　—*Mildred Plew Meigs*

The Pirate Cook

Oh, once there was a pirate bold
Who thought that he could cook;
He knew just how to bake a cake—
He'd read it in a book.

He stirred it up, he stirred it down,
He stirred it carefully.
He cooked it in a cooking pot
And served it up for tea.

The crew all took a hopeful bite
And then with one accord
They lifted up the pirate cook
And threw him overboard.

The cook was not so pleased at this,
Until with joy he found
That he could sit upon his cake
And paddle it around.

He paddled it, he paddled it,
He paddled night and day,
Until a porpoise came along
And carried it away.

"That only shows," the pirate said,
"That I know how to bake;
It is not usual for fish
To care for currant cake.

"I knew that I was right," he said
And gently sank below;
And now he keeps a cooking school
To which the mermaids go.

—*Marchette Gaylord Chute*

Antonio

Antonio, Antonio
Was tired of living alonio.
He thought he would woo
Miss Lissamy Lu,
Miss Lissamy Lucy Molonio.

Antonio, Antonio,
Rode off on his polo-ponio.
He found the fair maid
In a bowery shade,
A-sitting and knitting alonio.

Antonio, Antonio,
Said, "If you will be my ownio,
I'll love you true,
And I'll buy for you
An icery creamery conio!"

"Oh, *no*nio, Antonio!
You're far too bleak and bonio!
And all that I wish,
You singular fish,
Is that you would quickly begonio."

Antonio, Antonio,
He uttered a dismal monio;
Then ran off and hid
(Or I'm told that he did)
In the Ante-cat-arc-tical Zonio.

—*Laura E. Richards*

Eletelephony

Once there was an elephant,
Who tried to use the telephant—
No! no! I mean an elephone
Who tried to use the telephone—
(Dear me! I am not certain quite
That even now I've got it right.)

Howe'er it was, he got his trunk
Entangled in the telephunk;
The more he tried to get it free,
The louder buzzed the telephee—
(I fear I'd better drop the song
Of elephop and telephong!)

—Laura E. Richards

How Doth the Little Crocodile

How doth the little crocodile
　Improve his shining tail,
And pour the waters of the Nile
　On every golden scale!

How cheerfully he seems to grin,
　How neatly spreads his claws,
And welcomes little fishes in,
　With gently smiling jaws!

—Lewis Carroll

He Thought He Saw

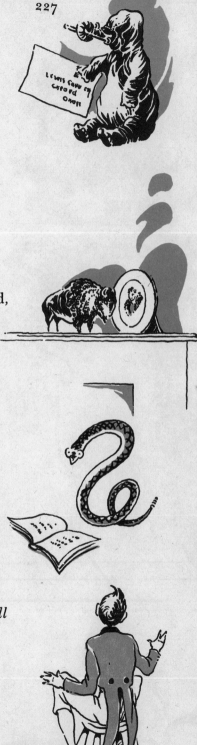

He thought he saw an elephant
That practiced on a fife:
He looked again, and found it was
A letter from his wife.
"At length I realize," he said,
"The bitterness of life."

He thought he saw a buffalo
Upon the chimney-piece:
He looked again, and saw it was
His sister's husband's niece.
"Unless you leave this house," he said,
"I'll send for the police!"

He thought he saw a rattlesnake
That questioned him in Greek:
He looked again, and found it was
The middle of next week.
"The one thing I regret," he said,
"Is that it cannot speak."

He thought he saw a banker's clerk
Descending from a bus:
He looked again, and found it was
A hippopotamus:
"If this should stay to dine," he said,
"There won't be much for us!"

—*Lewis Carroll*

The Mouse

I heard a mouse
Bitterly complaining
In a crack of moonlight
Aslant on the floor—

"Little I ask
And that little is not granted.
There are few crumbs
In this world any more.

"The bread-box is tin
And I cannot get in.

"The jam's in a jar
My teeth cannot mar.

"The cheese sits by itself
On the pantry shelf—

"All night I run
Searching and seeking,
All night I run
About on the floor,

"Moonlight is there
And a bare place for dancing,
But no little feast
Is spread any more."

—Elizabeth Coatsworth

The Young Calves

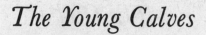

A hush had fallen on the birds,
    And it was almost night,
When I came round a turn and saw
    A whole year's loveliest sight.

Two calves that thought their month of life
    Meant June through all the year
Were coming down the grassy road
    As slender as young deer.

They stopped amazed and took me in,
    Putting their ears out far,
And in each of four round eyes
    There was an evening star.

They did not breathe, they stared so hard,
    Brother close to brother,
Then their legs awoke, and they
    Turned flank to flank for mother.

A small boy in torn knickers came
    And caught them as they fled,
He put a slender arm around
    Each slender, startled head.

He never looked at me at all,
    I was not in his mind;
The three of them went down the road
    And never glanced behind.

        —*Robert P. Tristram Coffin*

The Owl

When cats run home and light is come,
    And dew is cold upon the ground,
And the far-off stream is dumb,
    And the whirring sail goes round,
    And the whirring sail goes round,
Alone and warming his five wits,
The white owl in the belfry sits.

When merry milkmaids click the latch,
    And rarely smells the new-mown hay,
And the cock hath sung beneath the thatch
    Twice or thrice his roundelay,
    Twice or thrice his roundelay;
Alone and warming his five wits,
The white owl in the belfry sits.

                —*Alfred Tennyson*

This Is My Rock

This is my rock
And here I run
To steal the secret of the sun;

This is my rock
And here come I
Before the night has swept the sky;

This is my rock,
This is the place
I meet the evening face to face.

                —*David McCord*

The Year's at the Spring

The year's at the spring
And day's at the morn;
Morning's at seven;
The hillside's dew-pearled;
The lark's on the wing;
The snail's on the thorn;
God's in His heaven—
All's right with the world!

—*Robert Browning*

The Sandhill Crane

Whenever the days are cool and clear
The sandhill crane goes walking
Across the field by the flashing weir
Slowly, solemnly stalking.
The little frogs in the tules hear
And jump for their lives when he comes near,
The minnows scuttle away in fear,
When the sandhill crane goes walking.

The field folk know if he comes that way,
Slowly, solemnly stalking,
There is danger and death in the least delay
When the sandhill crane goes walking.
The chipmunks stop in the midst of their play,
The gophers hide in their holes away
And hush, oh, hush! the field mice say,
When the sandhill crane goes walking.

—*Mary Austin*

Night

Stars over snow,
   And in the west a planet
Swinging below a star—
   Look for a lovely thing and you will find it,
It is not far—
   It never will be far.

                 —Sara Teasdale

Green Moth

The night the green moth came for me,
   A creamy moon poured down the hill,
The meadow seemed a silver sea,
Small pearls were hung in every tree,
   And all so still, so still—

He floated in on my white bed,
   A strange and soundless fellow.
I saw the horns wave on his head,
He stepped across my pillow
In tiny ermine boots, and spread
   His cape of green and yellow.

He came so close that I could see
   His golden eyes, and sweet and chill,
His faint breath wavered over me.
"Come Child, my Beautiful," said he,
   And all so still, so still—

                 —Winifred Welles

Silver

Slowly, silently, now the moon
Walks the night in her silver shoon;
This way, and that, she peers, and sees
Silver fruit upon silver trees;
One by one the casements catch
Her beams beneath the silvery thatch;
Couched in his kennel, like a log,
With paws of silver sleeps the dog;
From their shadowy cote the white breasts peep
Of doves in a silver-feathered sleep;
A harvest mouse goes scampering by,
With silver claws, and silver eye;
And moveless fish in the water gleam,
By silver reeds in a silver stream.

—*Walter de la Mare*

Evening Hymn

The day is done;
The lamps are lit;
Woods-ward the birds are flown.
Shadows draw close,—
Peace be unto this house.

The cloth is fair;
The food is set.
God's night draw near.
Quiet and love and peace
Be to this, our rest, our place.

—*Elizabeth Madox Roberts*

Sea Song

A wet sheet and a flowing sea,
　A wind that follows fast
And fills the white and rustling sail,
　And bends the gallant mast!
And bends the gallant mast, my boys,
　While, like the eagle free,
Away the good ship flies, and leaves
　Old England on the lee.

O for a soft and gentle wind!
　I heard a fair one cry;
But give to me the swelling breeze,
　And white waves heaving high:
The white waves heaving high, my lads,
　The good ship tight and free;
The world of waters is our home,
　And merry men are we.

There's tempest in yon horned moon,
　And lightning in yon cloud;
And hark the music, mariners!
　The wind is wakening loud.
The wind is wakening loud, my boys,
　The lightning flashes free—
The hollow oak our palace is,
　Our heritage the sea.

—*Allan Cunningham*

The Sea Gypsy

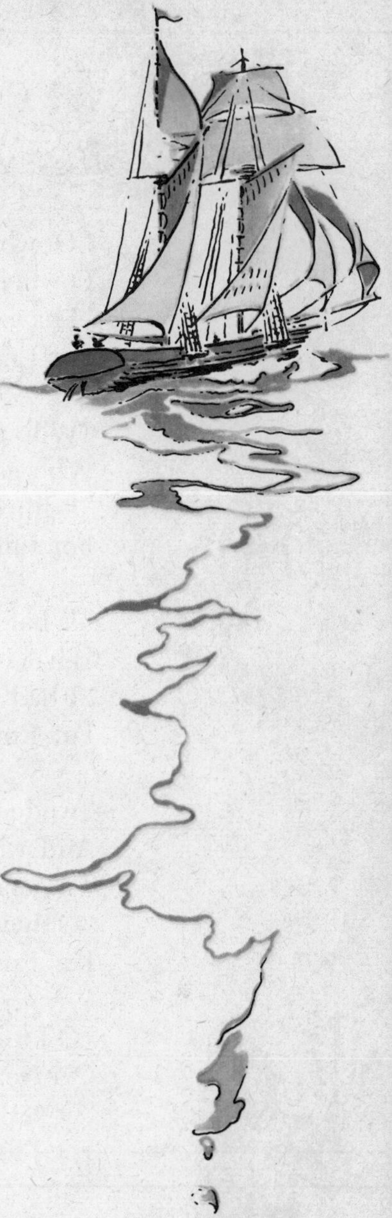

I am fevered with the sunset,
I am fretful with the bay,
For the wander-thirst is on me
And my soul is in Cathay.

There's a schooner in the offing,
With her topsails shot with fire,
And my heart has gone aboard her
For the Islands of Desire.

I must forth again tomorrow!
With the sunset I must be
Hull down on the trail of rapture
In the wonder of the Sea.

—Richard Hovey

Sea Horses

The wild sea horses lash
Their hooves against the land—
They thunder on the rocks,
They paw upon the sand.

They fling their wild white manes,
They whinny loud and free—
And then, at tide-turn, drift
To pastures far at sea.

—Dorothy Hall

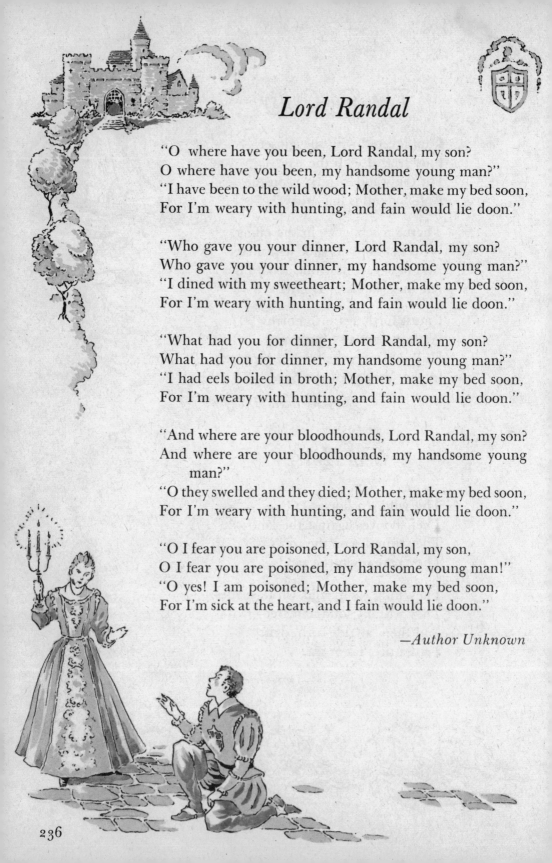

Lord Randal

"O where have you been, Lord Randal, my son?
O where have you been, my handsome young man?"
"I have been to the wild wood; Mother, make my bed soon,
For I'm weary with hunting, and fain would lie doon."

"Who gave you your dinner, Lord Randal, my son?
Who gave you your dinner, my handsome young man?"
"I dined with my sweetheart; Mother, make my bed soon,
For I'm weary with hunting, and fain would lie doon."

"What had you for dinner, Lord Randal, my son?
What had you for dinner, my handsome young man?"
"I had eels boiled in broth; Mother, make my bed soon,
For I'm weary with hunting, and fain would lie doon."

"And where are your bloodhounds, Lord Randal, my son?
And where are your bloodhounds, my handsome young
    man?"
"O they swelled and they died; Mother, make my bed soon,
For I'm weary with hunting, and fain would lie doon."

"O I fear you are poisoned, Lord Randal, my son,
O I fear you are poisoned, my handsome young man!"
"O yes! I am poisoned; Mother, make my bed soon,
For I'm sick at the heart, and I fain would lie doon."

—Author Unknown

Overheard on a Saltmarsh

Nymph, nymph, what are your beads?

Green glass, goblin. Why do you stare at them?

Give them me.

    No.

Give them me. Give them me.

    No.

Then I will howl all night in the reeds,
Lie in the mud and howl for them.

Goblin, why do you love them so?

They are better than stars or water,
Better than voices of winds that sing,
Better than any man's fair daughter,
Your green glass beads on a silver ring.

Hush, I stole them out of the moon.

Give me your beads, I desire them.

    No.

I will howl in a deep lagoon
For your green glass beads, I love them so.
Give them me. Give them.

    No.

—*Harold Monro*

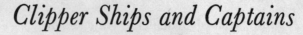

Clipper Ships and Captains

1843-1860

There was a time before our time,
It will not come again,
When the best ships still were wooden ships
But the men were iron men.

From Stonington to Kennebunk
The Yankee hammers plied
To build the clippers of the wave
That were New England's pride.

The "Flying Cloud," the "Northern Light,"
The "Sovereign of the Seas"
—There was salt music in the blood
That thought of names like these.

"Sea Witch," "Red Jacket," "Golden Age"
And "Chariot of Fame,"
The whole world gaped to look at them
Before the steamship came.

Their cargoes were of tea and gold,
Their bows a cutting blade,
And, on the bridge, the skippers walked,
Lords of the China trade.

The skippers with the little beards
And the New England drawl
Who knew Hong Kong and Marblehead
And the Pole Star over all.

Stately as churches, swift as gulls,
They trod the oceans, then—
No man had seen such ships before
And none will see again.

—*Rosemary and Stephen Vincent Benét*

The Arrow and the Song

I shot an arrow into the air,
It fell to earth, I knew not where;
For, so swiftly it flew, the sight
Could not follow it in its flight.

I breathed a song into the air,
It fell to earth, I knew not where;
For who has sight so keen and strong,
That it can follow the flight of song?

Long, long afterward, in an oak
I found the arrow, still unbroke;
And the song, from beginning to end,
I found again in the heart of a friend.

—*Henry Wadsworth Longfellow*

The Wilderness Is Tamed

The ax has cut the forest down,
The laboring ox has smoothed all clear,
Apples now grow where pine trees stood,
And slow cows graze instead of deer.

Where Indian fires once raised their smoke
The chimneys of a farmhouse stand,
And cocks crow barnyard challenges
To dawns that once saw savage land.

The ax, the plow, the binding wall,
By these the wilderness is tamed,
By these the white man's will is wrought,
The rivers bridged, the new towns named.

—*Elizabeth Coatsworth*

Spirit Hunt

The wind blows wild tonight and They are riding:
  Slim brown flames on ghostly ponies flying—
Now soundless in the moonlight's glimmer gliding,
  Now whooping in the wind's long moan and dying.

Cloud shadows move—the buffalo are coming!
  The moon is hidden though the night is starry;
And fierce yells mingle with the hoofbeats' drumming
  As spirit hunters slay the spirit quarry.

—*Dorothy Hall*

I Hear America Singing

I hear America singing, the varied carols I
hear,
Those of mechanics, each one singing his, as
it should be, blithe and strong,
The carpenter singing his, as he measures his
plank or beam,
The mason singing his, as he makes ready for
work, or leaves off work,
The boatman singing what belongs to him in
his boat, the deckhand singing on the
steamboat deck,
The shoemaker singing as he sits on his bench,
the hatter singing as he stands,
The wood-cutter's song, the ploughboy's on
his way in the morning, or at the noon
intermission, or at sundown,
The delicious singing of the mother, or of
the young wife at work, or of the girl
sewing or washing,
Each singing what belongs to him or her and
to none else,
The day what belongs to the day—at night the
party of young fellows, robust, friendly,
Singing with open mouths their strong melo-
dious songs.

—Walt Whitman

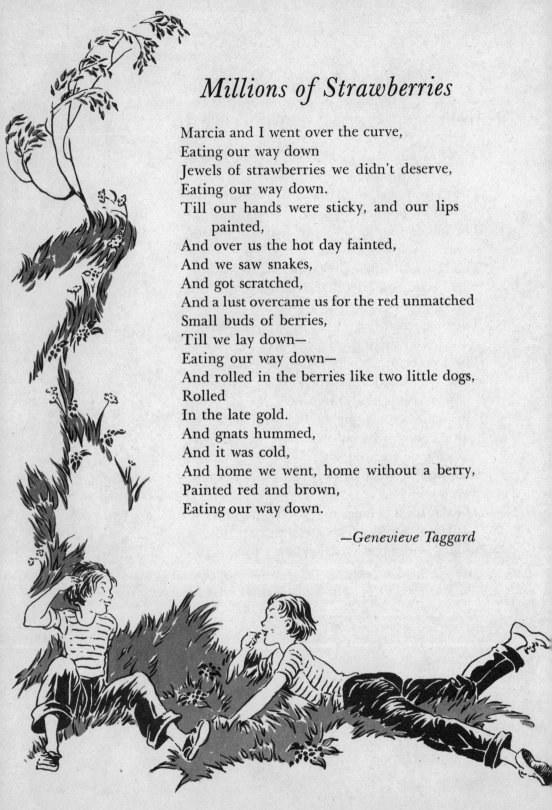

Millions of Strawberries

Marcia and I went over the curve,
Eating our way down
Jewels of strawberries we didn't deserve,
Eating our way down.
Till our hands were sticky, and our lips
    painted,
And over us the hot day fainted,
And we saw snakes,
And got scratched,
And a lust overcame us for the red unmatched
Small buds of berries,
Till we lay down—
Eating our way down—
And rolled in the berries like two little dogs,
Rolled
In the late gold.
And gnats hummed,
And it was cold,
And home we went, home without a berry,
Painted red and brown,
Eating our way down.

—Genevieve Taggard

Lone Dog

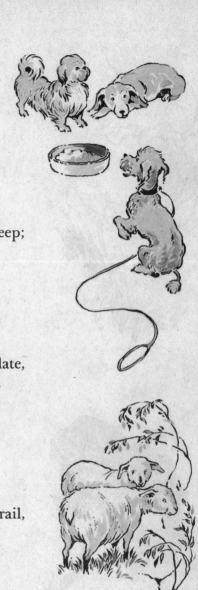

I'm a lean dog, a keen dog, a wild dog,
    and lone;
I'm a rough dog, a tough dog, hunting
    on my own;
I'm a bad dog, a mad dog, teasing silly sheep;
I love to sit and bay the moon, to keep
    fat souls from sleep.

I'll never be a lap dog, licking dirty feet,
A sleek dog, a meek dog, cringing
    for my meat,
Not for me the fireside, the well-filled plate,
But shut door, and sharp stone, and cuff,
    and kick, and hate.

Not for me the other dogs, running
    by my side,
Some have run a short while, but none
    of them would bide.
O mine is still the lone trail, the hard trail,
    the best,
Wide wind, and wild stars, and hunger
    of the quest!

—Irene Rutherford McLeod

Afternoon on a Hill

I will be the gladdest thing
   Under the sun!
I will touch a hundred flowers
   And not pick one.

I will look at cliffs and clouds
   With quiet eyes,
Watch the wind bow down the grass,
   And the grass rise.

And when the lights begin to show
   Up from the town,
I will mark which must be mine,
   And then start down!

       —*Edna St. Vincent Millay*

I Meant To Do My Work

I meant to do my work today—
   But a brown bird sang in the apple-tree,
And a butterfly flitted across the field,
   And all the leaves were calling me.

And the wind went sighing over the land,
   Tossing the grasses to and fro,
And a rainbow held out its shining hand—
   So what could I do but laugh and go?

       —*Richard LeGallienne*

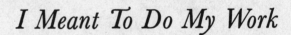

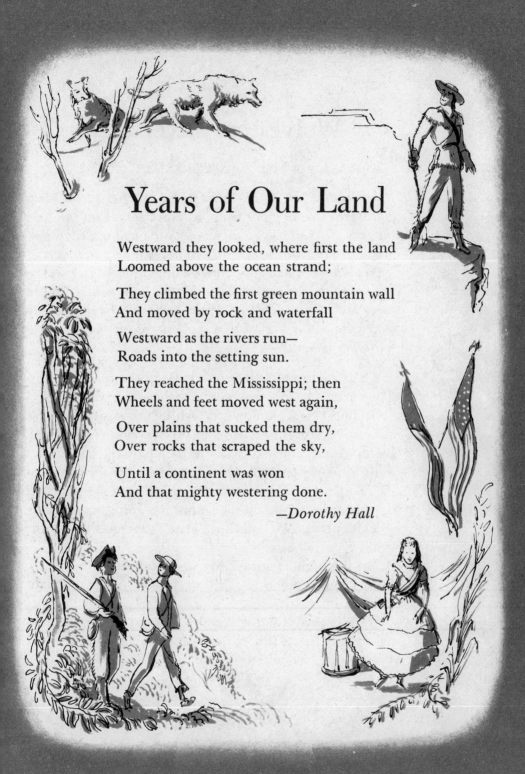

Years of Our Land

Westward they looked, where first the land
Loomed above the ocean strand;

They climbed the first green mountain wall
And moved by rock and waterfall

Westward as the rivers run—
Roads into the setting sun.

They reached the Mississippi; then
Wheels and feet moved west again,

Over plains that sucked them dry,
Over rocks that scraped the sky,

Until a continent was won
And that mighty westering done.

—Dorothy Hall

Wolves on Silver Lake

Laura Ingalls Wilder

Laura and her family—Ma and Pa, and her sisters Mary and Carrie—were pioneering in North Dakota at the time the first railroad was going through. Pa had served as paymaster for the railroad construction crews that summer.

Now the men had gone, and the Ingalls family were staying alone on the prairie through the long winter, in the surveyors' house. Pa's idea was to find a homestead on which he could file a claim and where his family could settle permanently.

There came a night when moonlight shone silver clear. The earth was endless white and the wind was still.

Beyond every window, the white world stretched far away in frosty glitter and the sky was a curve of light. Laura could not settle down to anything. She didn't want to play games. She hardly heard even the music of Pa's fiddle. She did not want to dance, but she felt that she must move swiftly. She must be going somewhere.

Suddenly she exclaimed, "Carrie! Let's go slide on the ice!"

"In the night, Laura?" Ma was astonished.

"It's light outdoors," Laura replied. "Almost as light as day."

"It will be all right, Caroline," Pa said. "There's nothing to hurt them, if they don't stay too long and freeze."

So Ma told them, "You may go for a quick run. Don't stay until you get too cold."

Laura and Carrie hurried into their coats and hoods and mittens. Their shoes were new and the soles thick. Ma had knit their stockings of woolen yarn, and their red flannel underclothes came down over their knees and buttoned in a snug band around each stocking. Their flannel petticoats were thick and warm, and their dresses and their coats were wool, and so were their hoods and mufflers.

Out of the warm house they burst into the breath-taking air that tingled with cold. They ran a race on the snowy path down the low hill to the stables. Then they followed the path that the horses and the cow had made when Pa led them through the snow to water at the hole he had cut in the lake ice.

"We mustn't go near the water hole," Laura said, and she led Carrie along the lake shore until they were well away from it. Then they stopped and looked at the night.

It was so beautiful that they hardly breathed. The great round moon hung in the sky and its radiance poured over a silvery world. Far, far away in every direction stretched motionless flatness, softly shining as if it were made of soft light. In the midst lay the dark, smooth lake, and a glittering moonpath stretched across it. Tall grass stood up in black lines from the snow drifted in the sloughs.

The stable lay low and dark near the shore, and on the low hill stood the dark, small, surveyors' house, with the yellow light in the window twinkling from its darkness.

"How still it is," Carrie whispered. "Listen how still it is."

Laura's heart swelled. She felt herself a part of the wide land, of the far deep sky and the brilliant moonlight. She wanted to fly. But Carrie was little and almost afraid, so she took hold of Carrie's hand and said, "Let's slide. Come on, run!"

With hands clasped, they ran a little way. Then, with right foot first, they slid on the smooth ice much farther than they had run.

"On the moonpath, Carrie! Let's follow the moonpath," Laura cried.

And so they ran and slid, and ran and slid again, on the glittering moonpath into the light from the silver moon. Farther and farther from shore they went, straight toward the high bank on the other side.

They swooped and almost seemed to fly. If Carrie lost her balance, Laura held her up. If Laura was unsteady, Carrie's hand steadied her.

The Wolf

Close to the farther shore, almost in the shadow of the high bank, they stopped. Something made Laura look up to the top of the bank.

And there, dark against the moonlight, stood a great
wolf!

He was looking toward her. The wind stirred his fur
and the moonlight seemed to run in and out of it.

"Let's go back," Laura said quickly, as she turned,
taking Carrie with her. "I can go faster than you."

She ran and slid and ran again as fast as she could, but
Carrie kept up.

"I saw it too," Carrie panted. "Was it a wolf?"

"Don't talk!" Laura answered. "Hurry!"

Laura could hear their feet running and sliding on
the ice. She listened for a sound behind them, but there
was none. Then they ran and slid without a word until
they came to the path by the waterhole. As they ran up
the path, Laura looked back but she could see nothing
on the lake nor on the bank beyond.

Laura and Carrie didn't stop running. They ran up
the hill to the house, opened the back door, and ran into

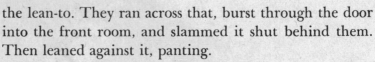

the lean-to. They ran across that, burst through the door into the front room, and slammed it shut behind them. Then leaned against it, panting.

Pa sprang to his feet. "What is it?" he asked. "What has frightened you?"

"Was it a wolf, Laura?" Carrie gasped.

"It was a wolf, Pa," Laura gulped, catching her breath. "A great, big wolf! And I was afraid Carrie couldn't run fast enough, but she did."

"I should say she did!" Pa exclaimed. "Where is this wolf?"

"I don't know. It is gone," Laura told him.

Ma helped them take off their wraps. "Sit down and rest! You are all out of breath," she said.

"Where was the wolf?" Pa wanted to know.

"Up on the bank," Carrie said, and Laura added, "The high bank across the lake."

"Did you girls go clear there?" Pa asked in surprise. "And ran all the way back after you saw him! I had no idea you would go so far. It is a good half-mile."

"We followed the moonpath," Laura told him.

Pa looked at her strangely. "You would!" he said. "I thought those wolves had gone. It was careless of me. I'll hunt them tomorrow."

Mary sat still, but her face was white. "Oh, girls," she almost whispered. "Suppose he had caught you!"

Then they all sat silent while Laura and Carrie rested. Laura was glad to be safe in the warm room with the desolate prairie shut out. If anything had happened to Carrie, it would have been her fault for taking her so far across the lake.

But nothing had happened. She could almost see again

the great wolf with the wind ruffling the moonlight on his fur.

"Pa!" she said in a low voice.

"Yes, Laura?" Pa answered.

"I hope you don't find the wolf, Pa," Laura said.

"Why ever not?" Ma wondered.

"Because he didn't chase us," Laura told her. "He didn't chase us, Pa, and he could have caught us."

A long, wild wolf howl rose and faded away on the stillness. Another answered it. Then silence again.

Laura's heart seemed to turn over with a sickening flop and she found herself on her feet. She was glad of Ma's steadying hand on her arm.

"Poor girl! You are nervous as a witch and no wonder," Ma said softly. Ma took a hot flatiron from the back of the stove, wrapped it tightly in a cloth, and gave it to Carrie.

"It is bedtime," she said. "Here is the hot iron for your feet. And here is yours, Laura," as she wrapped another. "Be sure you put it in the middle of the bed so Mary's feet can reach it too."

As Laura shut the stair door behind them, Pa was talking earnestly to Ma. But Laura could not hear what he said for the ringing in her ears.

Pa Finds the Homestead

After breakfast next morning, Pa took his gun and set out. All that morning Laura was listening for a shot and not wanting to hear it. All morning she remembered the great wolf sitting quiet in the moonlight that shimmered through his thick fur.

Pa was late for dinner. It was long past noon when

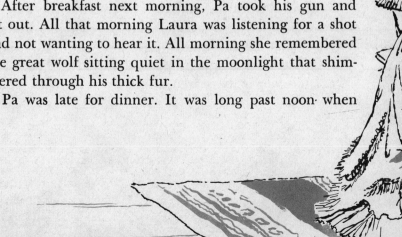

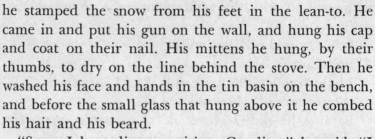

he stamped the snow from his feet in the lean-to. He came in and put his gun on the wall, and hung his cap and coat on their nail. His mittens he hung, by their thumbs, to dry on the line behind the stove. Then he washed his face and hands in the tin basin on the bench, and before the small glass that hung above it he combed his hair and his beard.

"Sorry I kept dinner waiting, Caroline," he said. "I was gone longer than I thought. Went farther than I intended."

"It doesn't matter, Charles. I've kept dinner warm," Ma replied. "Come to the table, girls! Don't keep Pa waiting."

"How far did you go, Pa?" Mary asked.

"Better than ten miles, all told," said Pa. "Those wolf tracks led me a chase."

"Did you get the wolf, Pa?" Carrie wanted to know. Laura did not say anything.

Pa smiled at Carrie and said, "Now, now, don't ask questions. I'll tell you all about it. I went across the lake, followed the marks you girls made last night. And what do you suppose I found in that high bank where you saw the wolf?"

"You found the wolf," Carrie said confidently. Laura still said nothing. Her food was choking her. She could hardly swallow the smallest mouthful.

"I found the wolves' *den*," said Pa. "And the biggest wolves' tracks I ever saw. Girls, there were two big buffalo wolves at that den last night."

Mary and Carrie gasped. Ma said, "Charles!"

"It's too late to be scared now," Pa told them. "But

that's what you girls did. You went right up to the wolves' den and there were the wolves.

"Their tracks were fresh, and all the signs show plain as day what they were doing. It's an old den, and from their size they're no young wolves. I'd say they'd been living there for some years. But they haven't been living there this winter.

"They came down from the northwest sometime yesterday evening and went pretty straight to that den. They stayed around it, in and out of it, maybe till this morning. I followed their tracks from there, down along the Big Slough and out on the prairie, southwest.

"From the time they left the old den, those wolves never stopped. They trotted along, side by side, as if they had started on a long journey and knew where they were going. I followed them far enough to be sure that I couldn't get a shot at them. They've left for good."

Laura took a deep breath as though she had forgotten to breathe till now. Pa looked at her. "You are glad they got away, Laura?" he asked.

"Yes, Pa, I am," Laura answered. "They didn't chase us."

"No, Laura, they didn't chase you. And for the life of me, I can't figure out why they didn't."

"And what were they doing at that old den?" Ma wondered.

"They were just looking at it," said Pa. "My belief is they came back to visit the old place where they lived before the graders came in and the antelope left. Maybe they used to live here before the hunters killed the last buffalo. Buffalo wolves were all over this country once, but there's not many left now, even around here. The railroads and settlements kept driving them farther West. One thing's certain if I know anything about wild animal tracks; those two wolves came straight from the West and went straight back West, and all they did here was to stop one night at the old den. And I wouldn't wonder if they're pretty nearly the last buffalo wolves that'll ever be seen in this part of the country."

"Oh, Pa, the poor wolves," Laura mourned.

"Mercy on us," Ma said briskly. "There's enough to be sorry for, without being sorry for the feelings of wild beasts! Be thankful the brutes didn't do any worse than scare you girls last night."

"That isn't all, Caroline!" Pa announced. "I've got some news. I've found our homestead."

"Oh, where, Pa! What's it like? How far is it?" Mary and Laura and Carrie asked, excited. Ma said, "That's good, Charles."

Pa pushed back his plate, drank his tea, wiped his mustache, and said, "It is just right in every way. It lies south of where the lake joins Big Slough, and the slough curves around to the west of it. There's a rise in the prairie to the south of the slough, that will make a nice place to build. A little hill just west of it crowds the slough back on that side. On the quarter section there's upland hay and plow land lying to the south; and good grazing on all of it, everything a farmer could ask for. And it's near the townsite, so the girls can go to school."

"I'm glad, Charles," said Ma.

"It's a funny thing," Pa said. "Here I've been looking around this country for months and never finding a quarter section that just exactly suited me. And that one was lying there all the time. Likely enough I wouldn't have come across it at all, if this wolf chase hadn't taken me across the lake and down along the slough on that side."

"I wish you had filed on it last fall," Ma worried.

"Nobody'll be in here this winter," Pa said confidently. "I'll get out to Brookins and file on that claim next spring before anybody else is looking for a homestead."

Kit Carson and the General

Edgar Wyatt

Colonel Christopher Carson turned away from the window of his adobe quarters at Fort Stanton. Outside, the New Mexico sun baked the dusty parade ground. A long line of blue-clad troopers stood ready beside their mounts. Kit Carson could hear their laughing talk and the shouts of their sergeants. He heard the pawing horses, the jingling spurs.

Yesterday, a band of Mescalero Apaches had raided the corrals at Fort West. Yelling Indians stampeded the fort's horses, then vanished into the rugged mountains above Dog Canyon. Kit Carson, in command at Fort Stanton, was ordered to "pursue and defeat the Indians and recover the animals."

Kit was anxious to be on his way. "If you're ready, Major," he said, "let's go. It's a long ride to Dog Canyon."

Major William McCleave was at his desk. A rider had galloped in just now with dispatches from the General at Santa Fe. McCleave was hastily reading through them. He frowned as he glanced up.

"In a moment—Colonel," snapped McCleave. He added the *Colonel* as if it hurt to say the word.

Kit turned back to the window. As McCleave watched him, his lip curled. This little bow-legged scout a colonel! Why, he couldn't even read or write. McCleave had to read his orders to him. He didn't look like a soldier— Kit's leathery cheeks were freckled and his sandy hair was always tousled. And he didn't act like an officer. Every man at the fort, privates and all—except Major McCleave —called him "Kit," never "Colonel Carson."

People said that Kit Carson was a great Indian fighter. "He sounds more like an Indian-lover to me," thought Major McCleave, "always talking about a 'square deal' for Apaches. Indians are savages—animals—and should be treated so."

Now McCleave was reading the last dispatch from Santa Fe. Then he read it again. There was triumph in his smile now as he glanced up at Kit. "Here's an order from the General."

Kit sighed. The troopers outside would have to wait a little longer. Generals, thought Kit, must spend all their time writing orders.

"Very well, Major," he said. "Read it to me."

McCleave read slowly, as if he liked the taste of every word:

"There must be no council held with the Indians, nor any talks. The men must be killed whenever and wherever you can find them."

Kit slowly shook his head. "The General signed that?"

McCleave flipped the paper across his desk. "General James H. Carleton, himself. There's his signature." Major McCleave pounded a fist into his broad palm. "That's the way to fight Apaches! I've always said it: Don't coddle 'em. Kill 'em."

"Apaches are people," said Kit softly. "They're good and they're bad, like us—"

"They're savages, all of them," snapped Major Mc-Cleave, "and we ought to wipe them out."

"No," said Kit Carson. "We have to fight them until

they're beaten. Then we should give them a square deal, a place to live, hunting grounds in their own country—"

"Their country!"

"It was theirs before we got here," said Kit. "And they want to keep it. That's what the fighting is about."

McCleave tapped the paper on his desk. "From now on we kill them on sight. The General says so. No treaties, no talks, no promises. Bullets, that's all!"

Kit shrugged and turned toward the door. Outside, an impatient bugler tried a few notes of *Boots and Saddles*. "Let's go, Major. We've got some fighting to do at Dog Canyon."

Kit Carson and Major McCleave led the column of troopers toward the mountains. A choking cloud of dust rose above the horses and men. Kit scarcely noticed it. He was deep in thought.

You could understand, thought Kit, why the General was bitter toward Apaches. When the Civil War began two years ago, General Carleton had raised two thousand California Volunteers. He marched them eastward through the desert country to join the Union armies.

But the Apache Indians had never heard of the Civil War. They thought Carleton was marching against them. In Arizona and New Mexico, swarms of Apache raiders stung his flanks. They kidnapped his scouts and messengers and ambushed his patrols.

General Carleton was still fighting his way across the desert when new orders came to him from Washington. This route from California must be protected. Carleton was ordered to stay in the Apache country and keep it open.

The Army sent Kit Carson, its finest Indian fighter, to serve with Carleton. Kit knew Apaches and spoke their language. He knew their trails, their signs and signals. All Apaches respected him. Some were his friends and called him "Father Kit."

General Carleton knew nothing at all about Apaches. He only knew that now, in 1863, there were great battles in the East. He was still chasing Indians two thousand miles away.

This trail toward Dog Canyon was winding now

through the lower foothills. Kit halted his troopers where the trail divided. He spoke to Major McCleave.

"Take Lieutenant French and eighty men. Ride straight ahead. I'll lead the others around to the north. We'll try to catch the Indians between us."

McCleave touched his hat in a careless salute and rode away.

Apache scouts, perched on high peaks, watched McCleave lead his troopers toward Dog Canyon. They saw Kit Carson circle the mountains to the north and begin to climb. Now they raced through the mountain passes to their chief, Gian-nah-tah, whose name meant "Always Ready."

"Father Kit leads many soldiers against us," said the scouts.

The End of the Trail

Gian-nah-tah listened in stony-faced silence, but his heart was heavy. His long warpath began when the first American settlers came to the Apache country. As more white men came, they drove the Indians from their desert homes. The Apaches were safe for a while in the high mountains. From here, they swooped down to raid the white man's ranches for food and his forts for horses. But now Kit Carson was coming to attack their last stronghold. Gian-nah-tah knew that his warpath soon must end.

Still he would not give up without a fight. "Ride!" he said to the scouts. "Make smoke on the peaks. Gather all our warriors."

Gian-nah-tah prepared his ambush skillfully as McCleave's troopers approached Dog Canyon. Apache braves

hid behind great boulders where the narrow pass twisted beneath overhanging rocks. They waited in perfect silence for the soldiers to ride into their trap.

But McCleave's troopers were veterans now. They had long ago learned that a narrow pass was dangerous in Indian country. They left the trail and climbed through cactus-studded foothills. Soon they were above and behind the hidden Indians.

A bugle call was the signal for the attack. A hail of bullets poured down on the Apaches and drove them tumbling from their rocky cover.

Loco, a brave young subchief, tried to rally the panicky Indians. He leaped through the rain of bullets and crouched behind a huge rock. He gave the rallying cry— the shrill bark of the coyote.

But these Americans knew that trick, too. A soldier crept up to the same boulder and knelt behind it on the other side. The soldier repeated the coyote's cry. The startled Indian raised his head. The soldier shot him at point-blank range.

The Indians retreated higher and higher into the mountains. The troopers drove them from village after village. They recaptured Fort West's horses. They burned the Apache wickiups.

Finally, Gian-nah-tah and his braves reached the deep pine forest that spread across the very top of this mountain range. There, in shadowy canyons, the chief hid five hundred Indians—old men, women, children. He left the warriors to guard them. Then, with four subchiefs, he started down the northern slope of the mountain.

"We must speak with Father Kit," said Gian-nah-tah. "Our warpath is ended."

Kit Carson's troopers, still climbing the northern slopes, were startled when five Indians appeared, it seemed, from nowhere.

"Apaches!" shouted a soldier and raised his rifle.

"Don't fire," called Kit. "They're carrying a white flag."

The Indians came closer. One of them held a flag made of a rag tied to a stick.

Kit watched Gian-nah-tah. There was a little grey now in the tall chief's hair, but he was lean and powerful and straight.

Gian-nah-tah spread his hands in a proud appeal.

"Your soldiers have driven us from our homes. There is nowhere now for us to go. Father Kit, you are a chief among white men. My people will surrender to you because they know your tongue is straight. Show us a place where we may live in peace. Tell us what to do."

Kit said, "My General in Santa Fe is a greater chief than I. Only he can answer Gian-nah-tah."

"Then let us ride to Santa Fe and speak with this great white chief."

Before Kit could answer, there was the sound of many riders on the trail. Major McCleave appeared at the head of his troopers.

He shouted triumphantly to Kit. "We drove them out of Dog Canyon and burned their filthy huts—"

McCleave caught sight of the five Apaches surrounded by Kit's soldiers.

"What are those Indians doing here alive?"

"Gian-nah-tah will take his people to a reservation. He'll leave the warpath—" Kit began.

"No more treaties with Apaches!" snapped McCleave. "We have our orders from the General." He was scornfully polite. "Do I have the Colonel's permission to obey him?"

McCleave twisted in his saddle. "Lieutenant French!" he shouted. "A firing squad, at once!"

Kit spoke quietly. "These Indians came here under a white flag, Major."

"I'll obey my orders," said McCleave stubbornly.

Kit shook his head. He met the Major's stormy glare. "Dismiss your firing squad, Major. It won't be needed. These are my prisoners. They'll be safe while I'm commanding here."

"That won't be long! When the General hears of this—"

Kit grinned. "Suppose you ride ahead and tell him, Major. Maybe he'll have you shoot me."

McCleave galloped furiously away. Kit turned to Gian-nah-tah.

"If you go to Santa Fe with me, you'll risk your life. The General may agree to a treaty with your people, and he may not. He has said that all Apaches must be shot."

Gian-nah-tah nodded. "I must try to make peace for my people. Let us go to this white chief."

At Santa Fe, curious sentries stared at Kit and the war-painted Indians. In General Carleton's quarters, Major McCleave stood, flushed and angry, beside the General's desk. He looked triumphantly at Kit.

General Carleton's gray eyes were frosty. "Colonel Carson, you have disobeyed me. Explain if you can. If not, you will await court martial."

"Gian-nah-tah will speak for both of us, General," said Kit.

The General turned hostile eyes toward Gian-nah-tah. The Apache chieftain stepped forward to face the white chief.

"This was our country," said Gian-nah-tah, "until white men came from far away to take it from us. We fought

you as long as we had warriors and weapons. But now you are stronger, your weapons are better than ours. We have no food, no means to live. Your troops are everywhere and we have no more heart for battle. We wish to live in peace, if you will let us live. You must decide. Do what you will with us, but do not forget that we are men and braves."

Gian-nah-tah finished. Red man looked at white man as one strong warrior to another. There was no fear in Gian-nah-tah's eyes as General Carleton looked into them for a long silent moment.

"Could you shoot him, General?" asked Kit softly.

Carleton slowly shook his head. "Bring your people here," he said to the Apache chieftain. "They will not be harmed."

"Major McCleave," said General Carleton, "see that the Indians are taken safely to the reservation on the Pecos River."

McCleave saluted stiffly and strode from the room, his face an angry red.

General Carleton looked at Kit. There was the hint of a twinkle now in the frosty gray eyes.

"Kit," he said—the General had never called him Kit before— "you understand that generals usually like to be obeyed—even when they give stupid orders?"

"Yes, sir," said Kit Carson.

"Then we'll say no more about it. Except this. You've taught me something about Apaches today. They're human beings and we will treat them so."

"I've learned something about generals today," said Kit, and a grin wrinkled his freckled face. "They're human, too."

—1755—

Horses for the King

Cornelia Meigs

Rolfe Turner, riding his own horse Hector and leading three cart horses behind him, was too busy getting this awkward procession along the sun-spotted forest trail to think much about how strangely and suddenly things can happen. Rolfe had heard only uncertain reports of the war with the French and Indians, until the town crier made his announcement on the village green of the little settlement in western Pennsylvania.

"Be it known that good Dr. Benjamin Franklin of Philadelphia town has promised that beasts and vehicles shall be found to carry General Braddock's food and military supplies on his march to the Ohio. Dr. Franklin urges all men to lend their horses and wagons to the army, in return for excellent payment from the king. Who will offer? Who will offer?"

Horses were offered, but who was to drive them over the hills to Fort Cumberland, where Braddock waited? None of the farmers seemed to have much desire to leave their fields. Yet here was tall Mr. Timothy Allen, with his rifle over his arm and his blue eyes sparkling with excitement. He was going to join Colonel Washington

 Adapted from "Horses for the King" by Cornelia Meigs from YOUNG AMERICANS, by permission of the publisher, Ginn and Company.

of Virginia, who marched with the British army. Timothy's young cousin, David Hale, was to go with him. And here was Rolfe Turner, touching the town crier's arm and saying eagerly, "I can drive horses, sir. With Mr. Allen to guide, I can get them to General Braddock's army. David Hale is going, and he is only two years bigger than I am."

There was no one to refuse. For Rolfe Turner had no parents—only his old cousin, Abner Harrowgate, who with much grumbling had taken him in to keep him until he was grown.

Plans were settled quickly. The company set out; and now Timothy Allen, the two boys, and the string of horses had come almost to the end of their hard march over the hills. By Allen's order, they tied the beasts in a thicket and climbed the next steep and rocky hill to look over the country. The British Army must surely be camped in the valley beyond.

Just as he reached the top, with David Hale and Rolfe behind him, Timothy Allen lifted his hand suddenly and threw himself flat upon the grass. The boys obeyed his silent order. Rolfe crept a few feet forward until he could look over the edge of the hill. He drew his breath suddenly. He had never seen Indians before, and these Indians were scarcely a dozen yards away.

They were no peace-time red men. Their faces were streaked with war paint. They were armed with knives, hatchets, and guns. Ten of them were spread out in a silently moving row, all looking closely at something on the slope below them. At the end of the line walked a bareheaded man dressed in worn buckskin. His face was brown with sunburn instead of copper color. Timothy

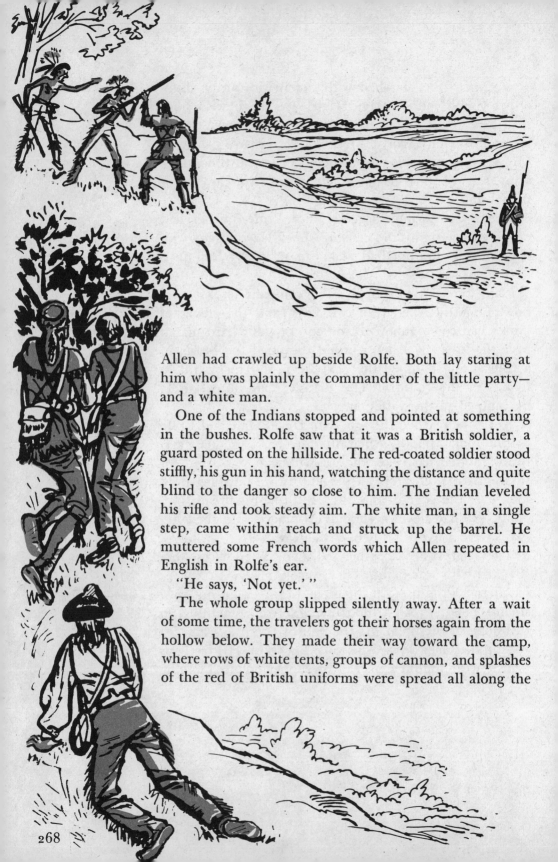

Allen had crawled up beside Rolfe. Both lay staring at him who was plainly the commander of the little party—and a white man.

One of the Indians stopped and pointed at something in the bushes. Rolfe saw that it was a British soldier, a guard posted on the hillside. The red-coated soldier stood stiffly, his gun in his hand, watching the distance and quite blind to the danger so close to him. The Indian leveled his rifle and took steady aim. The white man, in a single step, came within reach and struck up the barrel. He muttered some French words which Allen repeated in English in Rolfe's ear.

"He says, 'Not yet.'"

The whole group slipped silently away. After a wait of some time, the travelers got their horses again from the hollow below. They made their way toward the camp, where rows of white tents, groups of cannon, and splashes of the red of British uniforms were spread all along the

river. The command of a guard on the hillside brought them to a sudden halt.

"We allow no strangers near the camp," he began. But on seeing the string of horses, he was persuaded to let them pass.

A blue-coated rider passing along the lines turned and came galloping out to meet them. Timothy Allen flung himself off his horse to run up and grasp the soldier's outstretched hand.

"It's Colonel Washington," David Hale said breathlessly to Rolfe. A moment later, Rolfe was brought forward to be introduced. He found himself looking up into a strong, sober face lighted quickly by a sudden smile of friendliness. A queer, warm feeling such as he had never known before ran suddenly through Rolfe. He was fond of David. He liked and admired Timothy Allen. But he had never felt anything like the wave of whole-souled devotion which now filled his entire being.

It seemed that David Hale had the same feelings as Rolfe about this erect Virginian of twenty-three. Through all the days of the march that followed, Rolfe and David always knew just where Washington was. Over their

evening meal, the lads would compare notes on the events of the day. Nearly always their talk was of Washington.

"He spoke to me this morning," Rolfe would report. "He looked at Hector in the team with the others, and said it was hard that so fine a horse should be pulling his heart out trying to move a heavy wagon. But he said that the army must go forward."

Colonel George Washington was often in Timothy Allen's tent, for the two had many things of which they liked to talk together. One evening when the boys came in, they found the men bending their heads together over a sheet of paper spread on the colonel's knee. It was General Braddock's map. On it was marked the route they were all taking along the Monongahela River toward Fort Duquesne.

"Here runs the river," Washington was saying. "Here is where it meets the Allegheny and makes the bigger stream of the Ohio. Here is Fort Duquesne." He traced the larger river a little way, and then laid down the quill pen. He smiled up at the two boys as they came in. "The fort is at the head of a great river. I would give much to know how it runs to the sea."

"At least we shall soon add something to our knowledge," said Timothy Allen. "We cannot be far from the Ohio now. It is strange and ever stranger that we see nothing of our French and Indian enemies."

The Ambush

Two days later they passed a broad, open space in the forest. They could see rising hills which must be at the edge of the Ohio. After crossing the meadow, they

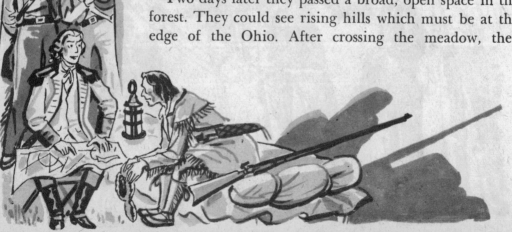

plunged once more into the narrow lane cut through
the forest by the advance guard. The Virginia Rangers
were well into the wood. The last column of soldiers
on foot had just come into the forested trail. The wagons
carrying supplies still toiled across the open. Suddenly
there arose that fearful cry which every man had dreamed
of and dreaded for a month of marching—the yell of the
attacking Indians.

To those who are in the midst of it, a battle is apt
to seem like nothing but a blind uproar. Rolfe heard
the sudden reports of guns, then the thunder of the
British cannon echoing among the crowded trees. A wave
of red-coated soldiers broke against the wagons, drew
together again and went forward, then fell back once
more. Suddenly the whole army was pouring back past
the halted supply train. In the disorder, Rolfe saw General
Braddock on his horse trying to turn back his men, who
went driving past. Finally they carried him and his horse
away in their midst.

The Virginia Rangers were passing, dropping back
slowly from one bit of shelter to another. Timothy Allen
went by, the light of battle in his eyes. It was possible
now to make out naked red figures slipping through the
trees and to see leather-shirted French riflemen. David
Hale broke from the stream of retreat and came running
to where Rolfe stood.

"Where is he?" David shouted above the noise. "Have
you seen him?"

Rolfe pointed. Here came Colonel Washington at last,
firing his pistol, then dropping it, empty of bullets, to
draw his sword. A rifleshot rang from the bushes. The

knees of the Virginian's horse bent, and the animal came
down upon the grass. The boys rushed up to Washington,
but he was up in an instant.

"I'm not hurt. Find me another horse," he cried.

Rolfe ran to his wagon. He caught up the sword of a
fallen redcoat, and began hacking at the harness to cut
Hector out of the traces. With wild haste, David helped
Washington snatch the saddle from the fallen beast and
throw it over the back of the new horse. As the colonel
galloped away, he shouted over his shoulder, "Cut loose
the other horses and ride them away!"

A party of red braves ran out of the wood. The Virginian fought his way through them and spurred on. The
two boys stood watching anxiously, to make sure that he
got away to safety.

A heavy hand was laid on Rolfe's shoulder. A voice
said, "Do you prefer to be my prisoners, messieurs, or
to wait until my friends the Indians take you?"

Rolfe turned to look into the face of the same Frenchman whom they had seen on the hill above the British
camp. A whole mob of Indians had broken out of the
wood and were spreading across the meadow, robbing
the wagons, driving off the horses, and gathering up the
scattered guns.

"You had better come with me quickly, or these warriors will dispute with me as to whose prisoners you are."
He turned on his heel, as though certain that the boys
would be wise enough to follow him.

Rolfe, in hot anger, held back. Instantly, a brave, leaping behind him, bent a steel elbow about his neck and
dragged him backward with a jerk which almost strangled
him. The Frenchman turned and sent the Indian spinning
with a great blow of his fist. The warriors fell away to a
respectful distance, stood for a moment jabbering and
threatening, and then scattered to the more welcome task
of collecting guns.

The noise died away behind them as the three climbed
to the top of the hill. Almost below them ran the great
Ohio, smooth and deep, with a suntouched ripple here
and there.

"Do you see," said the Frenchman, "where my boat lies upon the shore? My Indian canoemen are drunk with victory. But chance has sent me two stout fellows in their place. Probably you do not know how to paddle. You will learn before we come to the end of our journey to St. Louis. We are going all the way. Yes, you will learn."

St. Louis! A thousand miles from friends and home! The Frenchman, seeing refusal in their faces, cocked his rifle and settled it easily in the bend of his arm.

"You will go," he declared. "You will go down that trail to the river, and you will do it at once."

There was nothing to do but to carry out his order. It was of no use to look back. Ill luck had set their faces toward an unknown country.

The Frenchman taught the boys to paddle, and as the journey went on, their skill increased and their muscles grew hard. Jacques Perrin, the man who had captured them, began to turn into a friendly enemy. He was not a soldier, so he told them, but a trader who had happened to come to the head of the Ohio just at the moment when the French were preparing for battle with the English.

As they went forward, his gun was always by his side. He never let the boys out of his sight, whether they were traveling or camping or hunting. But he made the way easier with gay jokes and lighthearted talk.

"You like my river, eh?" he inquired several times, seeing approval in the boys' eyes. "I wonder what you will think of the Mississippi."

He began to teach them the fine points of handling the canoe and what to do in shoals and swift water. Above all, he taught them how to pass the great rapids where

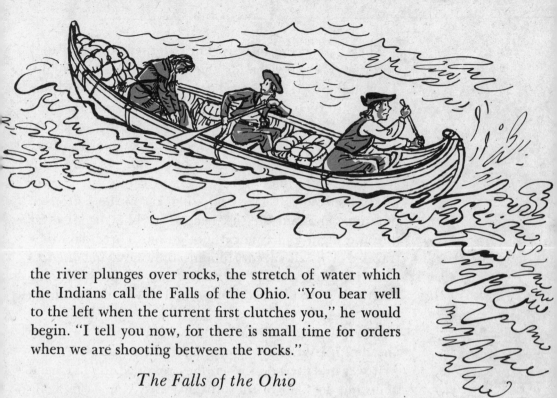

the river plunges over rocks, the stretch of water which the Indians call the Falls of the Ohio. "You bear well to the left when the current first clutches you," he would begin. "I tell you now, for there is small time for orders when we are shooting between the rocks."

The Falls of the Ohio

As the days passed, the Frenchman grew more silent. Miles would go by without his speaking at all. Then, late one afternoon when twilight was falling, Rolfe looked back to ask Monsieur Perrin if it were not time to make camp. He saw that the man's head had dropped upon his chest. His lips were moving in a silent mutter. His gun had slipped from his limp hand.

The boys brought the canoe to shore and lifted him out. When David accidentally touched his knee, his face contracted with pain and he cried out. Otherwise he made no sound. They cut away the leather of his worn breeches and saw a long knife wound, red and swollen.

They bathed the infected knee, dressed it as best they could, and watched beside the wounded man all night. They did not try to travel forward the next morning. But by afternoon, Perrin was so ill that David declared suddenly, "We shall have to get him on. He told us several days ago that St. Louis was not as far away now as where we came from. And he was to meet some friend of his at the mouth of the Ohio."

They spread soft grass and a blanket in the bottom of the canoe and laid the sick man in it. They paddled far into the night and rose early to go on. Three days they traveled with all speed, stopping only now and then to hunt for game to add to their small supplies. On the fourth day David, in the bow, laid down his paddle to listen.

"Do you hear it?" he asked. "That roar a long way ahead of us? We must be coming to the rapids."

It was midafternoon when they rounded the last bend and came in sight of the broken water. Rapids in a big river do not splash and sing as in a smaller stream. The rapids of the Ohio flowed down, rising and falling with little foam, with no racing ripples. The big waves lifted and swirled and sucked, while the whole stream cried a warning with its deep, hoarse roar.

They bore to the left, paddling wildly. Big waves rose as if to swamp them. Sharp stones pushed upward as though to rip the canoe's wooden sides. Luck and youthful strength and a quick following of the orders they had received—these three carried them through. An ugly, black lip of rock cut through the last wave, directly ahead. Rolfe saw it and dug with his paddle. The canoe gave a slight shudder. Then she slipped over the last

drop in the slope and floated easily in the pool below.

Rolfe heard a voice exclaim behind him. He turned around and saw Perrin, sitting up and staring about him, like a man suddenly awakened from sleep. His thin tired face broke into its old smile.

"I had a little attack of sickness some miles back," he began to tell the boys. "I could not even hold my gun. My captives might have got away, but by good luck you did not notice." He took up his rifle and laid it across his knees in his usual watchful manner.

For a few moments he watched the shores slipping past. Then he exclaimed in astonishment. "But this is the lower Ohio! We have passed the rapids!" There was a long pause before he spoke again. "How long, my children, have I been lying here helpless?"

"Nearly five days, sir," replied David. "We—we are very glad that you are beginning to be yourself again."

"Five days," repeated Perrin. "And in the name of the good Providence, what was there to keep you from leaving me beside the river and returning to your own people?"

The boys looked at each other blankly. Had they even thought of such a thing?

David spoke low and almost sheepishly. "It seemed that the best we could do was to carry you forward to find your friends."

They paddled for several days. Perrin grew better every hour. At last, in that stretch of water where the Ohio widens to its mouth, they came to a wooded island and there made camp. The boys were aroused at daylight by Perrin's hand shaking each by the shoulder.

"Arise, sluggards!" he ordered. "I have something to say to you."

He pointed to a small black dot, showing far downstream on the dull steel surface of the river. "That is the canoe of my friend and partner. Each year we meet here and go on to St. Louis together. Just beyond that last wooded hill is the mighty Mississippi. But I think you are not to see it. I took your liberty from you on the battlefield. Now I give it to you again. Take my canoe and return to your own land. The river is a safe guide, and you cannot miss your way. Slip by the fort in the night and follow the Monongahela until you come safely home."

He picked up his rifle and gave it to David. "Here is my gun. It will help you to find food along the way."

Some weeks later, a small company sat about the library table in a country house which looked out over the Potomac. Timothy Allen had brought the boys to

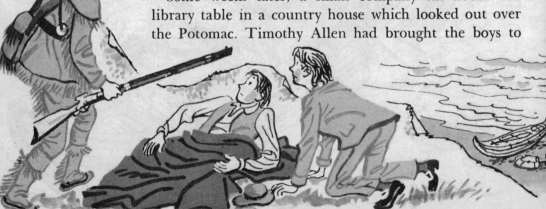

see the master of Mount Vernon and to deliver a message
to him. Colonel George Washington was worn from a
long illness following Braddock's battles with the French
and Indians. But he was as erect as ever, with color
returning to his thin cheeks. Once more he was drawing
upon a sheet of paper, tracing the course of the Ohio,
just below Fort Duquesne.

"Making maps is my business," he said. "I begin to
think that I am fit for no other. Here is a road which
leads to the heart of our country. At last I am to learn
something of it. Stand on each side of me, you two
explorers, and tell me, mile by mile, how these rivers
run."

Be Jubilant, My Feet!

Carol R. Brink

The Woodlawn girls were all getting new white dresses for the Independence Day celebration at Eau Galle.

"It really seems a waste of good material to make one for Caddie," said Mother, with a sigh. "She's ruined every white dress we ever made for her."

"But she's doing so much better now, Mother," said Clara gently. "Ever since that time when Annabelle was here and she and Tom played all the tricks, Caddie's been trying very hard to be a lady."

"I know," Mother said. "I'm proud of her, too. She's come a long way. It's only that there's something fatal about the combination of Caddie and a white dress. Either she tears it, or she cuts her finger and stains it with blood, or she sits on the grass and gets grass stains, or she accidentally spills a bottle of ink. There's no telling what will happen to this one."

"Well," said Mrs. Hyman, who, with Katie, had come to spend the week at the Woodlawns', "well, you've got plenty of extra material. I'd keep it if I was you. Later on, I can always put in a new skirt breadth or a front to the bodice, if she spills or tears."

Caddie and Katie came in just too late to hear these dire predictions. They had been to the far field to take a bucket of spring water to the men and boys who were haying.

"Come, now, Caddie," said Mother. "You're just in time to have a fit."

The phrase delighted Caddie. "Run away, now, children," she called to Hetty and Minnie, who were trailing along behind her. "I'm going to have a fit."

She slipped out of her old blue denim and into the yards and yards of white muslin, which Mrs. Hyman slid over her head.

"Mind the pins now, and the basting threads. Don't pull and squirm too much."

Caddie regarded herself in the mirror. "Is that me?" she said. "My goodness! I won't know how to act out of blue denim."

"You act like a lady, that's what you do," advised Mother. "You take small steps and turn out your toes when you walk, and keep away from horses and the snags on rail fences, and don't sit on the grass or climb the haymow or eat strawberries or write with ink."

"I might as well be dead," said Caddie, screwing up her nose. "Is a white dress worth it?"

"Oh, yes," said Katie. "You look lovely, Caddie. Honest, you do."

"Mother," said Caddie, her eyes twinkling, "they're going to have a log-rolling contest in the millpond at Eau Galle. I can walk logs just as well as the lumberjacks. Will you let me enter?"

"Now, Caddie," cried Mother, vexed beyond measure, "don't let me hear of such a thing! Don't even let a thought like that enter your head. The idea!"

"We'll keep her busy enough singing," said Clara. "The girls are all to sing, in their white dresses with loops of red, white, and blue bunting over one shoulder and

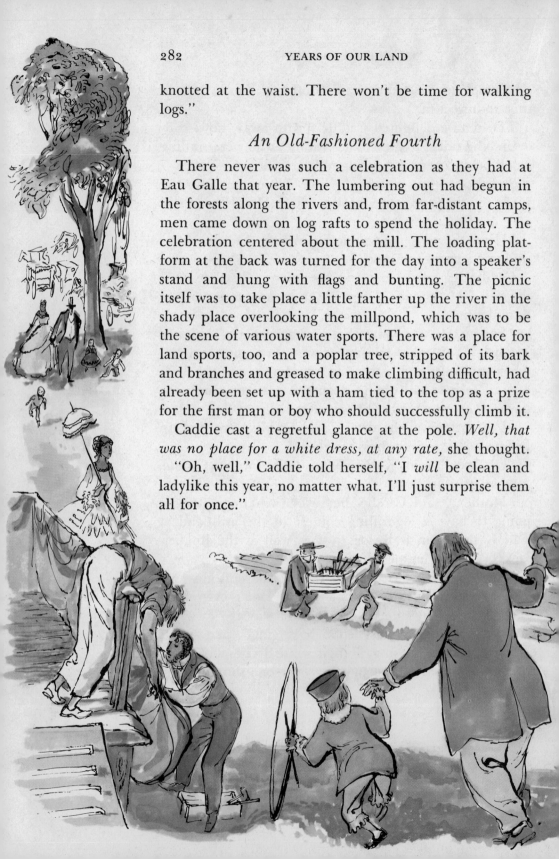

knotted at the waist. There won't be time for walking logs.''

An Old-Fashioned Fourth

There never was such a celebration as they had at Eau Galle that year. The lumbering out had begun in the forests along the rivers and, from far-distant camps, men came down on log rafts to spend the holiday. The celebration centered about the mill. The loading platform at the back was turned for the day into a speaker's stand and hung with flags and bunting. The picnic itself was to take place a little farther up the river in the shady place overlooking the millpond, which was to be the scene of various water sports. There was a place for land sports, too, and a poplar tree, stripped of its bark and branches and greased to make climbing difficult, had already been set up with a ham tied to the top as a prize for the first man or boy who should successfully climb it.

Caddie cast a regretful glance at the pole. *Well, that was no place for a white dress, at any rate,* she thought.

"Oh, well," Caddie told herself, "I *will* be clean and ladylike this year, no matter what. I'll just surprise them all for once."

Father had brought them all over early in the big hay wagon, together with Robert Ireton and Mrs. Conroy, Katie and her mother, and the McCantry family. It had been great fun — all riding together and talking and laughing, and practicing the songs which they were to sing later.

The sunshine seemed more golden on a day like this, and the smell of new-cut hay and clover bloom far sweeter than it was on ordinary days. Their own singing and the singing of the meadowlarks and red-winged blackbirds along the wayside seemed to mingle in a perfect harmony.

To celebrate the Fourth of July meant something definite in those days. Beyond the picnic lunches, the spread-eagle speeches, the greased pole, the water sports, and the fireworks in the evening, there was the consciousness of happiness and good fortune. It was a day in praise of freedom. It was a kind of summer Thanksgiving Day when they could raise their voices in gratitude for life, liberty, and the pursuit of happiness, and dedicate themselves anew to the self-evident truth that all men are created equal.

Father's voice, full of the spirit of the day, started them all to singing "The Battle Hymn of the Republic," and Caddie's heart swelled as she sang. Best of all, she loved the fourth stanza.

> *He has sounded forth the trumpet*
>   *That shall never call retreat;*
> *He is sifting out the hearts of men*
>   *Before His judgment seat;*
> *Oh, be swift, my soul, to answer Him!*
>   *Be jubilant, my feet!*
> *Our God is marching on.*

She kept humming it to herself as she and Emma and Katie wandered about the picnic grounds at Eau Galle.

Today her feet, in neat white slippers with satin rosettes, were jubilant indeed. The sky was very blue, and the hot sweet smell of new-cut lumber filled the air.

The three were early enough to greet the other girls as they arrived in their white dresses with red, white, and blue bunting looped over the shoulder and knotted at the waist. Maggie, Jane, Lida—all of them arrived in due time, with their hair unnaturally frizzed out from an uncomfortable night in curl papers, and their eyes sparkling with anticipation. All the girls of Dunnville and Eau Galle were to sit on the loading platform behind the speakers, and sing before and after the speeches were delivered. But until the speaking began, they were free to roam about as they wished.

Tom and Warren with a crowd of boys went past them to the millpond. Tom called back over his shoulder, "They're starting to roll logs. You better come watch."

"Let's do," said Caddie to Katie, and Katie said, "All right."

"Just look out for your dress, that's all," warned Clara.

"Oh, bother!" Caddie said. "They're always after me about my clothes. But nothing—*nothing's* going to happen to this one!"

A good many children were crowded along the banks of the quiet millpond watching the preliminary log-rolling contests. Caddie saw Hetty and Minnie and Pearly and Ezra McCantry playing "I Spy" with some of the other little children higher up the bank.

In the millpond floated several large peeled logs, and men from the various logging camps up the river were trying their skill upon them. From a boat each man would carefully mount his log, and balance himself on it while he rolled it under his feet. He appeared to be running on top of the water, and it was exciting to see how long he could keep it up. Much skill was required to stay on the slippery logs at all, and sooner or later one of the men would lose his balance, slip off, and go down with a great splash. Walking logs in the river was part of the lumberjacks' job.

The children soon had their favorites among the contestants, and cheered or shouted praise or disapproval. When Robert Ireton came out in old blue jeans with his strong brown arms folded across his bare chest, the Woodlawn children went mad with glee.

"Robert! Robert!" they shouted. "We're on your side, Robert! Beat the lumber camps, Robert! Show 'em Dunnville's got the champion log roller of the world!"

None of them had known that Robert was going to enter the contest. Caddie went as wild as the boys, shouting, "Robert! Robert! Lick the old tar out of 'em, Robert!"

The little children left their game of "I Spy" and came crowding down to the water's edge, echoing, "Robert! Robert! Beat 'em, Robert!"

Near the shore floated a number of smaller, unpeeled logs. Hetty and Minnie and the two little McCantrys came to stand in front of Caddie and Katie, and Caddie saw Ezra's toe go out experimentally to one of the floating logs.

"I c'n walk 'em, too," he said.

"Well, don't you try it, mister," Caddie advised.

Red, White, and Blue

Now Robert had reached his log and mounted it. His feet were light and quick on the rolling log. He might have been dancing one of his Irish jigs on the threshing floor of the barn at home, to see him lift his feet. The water flashed and sparkled over the rolling log. Everybody was looking at him. He was better, more light and graceful, than the lumbermen from up the river.

But suddenly, Caddie saw out of the tail of her eye that another log walker was performing near at hand.

Ezra McCantry was stepping gingerly from log to log, and running the length of them and back with arms outstretched to keep his balance.

"Come back here, Ezra!" Caddie cried.

But Ezra only ran a little farther out and called back mockingly, "Look at me! I c'n walk 'em, too!"

"Oh, dear!" Caddie said to Katie. "I just wish Emma had come down with us. She'd make him come back in pretty smart, I guess!"

Katie raised her gentle voice and called him, too. But Ezra was puffed up by the importance of the moment to even greater feats of daring. It seemed to him that everybody was looking at *him* now instead of Robert Ireton.

"Look-it me now! Look-it—"

Even as he uttered his howl of triumph, the log he was on began to roll. Slowly and gently it rolled, but it took Ezra by surprise and he rolled with it. He made a wonderful, big splash for such a very small boy.

"*Oh, dear!*" cried Caddie. "*Oh, dear!*"—and all sorts of disconnected things went like a panic through her mind. "*Be swift, my soul. Be jubilant, my feet* . . . But, oh, my dress! Whatever happens, it must not get wet."

And then she saw Ezra coming up to the surface and clawing the air an instant, trying to catch the log—and going down again. She knew that the millpond was deep, and that Ezra couldn't swim—and neither could she. She heard people behind her beginning to shout. Then, before she knew it, her clean white slippers were stepping out on the first logs and then the next ones, and she was frantically untying the long piece of bunting which had been over her shoulder.

She heard her own voice calling, "*Ezra! Ezra!*"

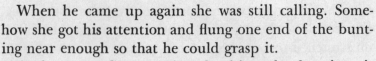

When he came up again she was still calling. Somehow she got his attention and flung one end of the bunting near enough so that he could grasp it.

As he went down again, clutching the bunting, it snapped out tight, and Caddie, holding the other end, felt the log she was on beginning to roll. She tried to make her feet go fast, like Robert's feet, in order to keep her balance. But still her log kept rolling, rolling—and the clean white slippers with the satin rosettes could not go fast enough. There was a second wonderful splash— and it was Caddie Woodlawn!

But she never let go of the bunting. Ezra was holding on to his end, too. There was a log between them, and with the bunting over it neither one of them could go down too far. Caddie struggled desperately up until she could cling to the log with one hand and pull in the bunting with the other. And presently Ezra was clinging to the other side of the log.

Robert was the first to reach them, swimming from his log in mid-pond with long, sure strokes.

"Oh, Robert!" Caddie cried, between gulps and coughs, "You had to get off your log! We made you lose the contest, Robert."

"Eh," Robert roared, "and my Caddie drowning! What do you think, lass? What do you think!"

When they were safe on shore again, Caddie looked down and saw that she was still clutching the Fourth of July bunting against her breast. The red and blue dye was running in gaudy little streams all down the front of her lovely new white dress. As she stood there speechless with this new calamity, she heard the first notes of the fife and drum calling the people to the speaking and the singing.

The crowd began to drift away, now that they saw Caddie and Ezra safe.

"Oh, come along now, Caddie," Katie said. "You'll dry out on the speakers' stand, with all the hot sun blazing in there. It's time we went to sing."

"But I can't! I can't—*like this,*" wailed Caddie.

Tom and Katie, Warren and Hetty and little Minnie, were all around her, helping her wring out the yards of white—and *blue* and *red*—muslin.

"Sure you can, Caddie," they were saying. "They need your high voice on the choruses."

"You can sit in the back," said Katie. "I'll spread my skirts out over yours."

"But Mother!" gasped Caddie. "She'll take one look at me and have a heart attack."

"You come along," they said.

A Good Citizen

Caddie and Katie had just time to squeeze in among the other girls at the back of the platform before the program began. Caddie was sure that Mother could not have seen the dreadful mess she was wearing.

When the fifes and drums were silent, the girls' chorus stood up and began to sing. Caddie remained seated so that she would not spoil the beautiful appearance of the other girls, but her voice soared clear and happy.

It seemed as if half of the men of Dunnville and Eau Galle made speeches that day. Dr. Nightingale, the physician, made the last one, and it was the best one too. He spoke very simply, as if he were talking to friends. He said that the truest way citizens could serve their country was by obeying its laws and by meeting daily life with courage and honesty.

Caddie forgot her troubles in listening to his earnest voice. Finally he said something which surprised her. He said, "There are many good citizens among us, but it has just been called to my attention that one of us today has proven particularly worthy of citizenship. This person, although one of the youngest members of our society, has proven equal to an emergency which called for quick thinking, courage, and a willingness to risk personal safety. You all know this young person. You have just heard her voice in the singing. When you know that Caddie Woodlawn saved a little boy's life this morning, I think you will want her to step forward and receive your cheers."

Until her name was mentioned, Caddie had been looking around trying to imagine whom Dr. Nightingale was speaking of. Now when she heard him saying, "Will Caddie Woodlawn please come forward?" Caddie was so filled with astonishment and alarm that she could do nothing but sit there and whisper, "Oh, I can't!"

But the girls were pulling her to her feet. "Don't be silly," they cried, pushing her forward.

To her surprise, Caddie found herself going up to the front of the platform where Dr. Nightingale stood with outstretched hand and welcoming smile. Caddie had tried to hold the worst parts of her bedraggled skirt together so that it would not show. But when she held out her hand, it all fell open. Everyone in Dunnville and Eau Galle could see that Caddie Woodlawn had spoiled another white dress.

Dr. Nightingale seemed to understand her distress just as he understood measles or mumps.

"Congratulations, Caddie," he said. "And don't be ashamed of your dress, my dear. I'm proud to shake the hand of a girl who can forget her vanity to risk her life for others."

Caddie looked up at him in pleased surprise, and then

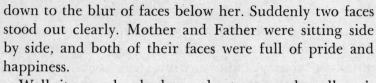

down to the blur of faces below her. Suddenly two faces stood out clearly. Mother and Father were sitting side by side, and both of their faces were full of pride and happiness.

Well, it was a lovely day—a day to remember all one's life!

Caddie did not roll logs or chase the greased pig, nor climb the greased pole. But even in her bedraggled dress she had a lovely time. In the evening, they all rode home on the hayload, tired but content; and as they rode they sang. An early moon was in the sky, and the odors of sweet clover and red clover and new-cut hay and pine mingled like perfume in the clear air.

And, when the song had drifted away again to silence, Caddie found herself softly humming the other tune which seemed so perfectly to fit the day, and the new, sweet country which they loved so well.

> *Oh, be swift, my soul, to answer Him!*
> *Be jubilant, my feet!*

Strange
and Wonderful

Sometimes two times two seem five;
   The moon is sometimes blue;
And fields of purple cows sometimes
   Sedately graze in view.

How strange and wonderful a world
   In which a lump of clay
Can turn itself into a rose
   Almost any day!

—*Dorothy Hall*

By Kite-String
Across the Grand Canyon

Robert Lawson

Professor Ambrose Augustus McWhinney loved bi-cycling. But he did not love to pump up his own bicycle tires. So he invented Z-Gas, which not only filled the tires but to his astonishment lifted the bicycle clear off the ground. With a little practice, the Professor found that he could fly. So he started off on his bicycle-airplane for Hollywood and the movies.

I was now approaching that most stupendous of all scenic wonders, the Grand Canyon of the Colorado. Although I had often read of it, no amount of reading or any number of pictures could really prepare one for its breath-taking beauty.

The hotel at which I stopped, located close to the edge of the chasm, was a magnificent affair and extremely expensive. Most of the guests were too.

While my finances were still in excellent shape, I did wish to have an ample supply of money on arriving in Hollywood. I therefore engaged in conversation with several of the wealthy gentlemen guests. After a time, I rather casually led up to the boast that I could ride my bicycle across the Canyon on a kite string.

Of course, this was met with a great deal of unbelief

and many heavy witticisms. However, as they were all bored, there being nothing to do except look at the scenery, the prospect of any sort of sporting event appealed to them greatly. Within a few moments they had collected a purse of $1,000. This was to be my reward should I succeed.

I set twelve noon of the following day as the hour for the attempt. I wanted my tires to have their maximum buoyancy. The Canyon looked awfully deep!

The next morning, I managed to procure a couple of miles of light string, such as children use in flying kites. Getting it across to the other side of the Canyon presented a problem. But one of the guests who had his private airplane kindly flew me across. On the far rim, I drove a stout stake and tied the string to it. Then we flew back, paying out the string as we came. Here I drove another stake, pulled the string as taut as possible, and made it fast.

By now many of the lady guests, convinced that my coming attempt was sheer suicide, protested to the manager of the hotel, demanding that he stop it. He, however, merely shrugged and said that "the guest is always right." He also added that I had paid my bill in advance. *He* had nothing to worry about.

They thereupon telephoned to the sheriff, who lived some ninety miles away. He promised to come as quickly as possible, but feared he could not make it before one o'clock.

Everything being prepared, I went to my room. I shaved, sent a picture post card to Mrs. McWhinney, oiled my bicycle thoroughly, and then took a short nap.

When I emerged and mounted my bicycle promptly

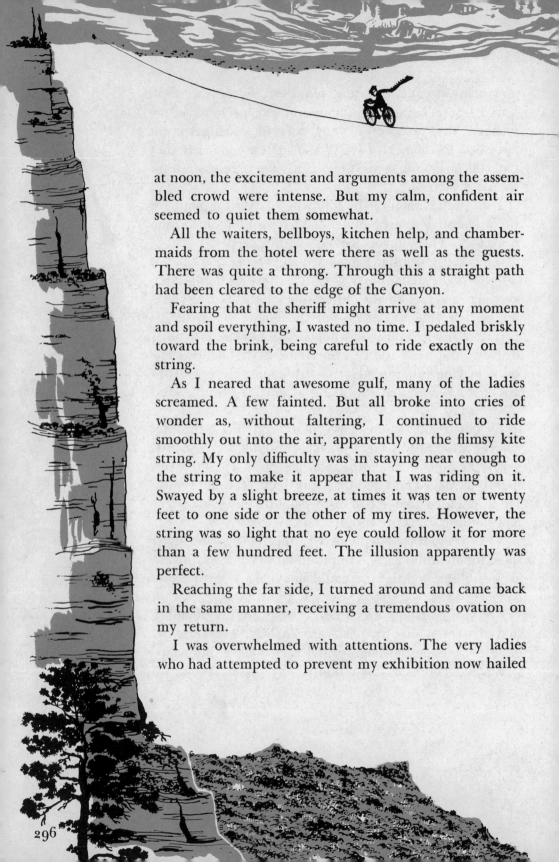

at noon, the excitement and arguments among the assembled crowd were intense. But my calm, confident air seemed to quiet them somewhat.

All the waiters, bellboys, kitchen help, and chambermaids from the hotel were there as well as the guests. There was quite a throng. Through this a straight path had been cleared to the edge of the Canyon.

Fearing that the sheriff might arrive at any moment and spoil everything, I wasted no time. I pedaled briskly toward the brink, being careful to ride exactly on the string.

As I neared that awesome gulf, many of the ladies screamed. A few fainted. But all broke into cries of wonder as, without faltering, I continued to ride smoothly out into the air, apparently on the flimsy kite string. My only difficulty was in staying near enough to the string to make it appear that I was riding on it. Swayed by a slight breeze, at times it was ten or twenty feet to one side or the other of my tires. However, the string was so light that no eye could follow it for more than a few hundred feet. The illusion apparently was perfect.

Reaching the far side, I turned around and came back in the same manner, receiving a tremendous ovation on my return.

I was overwhelmed with attentions. The very ladies who had attempted to prevent my exhibition now hailed

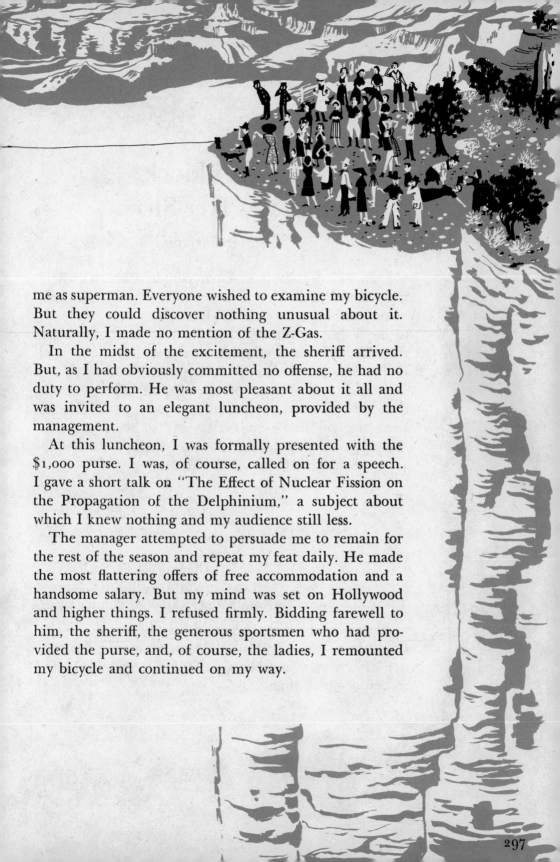

me as superman. Everyone wished to examine my bicycle. But they could discover nothing unusual about it. Naturally, I made no mention of the Z-Gas.

In the midst of the excitement, the sheriff arrived. But, as I had obviously committed no offense, he had no duty to perform. He was most pleasant about it all and was invited to an elegant luncheon, provided by the management.

At this luncheon, I was formally presented with the $1,000 purse. I was, of course, called on for a speech. I gave a short talk on "The Effect of Nuclear Fission on the Propagation of the Delphinium," a subject about which I knew nothing and my audience still less.

The manager attempted to persuade me to remain for the rest of the season and repeat my feat daily. He made the most flattering offers of free accommodation and a handsome salary. But my mind was set on Hollywood and higher things. I refused firmly. Bidding farewell to him, the sheriff, the generous sportsmen who had provided the purse, and, of course, the ladies, I remounted my bicycle and continued on my way.

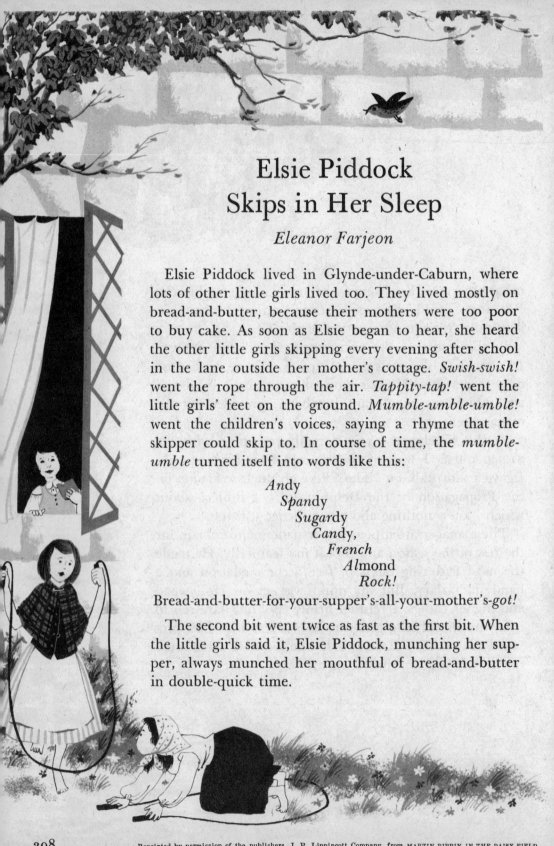

Elsie Piddock
Skips in Her Sleep

Eleanor Farjeon

Elsie Piddock lived in Glynde-under-Caburn, where lots of other little girls lived too. They lived mostly on bread-and-butter, because their mothers were too poor to buy cake. As soon as Elsie began to hear, she heard the other little girls skipping every evening after school in the lane outside her mother's cottage. *Swish-swish!* went the rope through the air. *Tappity-tap!* went the little girls' feet on the ground. *Mumble-umble-umble!* went the children's voices, saying a rhyme that the skipper could skip to. In course of time, the *mumble-umble* turned itself into words like this:

> *A*ndy
> *S*pandy
> *Suga*rdy
> *C*andy,
> *French*
> *Al*mond
> *Rock!*

Bread-and-butter-for-your-supper's-all-your-mother's-*got!*

The second bit went twice as fast as the first bit. When the little girls said it, Elsie Piddock, munching her supper, always munched her mouthful of bread-and-butter in double-quick time.

When Elsie Piddock was three years old, she asked her mother for a skipping rope.

"You're too little," said her mother. "Bide a bit till you're a bigger girl. Then you shall have one."

Elsie pouted, and said no more. But in the middle of the night her parents were wakened by something going *Slap-slap!* on the floor, and there was Elsie in her night-gown skipping with her father's braces.

"Bless my buttons, mother!" said Mr. Piddock. "The child's a born skipper."

And Mrs. Piddock jumped out of bed full of pride, and said, "There-a-there now! tomorrow you shall have a skip-rope all of your own."

In the morning, before he went to work, Mr. Piddock got a little cord, just the right length, and made two little wooden handles to go on the ends. With this Elsie skipped all day, scarcely stopping to eat her breakfast of bread-and-butter, and her dinner of butter-and-bread. And in the evening, when the school-children were gathered in the Lane, Elsie went out among them, and began to skip with the best.

"Oh!" cried Joan Challon, who was the champion skipper of them all. "Just look at little Elsie Piddock skipping as never so!"

By the time she was five she could outskip any of them. By the time she was six, her name and fame were known to all the villages in the county. And by the time she was seven, the fairies heard of her. For a whole year the fairies' Skipping-Master, Andy-Spandy, taught her all the tricks of the skipping rope.

He taught her the High Skip, the Sly Skip, the Skip like a Feather, the Long Skip, the Strong Skip, the Skip

All Together, the Slow Skip, the Toe Skip, the Skip Double-Double, the Fast Skip, the Last Skip, and the Skip Against Trouble. Nobody had ever found out how long Elsie Piddock could skip without getting tired, for everybody else got tired first. Even Andy-Spandy didn't know.

If Elsie had been famous for her skipping before this fairy year, you can imagine what she became after it. She created so much wonder, that she hardly dared to show all she could do. Nevertheless, for another year she did such amazing things, that people came from far and near to see her skip over the church spire, or through the split oak-tree in the Lord's Park, or across the river at its widest point. And on the night of the new moon, she always led the children up Mount Caburn, outside the village, where she skipped more marvelously than ever. In fact, it was Elsie Piddock who established the custom of New-Moon-Skipping on Caburn.

But at the end of another year she had grown too big to skip with her little rope. She laid it away in a box, and went on skipping with a longer one. She still skipped as never so, but her fairy tricks were laid by with the rope.

In time, Elsie grew up (though never very much), and became a little old woman, and gave up skipping, because skipping-time was over. After fifty years or so, nobody remembered that she had ever skipped at all.

Trouble Comes to Caburn

It was ever and ever so long afterwards. Three new Lords had walked in the Park since the day when Elsie Piddock had skipped through the split oak. Changes had come in the village. Farms had changed hands. But

Mount Caburn was as it always had been, and as the people came to think it always would be. And still the children kept the custom of going there each new moon to skip. Nobody remembered how this custom had come about. But customs are customs, and the child who could not skip the new moon in on Caburn stayed at home and cried.

Then a new Lord came to the Park. Soon after his coming, more changes began to take place. The new Lord began to shut up foot-paths and destroy rights of way.

Amongst the lands over which he possessed a certain power was Caburn. This had been always open to the people, and the Lord determined, if he could, to close it. Looking up the old deeds, he discovered that, though the Down was his, he was obliged to leave a way upon it by which the people could go from one village to another. For hundreds of years, they had made a short cut of it over Caburn's top.

"At least," snorted the Lord, "I can make them travel a long way round!"

And he had plans drawn up to enclose the whole of the top of Caburn, so that nobody could walk on it. This meant that the people must trudge miles round the base, as they passed from place to place. The Lord gave out that he needed Mount Caburn to build great factories on.

The village was up in arms to defend its rights. "Can he do it?" they asked those who knew; and they were told, "It is not quite certain, but we fear he can." The Lord himself was not quite certain either. But he went on with his plans, and each new move was watched with anger and anxiety by the villagers. And not only by the villagers; for the fairies saw that their own skipping-ground was threatened. How could they ever skip there again when the grass was turned to cinders, and the new moon blackened by chimney-smoke?

The Lord sent word to the villagers that, though he undoubtedly could do what he pleased, he would, out of his good heart, restore to them a footpath he had blocked, if they would give up all their claims to Caburn.

"Footpath, indeed!" cried stout John Maltman. "What's a footpath to Caburn? Why, our mothers skipped there as children, and our children skip there now. And we hope to see our children's children skip there. If Caburn top be built over, 'twill fair break my little Ellen's heart."

"Ay, and my Margery's," said another.

"And my Mary's and Kitty's!" cried a third.

The Lord was sure of his victory. He had great loads of bricks ordered; but he did not begin building for fear

the people might grow violent. The only thing he did was to put a wire fence round the top of Caburn, and set a keeper there to send the people round it.

One evening, just before the new moon was due, Ellen Maltman went into the woods to cry. For she was the best skipper under Mount Caburn, and the thought that she would never skip there again made her more unhappy than she had ever thought she could be. While she was crying in the dark, she felt a hand on her shoulder. A voice said to her, "Crying for trouble, my dear? That'll never do!"

The voice might have been the voice of a withered leaf, it was so light and dry; but it was also kind. So Ellen checked her sobs and said, "It's a big trouble, ma'am. There's no remedy *but* to cry."

"Why yes, there is," said the withered voice. "Ye should skip against trouble, my dear."

At this, Ellen's sobs burst forth anew. "I'll never skip no more!" she wailed. "If I can't skip the new moon in on Caburn, I'll never skip no more."

"And why can't you skip the new moon in on Caburn?" asked the voice.

Then Ellen told her. After a little pause, the voice spoke quietly out of the darkness.

"Well, Ellen, run you home and tell them this. They are to go to this Lord and tell him he shall have his way and build on Caburn, if he will first take down the fence and let all who have ever skipped there skip there once more by turns, at the new moon. *All,* mind you, Ellen. And when the last skipper skips the last skip, he may lay his first brick. And let it be written out on paper, and signed and sealed."

"But ma'am!" said Ellen, wondering.

"No words, child. Do as I tell you." And the withered voice sounded so compelling that Ellen resisted no more. She ran straight to the village, and told her story to everybody.

At first they could hardly swallow it. "What's the sense of it?" they said. But Ellen persisted and persisted. Something of the spirit of the old voice got into her words, and against their reason the people began to think it was the thing to do. They sent the message to the Lord next day.

The Last Skip on Caburn

The Lord could scarcely believe his ears. He rubbed his hands, and chortled at the people for fools. The paper was drawn out, signed by both parties in the presence of witnesses, and duly sealed. And on the night of the new moon, the Lord invited a party of his friends to go with him to Caburn to see the sight.

And what a sight it was for them to see! Every little girl

in the village was there with her skipping-rope, from the toddlers to those who had just turned up their hair. Nay, even the grown maidens and the young mothers were there; and the very matrons too had come with ropes. Yes, and others were there, others they could not see: Andy-Spandy and his fairy team, to watch with bright fierce eyes the last great skipping on their precious ground.

The skipping began. The toddlers first, a skip or so apiece, a stumble, and they fell out. After the toddlers, the little girls skipped in the order of their ages. And as they got older, the skipping got better. "This will take some time," said the Lord impatiently. And when Ellen Maltman's turn came, and she went into her thousands, he grew restive.

But even she, who could skip as never so, tired at last. Her foot tripped, and she fell on the ground with a little sob. None lasted even half her time. In the small hours, the older women were beginning to take their turn. Few of them kept it up for half a minute. They hopped and puffed bravely, but their skipping days were done.

"Soon over now," said the Lord, as the oldest of the women, a fat old dame of sixty-seven, stepped out and twirled her rope. Her foot caught in it. She staggered, dropped the rope, and hid her face in her hands.

"Done!" shouted the Lord. He brandished at the crowd a trowel and a brick which he had brought with him.

"I am going to lay the first brick. The skipping's ended!"

"No, if you please," said a gentle withered voice. "It is *my* turn now." And out of the crowd stepped a tiny,

tiny woman, so very old, so very bent and fragile, that she seemed to be no bigger than a little child.

"You!" cried the Lord. "Who are *you?*"

"My name is Elsie Piddock, if you please, and I am a hundred and nine years old. I was born in Glynde, and I skipped on Caburn as a child." She spoke like one in a dream, and her eyes were closed.

"Elsie Piddock! Elsie Piddock!" the name ran in a whisper round the crowd.

"Elsie Piddock!" murmured Ellen Maltman. "Why, mum, I thought Elsie Piddock was just a tale."

"Nay, Elsie Piddock was no tale!" said the fat woman who had skipped last. "My mother Joan skipped with her many a time, and told me tales you never would believe."

Signed and Sealed

"Elsie Piddock!" they all breathed again; and a wind seemed to fly around Mount Caburn, shrilling the name with glee. But it was no wind. It was Andy-Spandy and his fairy team.

But the new Lord had never even heard of Elsie Pid-

dock as a story. Laughing coarsely, he said, "One more bump for an old woman's bones! Skip, Elsie Piddock, and show us what you're worth."

"Yes, skip, Elsie Piddock," cried Andy-Spandy and the fairies, "and show them what you're worth!"

Then Elsie Piddock stepped into the middle of the onlookers, twirled her baby rope over her little shrunken body, and began to skip. And she skipped as *never so!*

First of all she skipped:

> *A*ndy
> *Sp*andy
> *Su*gardy
> *Ca*ndy,
> *Fr*ench
> *Al*mond
> *Rock!*

Bread-and-butter-for-your-supper's-all-your-mother's-*got!*

And nobody could find fault with her skipping. Even the Lord gasped, "Wonderful! wonderful for an old woman!"

But Ellen Maltman, who *knew*, whispered, "Oh, mum! 'tis wonderful for *any*body! And oh mum, do but see—she's skipping in her sleep!"

It was true. Elsie Piddock, shrunk to the size of seven years old, was sound asleep, skipping the new moon in with her baby rope that was up to all the tricks. An hour went by, two hours, three hours. There was no stopping her, and no tiring her. The people gasped, the Lord fumed, and the fairies turned head-over-heels for joy. When morning broke, the Lord cried, "That's enough!"

But Elsie Piddock went on skipping.

"Time's up!" cried the Lord.

"When I skip my last skip, you shall lay your first brick," said Elsie Piddock. The villagers broke into a cheer.

"Signed and sealed, my lord, signed and sealed," said Elsie Piddock.

"But hang it, old woman, you can't go on forever!" cried the Lord.

"Oh, yes, I can," said Elsie Piddock. And on she went.

At midday the Lord shouted, "Will the woman never stop?"

"No, she won't," said Elsie Piddock. And she didn't.

"Then I'll stop you!" stormed the Lord, and made a grab at her.

"Now for a Sly Skip," said Elsie Piddock. And she skipped right through his thumb and forefinger.

"Hold her, you!" yelled the Lord to his Lawyer.

"Now for a High Skip," said Elsie Piddock. As the Lawyer darted at her, she skipped right over the highest lark singing in the sun.

The villagers shouted for glee, and the Lord and his friends were furious. Forgotten was the compact signed and sealed. Their one thought now was to seize the maddening old woman, and stop her skipping by sheer force. But they couldn't. She played all her tricks on them: High Skip, Slow Skip, Sly Skip, Toe Skip, Long Skip, Fast Skip, Strong Skip, but never Last Skip. On and on and on she went. When the sun began to set, she was still skipping.

"Can we never rid the Down of the old thing?" cried the Lord desperately.

"No," answered Elsie Piddock in her sleep. "The Down will never be rid of me more. It's the children of Glynde I'm skipping for; it's Andy-Spandy I'm skipping for once again. Oh, Andy, even you never knew how long Elsie Piddock could go on skipping!"

"The woman's mad!" cried the Lord. "Signed and sealed doesn't hold with a madwoman. Skip or no skip, I shall lay the first brick!"

He plunged his trowel into the ground, and forced his brick down into the hole as a token of his possession of the land.

"Now," said Elsie Piddock, "for a Strong Skip!"

Right on the top of the brick she skipped, and down underground she sank out of sight, bearing the brick beneath her. Wild with rage, the Lord dived after her. Up came Elsie Piddock skipping blither than ever—but the Lord never came up again. The Lawyer ran to look down

the hole; but there was no sign of him. The Lawyer reached his arm down the hole; he dropped a pebble down the hole. No one heard it fall. So strong had Elsie Piddock skipped the Strong Skip.

The Lawyer shrugged his shoulders. He and the Lord's friends left Mount Caburn for good and all. Oh, how joyously Elsie Piddock skipped then!

"Skip Against Trouble!" cried she, and skipped so that everyone present burst into happy laughter. To the tune of it she skipped the Long Skip, clean out of sight. And the people went home to tea. Caburn was saved for their children, and for the fairies, forever.

But that wasn't the end of Elsie Piddock. She has never stopped skipping on Caburn since, for Signed and Sealed is Signed and Sealed. Not many have seen her, because she knows all the tricks. But if you go to Caburn at the new moon, you may catch a glimpse of a tiny bent figure, no bigger than a child, skipping all by itself in its sleep, and hear a gay little voice, like the voice of a dancing yellow leaf, singing:

> Andy
> Spandy
> Sugardy
> Candy,
> French
> Almond
> *Rock!*
> Bread-and-butter-for-your-supper's-all-your-mother's-*got!*

Stuart Little's Nautical Adventure

E. B. White

Although he was the second son of the Frederick C. Littles and had a boy brother named George, Stuart Little looked remarkably like a mouse. Naturally, this made many problems, both for his family and for Stuart himself. But he was a brave little fellow, and did not let difficulties discourage him.

One morning when the wind was from the west, Stuart put on his sailor suit and his sailor hat, took his spyglass down from the shelf, and set out for a walk, full of the joy of life and the fear of dogs. With a rolling gait he sauntered along toward Fifth Avenue, keeping a sharp lookout.

Whenever he spied a dog through his glass, Stuart would hurry to the nearest doorman, climb his trouser-leg, and hide in the tails of his uniform. And once, when no doorman was handy, he had to crawl into a yesterday's paper and roll himself up in the second section till danger was past.

At the corner of Fifth Avenue there were several people waiting for the uptown bus, and Stuart joined them. Nobody noticed him, because he wasn't tall enough to be noticed.

"I'm not tall enough to be noticed," thought Stuart, "yet I'm tall enough to want to go to Seventy-second Street."

When the bus came into view, all the men waved their canes and brief cases at the driver, and Stuart waved his spyglass. Then, knowing that the step of the bus would be too high for him, Stuart seized hold of the cuff of a gentleman's pants and was swung aboard without any trouble or inconvenience whatever.

Stuart never paid any fare on buses, because he wasn't big enough to carry an ordinary dime. The only time he had ever attempted to carry a dime, he had rolled the coin along like a hoop while he raced along beside it; but it had got away from him on a hill and had been snatched up by an old woman with no teeth. After that experience Stuart contented himself with the tiny coins which his father made for him out of tin foil. They were handsome little things, although rather hard to see without putting on your spectacles.

When the conductor came around to collect the fares, Stuart fished in his purse and pulled out a coin no bigger than the eye of a grasshopper.

"What's that you're offering me?" asked the conductor.

"It's one of my dimes," said Stuart.

"Is it, now?" said the conductor. "Well, I'd have a fine time explaining that to the bus company. Why, you're no bigger than a dime yourself."

"Yes I am," replied Stuart angrily. "I'm more than twice as big as a dime. A dime only comes up to here on me." And Stuart pointed to his hip. "Furthermore," he added, "I didn't come on this bus to be insulted."

"I beg pardon," said the conductor. "You'll have to forgive me, for I had no idea that in all the world there was such a small sailor."

"Live and learn," muttered Stuart, tartly, putting his change purse back in his pocket.

When the bus stopped at Seventy-second Street, Stuart jumped out and hurried across to the sailboat pond in Central Park. Over the pond the west wind blew, and into the teeth of the west wind sailed the sloops and schooners, their rails well down, their wet decks gleaming. The owners, boys and grown men, raced around the cement shores hoping to arrive at the other side in time  to keep the boats from bumping. Some of the toy boats were not as small as you might think, for when you got close to them you found that their mainmast was taller than a man's head, and they were beautifully made, with everything shipshape and ready for sea. To Stuart they seemed enormous, and he hoped he would be able to get aboard one of them and sail away to the far corners of the pond. (He was an adventurous little fellow and loved the feel of the breeze in his face and the cry of the gulls overhead and the heave of the great swell under him.)

As he sat cross-legged on the wall that surrounds the pond, gazing out at the ships through his spyglass, Stuart

noticed one boat that seemed to him finer and prouder than any other. Her name was Wasp. She was a big, black schooner flying the American flag. She had a clipper bow, and on her foredeck was mounted a three-inch cannon. She's the ship for me, thought Stuart. And the next time she sailed in, he ran over to where she was being turned around.

Stuart Signs On

"Excuse me, sir," said Stuart to the man who was turning her, "but are you the owner of the schooner Wasp?"

"I am," replied the man, surprised to be addressed by a mouse in a sailor suit.

"I'm looking for a berth in a good ship," continued Stuart, "and I thought perhaps you might sign me on. I'm strong and I'm quick."

"Are you sober?" asked the owner of the Wasp.

"I do my work," said Stuart crisply.

The man looked sharply at him. He couldn't help admiring the trim appearance and bold manner of this diminutive seafaring character.

"Well," he said at length, pointing the prow of the Wasp out toward the center of the pond, "I'll tell you what I'll do with you. You see that big racing sloop out there?"

"I do," said Stuart.

"That's the Lillian B. Womrath," said the man, "and I hate her with all my heart."

"Then so do I," cried Stuart loyally.

"I hate her because she is always bumping into my boat," continued the man, "and because her owner is a lazy boy who doesn't understand sailing and who hardly knows a squall from a squid."

"Or a jib from a jibe," cried Stuart.

"Or a luff from a leech," bellowed the man.

"Or a deck from a dock," screamed Stuart.

"Or a mast from a mist," yelled the man. "But hold on, now, no more of this! I'll tell you what we'll do. The Lillian B. Womrath has always been able to beat the Wasp sailing, but I believe that if my schooner were properly handled it would be a different story. Nobody knows how I suffer, standing here on shore, helpless, watching the Wasp blunder along, when all she needs is a steady hand on her helm. So, my young friend, I'll let you sail the Wasp across the pond and back, and if you can beat that detestable sloop I'll give you a regular job."

"Aye, aye, sir!" said Stuart, swinging himself aboard the schooner and taking his place at the wheel. "Ready about!"

"One moment," said the man. "Do you mind telling me *how* you propose to beat the other boat?"

"I intend to crack on more sail," said Stuart.

"Not in *my* boat, thank you," replied the man quickly. "I don't want you capsizing in a squall."

"Well, then," said Stuart, "I'll catch the sloop broad on, and rake her with fire from my forward gun."

"Foul means!" said the man. "I want this to be a boat race, not a naval engagement."

"Well, then," said Stuart cheerfully, "I'll sail the Wasp straight and true, and let the Lillian B. Womrath go yawing all over the pond."

"Bravo!" cried the man, "and good luck go with you!" And so saying, he let go of the Wasp's prow. A puff of air bellied out the schooner's headsails and she paid off and filled away on the port tack, heeling gracefully over to the breeze while Stuart twirled her wheel and braced himself against a deck cleat.

"By the by," yelled the man, "you haven't told me your name."

"Name is Stuart Little," called Stuart at the top of his lungs. "I'm the second son of Frederick C. Little, of this city."

"*Bon voyage*, Stuart," hollered his friend, "take care of yourself and bring the Wasp home safe."

"That I will," shouted Stuart. And he was so proud and happy, he let go of the wheel for a second and did a little dance on the sloping deck, never noticing how narrowly he escaped hitting a tramp steamer that was drifting in his path, with her engines disabled and her decks awash.

The Sailboat Race

When the people in Central Park learned that one of the toy sailboats was being steered by a mouse in a sailor suit, they all came running. Soon the shores of the pond were so crowded that a policeman was sent from headquarters to announce that everybody would have to stop pushing, but nobody did. People in New York like to push each other. The most excited person of all was the boy who owned the Lillian B. Womrath. He was a fat, sulky boy of twelve, named LeRoy. He wore a blue serge suit and a white necktie stained with orange juice.

"Come back here!" he called to Stuart. "Come back here and get on my boat. I want you to steer *my* boat. I will pay you five dollars a week and you can have every Thursday afternoon off and a radio in your room."

"I thank you for your kind offer," replied Stuart, "but I am happy aboard the Wasp—happier than I have ever been before in all my life." And with that he spun the wheel over smartly and headed his schooner down toward the starting line, where LeRoy was turning his boat around by poking it with a long stick, ready for the start of the race.

"I'll be the referee," said a man in a bright green suit. "Is the Wasp ready?"

"Ready, sir!" shouted Stuart, touching his hat.

"Is the Lillian B. Womrath ready?" asked the referee.

"Sure, I'm ready," said LeRoy.

"To the north end of the pond and back again!" shouted the referee. "On your mark, get set, GO!"

"Go!" cried the people along the shore.

"Go!" cried the owner of the Wasp.

"Go!" yelled the policeman.

And away went the two boats for the north end of the pond, while the seagulls wheeled and cried overhead and the taxicabs tooted and honked from Seventy-second Street and the west wind (which had come halfway across America to get to Central Park) sang and whistled in the rigging and blew spray across the decks, stinging Stuart's cheeks with tiny fragments of flying peanut shell tossed up from the foamy deep. "This is the life for me!" Stuart murmured to himself. "What a ship! What a day! What a race!"

Before the two boats had gone many feet, however, an

accident happened on shore. The people were pushing each other harder and harder in their eagerness to see the sport, and although they really didn't mean to, they pushed the policeman so hard they pushed him right off the concrete wall and into the pond. He hit the water in a sitting position, and got wet clear up to the third button of his jacket. He was soaked.

This particular policeman was not only a big, heavy man, but he had just eaten a big, heavy meal, and the wave he made went curling outward, cresting and billowing, upsetting all manner of small craft and causing every owner of a boat on the pond to scream with delight and consternation.

When Stuart saw the great wave approaching he jumped for the rigging, but he was too late. Towering above the Wasp like a mountain, the wave came crashing and piling along the deck, caught Stuart up and swept him over the side and into the water, where everybody supposed he would drown. Stuart had no intention of drowning. He kicked hard with his feet, and thrashed hard with his tail, and in a minute or two he climbed back aboard the schooner, cold and wet but quite unharmed. As he took his place at the helm, he could hear people cheering for him and calling, "Atta mouse, Stuart! Atta mouse!" He looked over and saw that the wave had capsized the Lillian B. Womrath but that she had righted herself and was sailing on her course, close by. And she stayed close alongside till both boats reached the north end of the pond. Here Stuart put the Wasp about and LeRoy turned the Lillian around with his stick, and away the two boats went for the finish line.

"This race isn't over yet," thought Stuart.

A Falling Glass and a Dirty Sky

The first warning he had that there was trouble ahead came when he glanced into the Wasp's cabin and observed that the barometer had fallen sharply. That can mean only one thing at sea—dirty weather. Suddenly a dark cloud swept across the sun, blotting it out and leaving the earth in shadow. Stuart shivered in his wet clothes. He turned up his sailor blouse closer around his neck, and when he spied the Wasp's owner among the crowd on shore he waved his hat and called out:

"Dirty weather ahead, sir! Wind backing into the southwest, seas confused, glass falling."

"Never mind the weather!" cried the owner. "Watch out for flotsam dead ahead!"

Stuart peered ahead into the gathering storm, but saw nothing except gray waves with white crests. The world

seemed cold and ominous. Stuart glanced behind him.
There came the sloop, boiling along fast, rolling up a
bow wave and gaining steadily.

"Look out, Stuart! Look out where you're going!"

Stuart strained his eyes, and suddenly, dead ahead,
right in the path of the Wasp, he saw an enormous paper
bag looming up on the surface of the pond. The bag
was empty and riding high, its open end gaping wide
like the mouth of a cave. Stuart spun the wheel over
but it was too late: the Wasp drove her bowsprit straight
into the bag and with a fearful *whooosh* the schooner
slowed down and came up into the wind with all sails
flapping. Just at this moment Stuart heard a splintering
crash, saw the bow of the Lillian plow through his rigging, and felt the whole ship tremble from stem to stern
with the force of the collision.

"A collision!" shouted the crowd on shore.

In a jiffy the two boats were in a terrible tangle. Little

boys on shore screamed and danced up and down. Meanwhile the paper bag sprang a leak and began to fill.

The Wasp couldn't move because of the bag. The Lillian B. Womrath couldn't move because her nose was stuck in the Wasp's rigging.

Waving his arms, Stuart ran forward and fired off his gun. Then he heard, above the other voices on shore, the voice of the owner of the Wasp yelling directions and telling him what to do.

"Stuart! Stuart! Down jib! Down staysail!"

Stuart jumped for the halyards, and the jib and the forestaysail came rippling down.

"Cut away all paper bags!" roared the owner.

Stuart whipped out his pocketknife and slashed away bravely at the soggy bag until he had the deck cleared.

"Now back your foresail and give her a full!" screamed the owner of the Wasp.

Stuart grabbed the foresail boom and pulled with all his might. Slowly the schooner paid off and began to gather headway. And as she heeled over to the breeze she rolled her rail out from under the Lillian's nose, shook herself free, and stood away to the southard. A loud cheer went up from the bank. Stuart sprang to the wheel and answered it. Then he looked back, and to his great joy he perceived that the Lillian had gone off in a wild direction and was yawing all over the pond.

Straight and true sailed the Wasp, with Stuart at the helm. After she had crossed the finish line, Stuart brought her alongside the wall, and was taken ashore and highly praised for his fine seamanship and daring. The owner

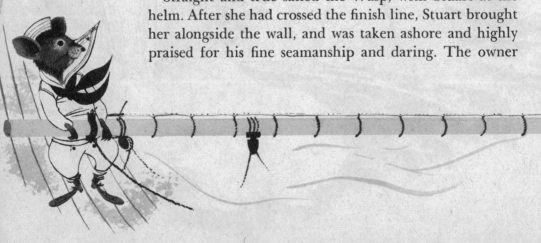

was delighted and said it was the happiest day of his life.
He introduced himself to Stuart, said that in private life
he was Dr. Paul Carey, a surgeon-dentist. He said model
boats were his hobby and that he would be delighted to
have Stuart take command of his vessel at any time.
Everybody shook hands with Stuart—everybody, that is,
except the policeman, who was too wet and mad to shake
hands with a mouse.

When Stuart got home that night, his brother George
asked him where he had been all day.

"Oh, knocking around town," replied Stuart.

The Little Green Orchard

Some one is always sitting there,
  In the little green orchard;
Even when the sun is high,
In noon's unclouded sky,
And faintly droning goes
The bee from rose to rose,
Some one in shadow is sitting there,
  In the little green orchard.

Yes, and when twilight's falling softly
  On the little green orchard;
When the grey dew distils
And every flower-cup fills;
When the last blackbird says,
"What—what!" and goes her way—ssh!
I have heard voices calling softly
  In the little green orchard.

Not that I am afraid of being there,
    In the little green orchard;
  Why, when the moon's been bright,
  Shedding her lonesome light,
  And moths like ghosties come,
  And the horned snail leaves home:
I've sat there, whispering and listening there,
    In the little green orchard;

Only it's strange to be feeling there,
    In the little green orchard;
  Whether you paint or draw,
  Dig, hammer, chop, or saw;
  When you are most alone.
  All but the silence gone . . .
Some one is waiting and watching there,
    In the little green orchard.

                    —*Walter de la Mare*

Four Generals

Arthur Bowie Chrisman

Prince Chang petitioned his father, the King. "My Honored Parent, give me permission to make a journey throughout the kingdom. I would learn how the people live, and note wherein they are contented and discontented. Thus I shall be prepared against the time when I ascend the throne."

The King nodded approval. "Your plan is good, my son. I shall immediately order that new gold tires be put upon the royal carriage, and summon ten troops of cavalry to guard you."

But the prince would not listen to such arrangements. "Oh, no, sire, I mean to go alone and in disguise. Instead of the carriage, a stick will serve for my vehicle. Instead of the troops, that selfsame stick will guard me."

Whereat, the King was greatly troubled, and the prince was put to much argument before he won his point. "Then do as you wish, my only and much beloved son," said the King, grudgingly. "But observe extreme care. There is disorder in the provinces. Go, and may your stick be as strong as the magic mace of Sun How Ehr."

"Farewell, my royal father."

"Farewell, my noble son."

Now it must be remembered that Prince Chang was

no graybeard. In years, he was nearing thirteen. Is it,
therefore, any wonder that before long, homesickness
caused his heels to drag, and his eyes to need the kerchief?
He had walked all of twenty *li*. That, he began to imagine, was journey enough for the present. He continued
to the edge of Hu Pei Forest. At the edge of the forest
he stopped. The woodland was so dark . . . so dark. The
wolves howled "Oo-o-o-o-o-wh—We starve." And such a
weak little stick with which to enter the forest of Hu Pei.
"Oo-o-o-o-owh." What wolves . . .

The prince had turned his face toward home when a
merry voice hailed him. "Ho, Brother, I'm glad you are
come. Tell me if my fiddle be in tune." A comical fellow
hopped down from a stump and chinned his fiddle while
Prince Chang stared. *Eek. Eek. Eeek.* "How does it sound,
little brother?"

"I dare say it—"

But the fiddler was not waiting for an answer. His
bow arm fell to sawing while his legs and voice joined

in the tune—"A beggar asked the King to dine." And that's a foolish song. Prince Chang thought he had never before heard or seen anything so funny by half. The more he laughed, the greater his need for laughter. Such a comical beggar, and how he could play and sing!

From one end of Hu Pei Forest to the other, Prince Chang laughed while the beggar capered and fiddled. No wolves at all appeared. Homesickness was a thing of the past—forgotten. "Let me give you a copper cash, merry stranger," said Chang, when they came to a Y of the road. "Not now," said he of the fiddle and bow. "I judge you are poorer than I."

"Indeed?" laughed the prince. "When I am King (he forgot himself there), I shall reward you handsomely."

"Ho, ho!" shrieked the beggar. "When you are King. When you are King, I'll accept a reward. Make me a general in your army."

"It shall be done," said Chang. "What is your very nice name?"

"My pitiful name is Tang—Tang, the fiddler. Farewell, my little King, who rides a bamboo horse." So they parted, both merry.

Sad to relate, Prince Chang's merriment was to be soon over. A band of robbers sprang up from the roadside and surrounded him, pounding him without mercy— all striking at one time. They took his stick and his clothing and the little bag of coins that hung from his neck. They left him in the road for dead. A sorry ending, that, to his journey.

Shortly, another traveler chanced by, and he was a man of warm heart. He revived Prince Chang and took him on his shoulder, carrying him to a village. There,

he set out food and clothing and bade the prince ask for what more he desired. Chang was deeply thankful. "How can I ever repay you?"

"*Ya ya pei* (Pish tush)," said the man. "It is nothing. What is a bit of food? And what is a gift of clothing? Besides, you must know that I am a tailor and will charge my next customer double. 'A tailor—a rogue,' says the proverb."

"I do not believe it," exclaimed Chang, "and when I become King—" (There he forgot himself again.)

"Ho, ho, ho!" roared the tailor. "When you become King. Ho, ho! When you are King, you may reward me. You may make me a general in your army."

"It shall be done," declared Chang. "What is your honorable name?"

"Wang is my miserable name. Wang, the tailor. Farewell, and good luck be with you, my future King." So they parted, merrily enough—each laughing at the excellent jest.

Third Adventure

Prince Chang continued his journey. For three days he saw no man of flesh and bone, nor came upon a dwelling. At the end of the third day, he was weak and unsteady from hunger. His stick broke beneath his weight and he lay beside the road, waiting for death to come.

Instead of death, there came a shepherd with sheep and goats. The shepherd picked up Chang and saw that the boy was far gone. It was plain that hunger had used him evilly. Promptly, the quick-witted fellow slung Chang on his shoulder and carried him off to a cave. Milk in bottles of leather hung on the cavern walls. Also,

there were cheeses. Chang was made to drink of the milk
—a little at first—only enough to moisten his throat. With
the return of strength, he drank greedily, completely
emptying a goatskin. And the emptier the bottle grew,
the more he thanked the shepherd.

"You have done me a great service," said Chang. "If
I had money I—"

"*Ya ya pei* (Pish tush)," said the shepherd. "It is
nothing. I fed you with no thought of reward."

"Nevertheless," declared Chang, "when I am made
King I—"

The shepherd was like to strain his throat with laughing. "Ho, ho, ho! When you are made King. What a
merry chap you seem to be. Very well, when you are
King, you may reward me. Make me a general in your
army. Ho, ho, ho!"

"I shall. I shall." The prince spoke firmly. "What

honorable name do you bear?" he inquired eagerly.

"My paltry name? Most folk call me Mang—Mang, the shepherd. And here, you must carry some food with you, for the nearest house is thirty *li* distant. Take this cheese— and may good luck be your companion, my King of the wandering road."

Burdened as he was, Prince Chang made slow work of getting over the mountain. He had begun to think seriously of dropping the cheese when a troop of soldiers clattered up the road behind him.

"How fortunate!" said Chang. "Here are my father's soldiers. They will take me on their horses to the next village."

But the soldiers halted and, scowling, asked fiercely, "Who are you, and what brings you here?" The prince stammered that he was sometimes called Chun, a most unfortunate invention, for Chun was the name of a local bandit.

The soldiers' frowns turned to pleased smiles (there was a reward offered), and the captain said: "So you are Chun, and you have just robbed some poor person of a new suit and a cheese. Off with his head, my braves."

Chang now saw that he was indeed in a tangle. A bold face seemed the only escape. He put on a stern look, saying: "How dare you execute men without a trial? Do you not know that I am Prince Chang, son of your noble King?"

The captain bowed in mock respect. "Your Highness seems large for such a tender age. I happen to know that King Yen Chi's eldest son is only two years old. Let your swords drink, men."

The terrible truth was made plain to Chang. He had wandered across the border of his father's kingdom. He was in a neighboring and hostile country.

The swords were lifted to strike, when—swish—came an arrow. After it, quickly, another, and another. Each found its mark. For each arrow, a soldier crumpled. The others dug heels in their horses, galloping wildly for their lives.

A sturdy youth stepped out from behind a pine. "You had better go quickly," he said to Chang. "The border of our own country lies a full mile back."

"I thank you with all my heart," declared Chang, "and shall reward you fittingly when—"

"When you are King?" finished the other. "I heard what you said to the soldiers, and wondered at your daring. Very well. Make me a general when you become King, and that will be ample reward."

"It shall be done," agreed the prince. "What brave name do you bear?"

"Name? Oh, you may call me Lang. Lang, the very so-so archer. And now you really must go, for more soldiers will come, and my arrows are few."

The Four New Generals

Prince Chang was not long returned from his journey when the King passed away in an illness. Immediately, the crown was placed on Chang's brow, and all the people burned much incense of *la ka* wood, crying, "Hail." And almost with their next breath they shouted *"Kou chou* (The enemy) ."* An enemy was marching upon Ku Hsueh. The new King had barely seated himself upon the throne before he found it necessary to see about raising an army.

There were two great troubles with the old army. It was dwarfish small, and it boasted more generals than bowmen. Of course, the generals never fought. They did nothing but plan—usually what they'd have for dinner, and which sword they'd wear to the King's next reception. Yet, King Chang added more generals to the army.

The first complaint raised against King Chang by his people was that he had added four more generals to the army. His new generals were named Tang, Wang, Mang, and Lang—though doubtless such information is hardly necessary. They were old friends of the King. The four arrived at the capital in time to see a huge enemy army encamp on the far side of the river that bordered the city. By great good fortune, the river was in flood, and held the enemy in check.

The King and his generals gazed across the river. Said Chang: "It is easily seen that the enemy has twenty men for every one we muster. What are your plans?"

Of all his generals, only Wang seemed to have so much

as the shadow of a plan. Wang said, "Give me all the tailors in the city, and all the cloth stored in the royal go-downs."

"Take them," said King Chang. "If you don't, the enemy will."

Throughout the night, General Wang and his tailors slaved with needle and thread. The click of thimbles made a continuous humming sound. The enemy on the farther shore heard, and wondered what strange warlike engines King Chang might be preparing.

With day's coming, Chang moved all his troops—he had only a thousand. The thousand men marched in parade along the river's brim. Their uniforms were old and dowdy. The words, "We are brave," that adorned the tattered jackets seemed a poor and weak boast. The soldiers were in rags. They marched as if weary. The enemy jeered.

But, lo. The first thousand had no sooner disappeared than another thousand circled past the river—stepping smartly, smartly uniformed in cloth of gold, the words "Very brave" embroidered upon their fronts. The enemy was not so quick to jeer.

Following the second thousand came a thousand men in smart red uniforms. Upon their breasts was broidered "Extremely brave." They stepped briskly, shouting dares across the river. The enemy replied with little heart.

Another thousand followed. Jade green uniforms clothed them. Rumble-dumble-de-dum sang their drums, and their steps kept perfect time. Upon their breasts were the words "Braver by far." Their taunts were hard to bear. Yet, the enemy remained silent.

A thousand men in pink, the same number in blue. Came white-clad men and orange-clad men. Violet uniforms and brown . . . The enemy thought it hardly fair. King Chang, evidently, had a million soldiers . . . How could they fight against a million? The tents came down and the enemy vanished.

General Wang continued to sew until the last enemy disappeared. He and his tailors were terribly tired. But the thousand soldiers were even more tired. All day long they had marched and changed uniforms, then marched again. They had changed from red to green, to black, to every color in the rainbow. They were color blind and weary.

But King Chang's happiness soon turned to gloom. The enemy had learned of Wang's clever trick, and resolved to march again. The army of Chang was scarcely larger than before. To come off victorious, each man would have to whip a dozen of the enemy. There was no time to increase the royal army. And the enemy lay on the other side of Ku Hsueh River, waiting for the waters to lower.

Two Cents' Worth of Rosin

King Chang rode with his generals to the river. Said he: "There lies the enemy. The depth of the river lessens with each minute. Who has a plan?" Some of the generals stroked their beards. Others twisted their mustaches. All wrinkled their brows. Not one of them parted his lips.

"Come, my brave generals. Have you no plan? General Tang?"

Tang bowed his head the three times required by law and courtesy. "Sire, with your permission, I have a small scheme that may serve."

"*Chen hao* (Very good); spare no expense. Draw on the treasury for whatever you may desire—silk, tailors, fans, or false faces—anything except more soldiers, for soldiers we have not."

"Then, please, Your Majesty," said Tang, "may I ask you to sign an order on the treasury for one ounce of pine rosin."

The King thought Tang was jesting. His first impulse was to strike off his head. But instead of doing so, he signed the order for two cents' worth of rosin.

At night, General Tang sat upon a cliff that towered above the river. He fondled his precious violin. A little breeze sprang up at his back. Tang the general was no more, but Tang the musician lived and thrilled. Bow swept strings with a magic sweetly sad. The breeze caught up the melody. The river was its sounding board. The soldiers on the farther shore turned in their blankets to listen. Than home there is no spot dearer—and the violin sang of home. More and more sad came the music. The musician wept. Across the river ten thousand eyes grew moist. The soldiers wept and were unashamed. Why had they left their warm hearthstones—to die in an alien land? Fierce resolve faded, and a longing took its stead, a longing for home and the loved ones it sheltered.

Morning saw the enemy camp deserted. Soldier after soldier had stolen away in the darkness, thinking only of home. Not one remained to threaten Ku Hsueh City.

King Chang assembled his generals and spoke high praise of Tang. Then he discussed the need of preparation for the future. He knew very well that the enemy would return. "Have any of you, my trusty generals, a plan for humbling the enemy in his next invasion?"

General Mang, the former shepherd, voiced a plan. "I would suggest that all horses be replaced by lean sheep of the mountain."

General Lang, the archer, said, "I would suggest that all cases at law be settled by trial with bow and arrow."

"So be it," said the King. "I grant both requests."

The enemy soon marched upon Ku Hsueh in greater

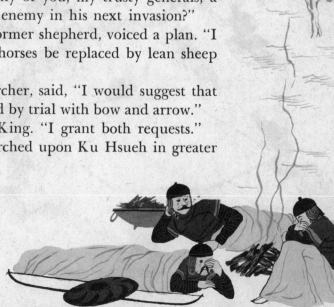

numbers than before. It was plain that only a miracle could save the city. All eyes were turned to General Mang —turned beseechingly, and rather doubtfully. Could a mountain shepherd save Ku Hsueh?

That night the question was answered. Mang herded his sheep in a tremendous body toward the enemy camp. At the proper moment, he raised a great din and startled the animals into flight. Through the camp of the enemy they rushed, and instantly the camp was confusion. The soldiers had fared none too well on their march. They were hungry. And here was good food to be had for the catching. Away went sheep. Away went soldiers. Thoroughly frightened, the lean-limbed sheep sped their fastest. Thoroughly desirous, the hungry soldiers followed at their fastest.

While the camp was empty, Mang and a score of daring men darted from tent to tent. In their hands were torches. Behind them rose a flare of ever-spreading flame. "To roast their meat when they catch it," said Mang. The wind was a helpful friend, scattering sparks with a will. The destruction was soon finished. What had been a white encampment became a red and rolling flame. Nothing was spared. A thoroughly unhappy enemy stole away from Ku Hsueh that night.

So far, General Lang had done nothing of a warlike nature—nothing at all—unless stepping upon the toes of a citizen be considered warlike. Lang had done that. Naturally, the citizen was indignant. He wished to see justice done and went to a court of law.

The judge said: "Take this bow and shoot five arrows in yonder target. He who shoots best has the right on his side." The young citizen shot first, and his marksmanship was poor to say the least. Whereupon, Lang drew the bow. Oddly enough, his aim was no better than that of the citizen. With that, the judge declared the suit undecided and set a future date for its retrial. General Lang left court well pleased. The young citizen went home to spend many hours in practice with bow and arrow.

Thereafter, the courts were flooded with lawsuits. From morn till night the bow strings twanged. It appeared that all the men of Ku Hsueh had quarrels to be settled. And they who were wise spent much time in archery practice before they went to court. Many became quite expert with the bow and arrow.

King Chang put all of them into his army. At last, he had a large force, a force that would give pause to any foe. Long the King waited for his enemy's return. But he

waited in vain. Spies had watched the men of Ku Hsueh at practice with the bow. They sent messages that Ku Hsueh was prepared. So the country was troubled no more by alarms of enemy armies.

Thus, without loss of a man, was the kingdom saved for Chang, by Wang, Tang, Mang, and Lang. A thousand years ago all this, but very learned men still dispute as to which was the greatest—Lang, Mang, Tang, or Wang—which of the four generals.

Down Our Street

Down our street, around the corner—
Around the corner and up our street—
I hear the shout of happy voices,
I hear the sound of flying feet.

Almost, I think, my eye can see them,
Almost I glimpse their figures fleet—
The boys and girls who in these pages
Live so near me, down our street.

Closer than the next-door neighbors,
Yet face to face we'll never meet:
I can only hear them call me,
Around the corner, up our street.

—*Dorothy Hall*

Rococo Skates

Marjorie Fischer

Twenty pairs of shoes clattered up the marble steps inside the Metropolitan Museum. The class was having Art today, and Miss Ryan had taken them to see the pictures. Miss Ryan walked beside the line, looking forward and backward along the double row of children.

Mary Ann was at the very end of the line. She was even behind Frances, the girl she was supposed to be walking with, who was her best friend in a way. Miss Ryan looked back.

"Close up the line, Mary Ann," said Miss Ryan.

Mary Ann stepped up and then fell back again. The Museum would be a good place to roller skate, she thought. The floors were hard wood, and today most of the galleries were empty. You could go shooting down the galleries and around corners yelling like anything. You could stop yourself with statues so big and heavy they couldn't fall. You'd go swinging around the statue, just holding lightly with one hand. And then you'd take off again—rolling, shooting, yelling. If you had skates, you could. Mary Ann didn't have any skates. Skates were what she had particularly wanted for a long time. Sometimes when she was in the park—if she had skates—she could play tag with Frances and the other kids who had skates. Maybe next Christmas—but Christmas was a long way off, and so was her birthday.

The twenty pairs of shoes clattered along the galleries. Here and there Miss Ryan would hold up her hand. The shoes stood still, and Miss Ryan told them about this picture or that.

Miss Ryan stopped before a medium-sized picture of a table with a bottle of wine, a loaf of bread, a knife, and a basket of fruit. It wasn't bad, Mary Ann thought. Right at one side of the picture was another picture on an easel. It was a medium-sized picture of a table with a bottle of wine, a loaf of bread, a knife, and a basket of fruit. It was, in fact, a copy of the picture on the wall, and so exactly like it that, except for the frame around it, nobody could have told one from the other.

"How is that, Miss Ryan?" asked Mary Ann.

"Artists get permission from the Museum to come in and copy," said Miss Ryan. "This is a very famous picture. So naturally, artists copy it."

"I'd never," said Mary Ann. "I'd rather do my own, even if it was bad."

Mary Ann hung back behind the class, standing before the easel and looking from one picture to the other. Maybe the paint was still wet on the copy, she thought. It would be easy enough to find out, but of course she shouldn't do that. Her right hand reached out all by itself, and her forefinger pressed against the picture on the easel. Oh, heavens! It *was* wet. She felt the paint slide a little under her finger.

Mary Ann hurriedly caught up with Frances and stepped along beside her.

"I saw you," whispered Frances. "You're just lucky Miss Ryan didn't see. Did it leave a mark?"

Mary Ann didn't answer. She walked along beside

Frances, swinging her skirt and breathing rather fast.

Miss Ryan walked on, with twenty pairs of shoes clopping behind her. They walked and stopped, walked and stopped. The pictures were like windows, Mary Ann thought. Through them, you saw how people used to look. Then they went through rooms full of furniture, and you could see how people used to sit and write and sew and sleep. There was one enormous bed with a canopy over it. The canopy was of heavy silk, held up with carved golden Cupids leaping through the air and holding carved wreaths of flowers.

"This is Rococo furniture," said Miss Ryan.

Rococo, Mary Ann thought to herself. It might be the name of something to play, or a pigeon cooing, or something you shouted as you slid along on roller skates.

"Rococo," Mary Ann said out loud. Frances looked at her and repeated it after her.

"Rococo," said Frances.

"Rococo," said Mary Ann, trying it out as a pigeon.

Mary Ann and Frances began to laugh. They hit against each other as they walked. "Rococo!" they said, and swayed away.

The class walked and looked, walked and looked. Mary Ann was *tired*.

"All right, children," Miss Ryan said at last. "That's enough for today. Turn right around as you are and we'll find our way out."

The class turned. Now Mary Ann and Frances were at the head of the line. They walked along, past the furniture—"Rococo!" said Mary Ann and Frances. They walked past pictures and pictures. Now they were in the room where the picture on the easel had been.

"Look," said Frances. "The copy's gone."

The Stolen Picture

Mary Ann was next to the wall. When she came to the medium-sized picture of the table with the bottle of wine, the loaf of bread, the knife, and the basket of fruit, she gave such a loud cry that everyone stopped.

"Look!" cried Mary Ann. "It's the other one. The real one's been stolen!"

"How can you tell?" said Frances.

"Quick!" said Mary Ann. "We've got to tell someone important."

Miss Ryan came between Mary Ann and Frances.

"What is the meaning of all this?" she said.

"The picture!" said Mary Ann. "The real picture's been stolen. This is the one that was on the easel."

"Nonsense," said Miss Ryan.

"Honestly!" cried Mary Ann. "We must tell the head of the Museum right away."

"Come along now," said Miss Ryan.

By this time one or two other people had heard the racket. They were standing about, trying to find out what had happened. A guard in a blue uniform strolled in and told everyone to keep quiet.

Miss Ryan was getting ready to march them straight out—Mary Ann saw that.

"I must tell someone," cried Mary Ann. She spun about and began to run, back along the way she had come. She ran past pictures and pictures, dodging people or bumping against them. Everyone turned to look, and then—there came the clatter of nineteen pairs of shoes, running along the galleries after her.

Mary Ann came to the furniture room. There were two guards coming towards her, one from each doorway. She sprang over the rope around the Rococo bed, and the guards came nearer. They reached out their hands for her, and she leaped on to the bed and stood on it. How hard the mattress was, like a board! She ran a little one way, under the canopy, and as both guards ran to get her, she doubled, leaped from the bed, sprang over the rope, and made off again, with everyone clopping after her.

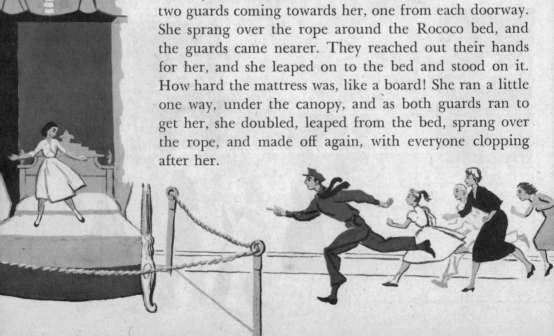

She ran out into a marble hall. At her left she saw a door marked—marked—why, it was marked *Office of the Director*. The *Director*. She turned about and swung open the heavy door and dashed inside, just as everyone caught up with her.

"A picture's been stolen!" gasped Mary Ann to the people in the office. "I know it's been stolen. You just come along with me and I'll show you. No one believes me, but I'll show you. Only hurry!"

While she was talking, a nice old man had come out of an inner office. Miss Ryan and four guards had come through the outer door.

"Let's just go along and have a look to make sure," said the nice old man. "It's pretty hard to steal a picture here, but just to make sure."

Back they went, all of them—first the nice old man and Mary Ann, then Frances and Miss Ryan, and then the class, and the other people, and the guards. When they got to the picture, the nice old man put on a pair of glasses with a black ribbon attached to them. He looked at the picture very carefully. After quite a while, he turned to Mary Ann.

"This is a very good copy," said the nice old man. "But it *is* a copy. The real picture has been stolen. I am going back to my office now. Won't you wait for me outside?"

While they waited for the nice old man, Miss Ryan told Mary Ann that she quite understood how it was, that Mary Ann had really *had* to run. When the nice old man came out, he had a great book bound in blue leather in his arms.

"This is for you, Mary Ann," he said. "It has colored pictures of most of the pictures in the Museum. It even has the stolen picture. If it had not been for you, the theft might not have been noticed until the picture had been taken out of the country. You have done a very remarkable thing. Almost anyone would have been fooled by that copy."

"I guess I couldn't be fooled," said Mary Ann.

"Here's the book then, Mary Ann," said the nice old man.

Mary Ann took the great book bound in blue leather and said thank you politely. The nice old man watched her.

"Maybe there was something you specially wanted, Mary Ann," he said. "Besides the book."

"She wants roller skates," Frances burst out.

"Roller skates it is," said the nice old man. He called a nice young man from his office.

In a few minutes, Mary Ann and Frances were going down the steps outside the Museum with the nice young man. The rest of the class and Miss Ryan stood and watched Mary Ann and Frances climb into a beautiful automobile, and waved to them as they drove away.

"How did you know about that copy, Mary Ann?"

asked the nice young man as they were driving along.

"I pushed the copy with my finger and it left a mark," said Mary Ann. "Right in the middle of the basket."

"Oh, so that was how," said Frances. "But I wouldn't tell on you."

"Neither would I," said the nice young man. "What do you say, Mary Ann and Frances—skates first or sodas first?"

"Sodas," said Frances.

"Skates," said Mary Ann. "She's got skates. Anyway, I marked the picture."

"Oh, all right," said Frances.

"I thought we could make up a new game," said Mary Ann. "Rococo Skates."

"What!" said the nice young man.

"Something like tag on skates," said Mary Ann.

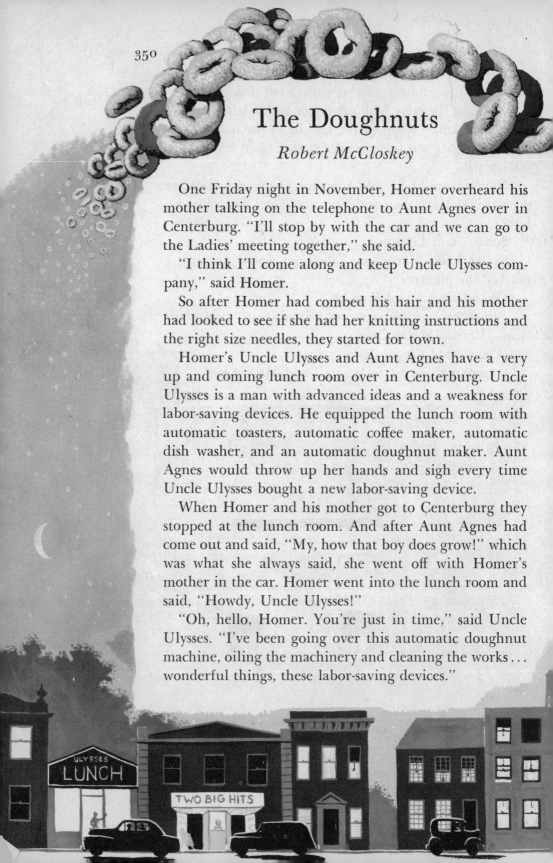

The Doughnuts

Robert McCloskey

One Friday night in November, Homer overheard his mother talking on the telephone to Aunt Agnes over in Centerburg. "I'll stop by with the car and we can go to the Ladies' meeting together," she said.

"I think I'll come along and keep Uncle Ulysses company," said Homer.

So after Homer had combed his hair and his mother had looked to see if she had her knitting instructions and the right size needles, they started for town.

Homer's Uncle Ulysses and Aunt Agnes have a very up and coming lunch room over in Centerburg. Uncle Ulysses is a man with advanced ideas and a weakness for labor-saving devices. He equipped the lunch room with automatic toasters, automatic coffee maker, automatic dish washer, and an automatic doughnut maker. Aunt Agnes would throw up her hands and sigh every time Uncle Ulysses bought a new labor-saving device.

When Homer and his mother got to Centerburg they stopped at the lunch room. And after Aunt Agnes had come out and said, "My, how that boy does grow!" which was what she always said, she went off with Homer's mother in the car. Homer went into the lunch room and said, "Howdy, Uncle Ulysses!"

"Oh, hello, Homer. You're just in time," said Uncle Ulysses. "I've been going over this automatic doughnut machine, oiling the machinery and cleaning the works... wonderful things, these labor-saving devices."

"Yep," agreed Homer. He picked up a cloth and started polishing the metal trimmings.

"Look here, Homer, you've got a mechanical mind. See if you can find where these two pieces fit in. I'm going across to the barber shop for a spell. There won't be much business here until the double feature is over. I'll be back before then."

Then as Uncle Ulysses went out the door he said, "Uh, Homer, after you get the pieces in place, would you mind mixing up a batch of doughnut batter and put it in the machine? You could make a few doughnuts to have on hand for the crowd after the movie . . ."

"O. K.," said Homer, "I'll take care of everything."

A few minutes later a customer came in and said, "Good evening, Bud."

Homer looked up from putting the last piece in the doughnut machine. "Good evening, Sir, what can I do for you?"

"Well, young feller, I'd like a cup o'coffee and some doughnuts," said the customer.

"I'm sorry, Mister, but we won't have any doughnuts for about half an hour, until I can mix some dough and start this machine. I could give you some very fine sugar rolls instead."

"Well, Bud, I'm in no real hurry. I'll just have a cup o'coffee and wait around a bit for the doughnuts."

"O.K.," said Homer, and he drew a cup of coffee from Uncle Ulysses' super automatic coffee maker.

"Nice place you've got here," said the customer.

"Oh, yes," replied Homer. "This is a very up and coming lunch room with all the latest improvements."

"Yes," said the stranger, "must be a good business. I'm in business too. A traveling man in outdoor advertising. I'm a sandwich man, Mr. Gabby's my name."

"My name is Homer. I'm glad to meet you, Mr. Gabby. It must be a fine profession, traveling and advertising sandwiches."

"Oh no," said Mr. Gabby, "I don't advertise sandwiches. I just wear any kind of an ad, one sign on front and one sign on behind, this way . . . Like a sandwich. Ya know what I mean?"

"Oh, I see. That must be fun," said Homer as he got out the flour and the baking powder.

Just then a large shiny black car stopped in front of the lunch room. A chauffeur helped a lady out of the rear door. They both came inside and the lady smiled and said, "We've stopped for a light snack. Some doughnuts and coffee would be simply marvelous."

Then Homer said, "I'm sorry, Ma'am, but the doughnuts won't be ready until I make this batter and start Uncle Ulysses' doughnut machine."

"Well now aren't *you* a clever young man to know how

to make *doughnuts!* You simply must allow me to help.
I know the best receipt for doughnuts."

"But, Ma'am . . ." said Homer.

"Now just *wait* till you taste these doughnuts," said
the lady. "Do you have an apron?" she asked, as she took
off her fur coat and her rings and her jewelry and rolled
up her sleeves. "Charles," she said to the chauffeur,
"hand me that baking powder, that's right. Young man,
we'll need some nutmeg."

So Homer and the chauffeur stood by and handed
things and cracked the eggs while the lady mixed and
stirred.

"It looks like an awful lot of batter," said Homer as he
stood on a chair and poured it into the doughnut
machine with the help of the chauffeur. "It's about *ten*
times as much as Uncle Ulysses ever makes."

"But wait till you taste them!" said the lady.

Homer got down from the chair and pushed a button
on the machine marked, *"Start."* Rings of batter started
dropping into the hot fat. After a ring of batter was
cooked on one side an automatic gadget turned it over
and the other side would cook. Then another automatic
gadget gave the doughnut a little push and it rolled
neatly down a little chute, all ready to eat.

"That's a simply *fascinating* machine," said the lady.
"Here, young man, *you* must have the first one. Now
isn't that just *too* delicious?"

"Yes, Ma'am, it's very good," replied Homer as the
lady handed doughnuts to Charles and to Mr. Gabby.

"It's an old family receipt!" said the lady with pride.

Homer poured some coffee for the lady and her chauffeur and for Mr. Gabby, and a glass of milk for himself.

Then they all sat down at the lunch counter to enjoy another few doughnuts apiece.

"I'm so glad you enjoy my doughnuts," said the lady. "But now, Charles, we really must be going. If you will just take this apron, Homer, and put two dozen doughnuts in a bag to take along, we'll be on our way. And, Charles, don't forget to pay the young man." She rolled down her sleeves and put on her jewelry. Then Charles managed to get her into her big fur coat.

"Good night, young man, I haven't had so much fun in years," said the lady, as she went out the door.

"Those are sure good doughnuts," said Mr. Gabby.

"You bet!" said Homer. Then he and Mr. Gabby stood and watched the automatic doughnut machine make doughnuts. After a few more dozen doughnuts had rolled down the little chute, Homer said, "I guess that's about enough doughnuts to sell to the after theater customers."

Homer pushed the button marked *"Stop"* and there was a little click, but nothing happened. The rings of batter kept right on dropping into the hot fat, and an automatic gadget kept right on turning them over, and another automatic gadget kept right on giving them a little push and the doughnuts kept right on rolling down the little chute, all ready to eat.

"That's funny," said Homer. He pushed the button again. But the automatic doughnut maker kept right on making doughnuts.

"Well, I guess I must have put one of those pieces in backwards," said Homer.

"Then it might stop if you pushed the button marked *'Start,'*" said Mr. Gabby.

Homer did, and the doughnuts still kept rolling down the little chute, just as regular as a clock can tick.

"I'd better telephone Uncle Ulysses over at the barber shop." Homer gave the number. While he waited for someone to answer, he counted thirty-seven doughnuts roll down the little chute.

Finally someone answered "Hello! This is the sarber bhop, I mean the barber shop."

"Oh, hello, sheriff. This is Homer. Could I speak to Uncle Ulysses?"

"Well, he's playing pinochle right now," said the sheriff. "Anythin' I can tell 'im?"

"Yes," said Homer. "I pushed the button marked '*Stop*' on the doughnut machine but it won't stop!"

"O.K. Wold the hire, I mean, hold the wire and I'll tell 'im." Then Homer looked over his shoulder and counted another twenty-one doughnuts roll down the little chute. Then the sheriff said, "He'll be right over. . . . Just gotta finish this hand."

The window was full of doughnuts by now, so Homer and Mr. Gabby had to hustle around and start stacking them on plates and trays on the counter.

"Sure are a lot of doughnuts!" said Homer.

"You bet!" said Mr. Gabby. "I lost count at twelve hundred and two and that was quite a while back."

People had begun to gather outside the lunch room window. Someone was saying, "There are almost as many doughnuts as there are people in Centerburg. I wonder how in thunder Ulysses thinks he can sell all of 'em!"

By the time Uncle Ulysses and the sheriff arrived, the lunch room was a calamity of doughnuts! Doughnuts in the window, doughnuts piled high on the shelves, doughnuts stacked on plates, doughnuts lined up twelve deep all along the counter, and doughnuts still rolling down the little chute, just as regular as a clock can tick.

"Hello, sheriff, hello, Uncle Ulysses, we're having a little trouble here," said Homer.

"Well, I'll be dunked!" said Uncle Ulysses.

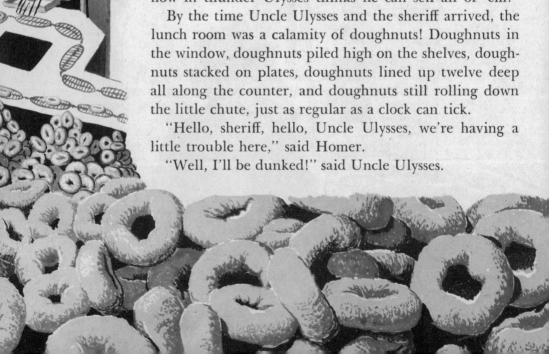

"Mighty fine doughnuts though. What'll you do with 'em all, Ulysses?"

Uncle Ulysses groaned and said, "What will Aggy say?"

Then Mr. Gabby stopped piling doughnuts and said, "What you need is an advertising man. You got the doughnuts, ya gotta create a market . . . Understand? . . . It's balancing the demand with the supply . . . That sort of thing."

"Yep!" said Homer. "Mr. Gabby's right. We have to enlarge our market. He's an advertising sandwich man. He can walk up and down in front of the theater and get the customers."

"You're hired, Mr. Gabby!" said Uncle Ulysses.

Then everybody pitched in to paint the signs and to get Mr. Gabby sandwiched between.

The sheriff went outside to keep order, because there was quite a crowd by now. Homer and Uncle Ulysses kept stacking doughnuts. Once in a while somebody bought a few, but not very often.

Then Mr. Gabby came back and said, "The show's all over. Besides, almost everybody in town is out front watching that machine make doughnuts!"

"Zeus!" said Uncle Ulysses. "We must get rid of these doughnuts before Aggy gets here!"

"Looks like you will have ta hire a truck to waul 'em ahay, I mean haul 'em away!" said the sheriff, who had just come in. Just then there were a noise and a shoving out front. The lady from the shiny black car and her chauffeur came pushing through the crowd and into the lunch room.

"Oh, gracious!" she gasped, ignoring the doughnuts. "I've lost my diamond bracelet. I know I left it here on the counter," she said, pointing to a place where the doughnuts were piled in stacks of two dozen.

"Yes, Ma'am, I guess you forgot it when you helped make the batter," said Homer.

Then they moved all the doughnuts around, but they couldn't find the bracelet anywhere. Meanwhile the doughnuts kept rolling down the little chute, just as regular as a clock can tick.

After they had looked all around, the sheriff cast a suspicious eye on Mr. Gabby. But Homer said, "He's all right, sheriff. He's a friend of mine."

Then the lady said, "I'll offer a reward of one hundred dollars for that bracelet! It really *must* be found! . . . it *really* must!"

"Now don't you worry, lady," said the sheriff. "I'll get your bracelet back!"

While the lady wrung her hands and said, "We must find it, we *must!*" and Uncle Ulysses was moaning about what Aunt Agnes would say, and the sheriff was eyeing Mr. Gabby, Homer sat down and thought hard.

Before twenty more doughnuts could roll down the little chute he shouted, "SAY! I know where the bracelet

FRESH
DOUGHNUTS
2
FOR
5¢

is! It was lying here on the counter and got mixed up in the batter by mistake! The bracelet is cooked inside one of these doughnuts!"

"Why . . . I really believe you're right," said the lady through her tears. "Isn't that *amazing?*"

"I'll be hog-tied!" said the sheriff.

"OhH-h!" moaned Uncle Ulysses. "Now we have to break up all these doughnuts to find it. Think of the *pieces!* Think of the *crumbs!* Think of what *Aggy* will say!"

"Nope," said Homer. "We won't have to break them up. I've got a plan."

So Homer and the advertising man took some cardboard and some paint and printed another sign. They put this sign in the window.

F R E S H   D O U G H N U T S
2 for 5c
While They Last
$100.00 PRIZE
For Finding
A Bracelet
inside a doughnut
P.S. You have to give the
bracelet back

THEN . . . The doughnuts began to sell! *Everybody* wanted to buy doughnuts, *dozens* of doughnuts!

And that's not all. Everybody bought coffee to dunk the doughnuts in, too. Those that didn't buy coffee bought milk or soda. It kept Homer and the lady and the chauffeur and Uncle Ulysses and the sheriff busy waiting on the people who wanted to buy doughnuts.

When all but the last couple of hundred doughnuts had been sold, Rupert Black shouted, "I GOT IT!" And sure enough . . . there was the diamond bracelet inside of his doughnut!

Then Rupert went home with a hundred dollars, the citizens of Centerburg went home full of doughnuts, the lady and her chauffeur drove off with the diamond bracelet, and Homer went home with his mother when she stopped by with Aunt Aggy.

As Homer went out of the door he heard Mr. Gabby say, "Neatest trick of merchandising I ever seen." Aunt Aggy was looking skeptical while Uncle Ulysses was saying, "The rings of batter kept right on dropping into the hot fat, and the automatic gadget kept right on turning them over, and the other automatic gadget kept right on giving them a little push, and the doughnuts kept right on rolling down the little chute just as regular as a clock can tick—they just kept right on a-comin', an' a-comin', an' a-comin', an' a-comin'."

The Baby Sea Lion

Doris Gates

*Kate, red-headed and an orphan, had just come to a
foster home in one of the fishing towns along the California coast. Among her new friends was Vic Corsatti,
who was in her class in school, and whose big brother Leo
had a fishing boat.*

The wharf ran far out into the blue bay. There were
buildings out near the end. Automobiles and pedestrians
moved back and forth along the whole length of it.
People were fishing along each side, sitting in the sun
with their feet swinging over the edge and their poles
reaching out patiently in front of them. Brilliant light
danced over the lifting water, on which floating gulls
bobbed like feathered corks. Lifting and falling in the
same rhythm, Kate saw, were the masts of the fishing fleet
tied at one side near the end of the wharf. The boats were
not yet visible, but as she and Vic quickened their steps,
the masts lengthened and finally the hulls of the little
craft bobbed in full view. Now the two came to where
the fishing nets were spread to dry. Some were stretched
along the edge of the wharf, and men on up-ended boxes
were mending them. Vic stopped beside one of them.

"Something make you a lot of trouble, Louie?" he
asked.

The old man glanced up from his work, squinting at Vic through bushy gray eyebrows. His face was deeply tanned and deeply lined.

"Yeh, I have tough luck. Last night a baby sea lion he get all tangled up in my net and the mother she try to rescue him. So when I come home from fishing this morning, I have in my net one baby sea lion and many big holes. And no fish."

"What happened to the baby sea lion?" asked Vic.

"Oh, we bring him up and look at him a little bit and then I give him to one of the fellows. Later on, we kill him."

He shrugged, looked out across the water, and went on with his work. But now Kate broke into the conversation.

"No," she said quickly. "You musn't kill him ever. Sea lions don't do any harm. We learned all about them in school. And besides, it's against the law to kill them."

Louie continued his mending in silence for a moment. Then he laid his gnarled old hands on his knees and regarded her curiously, his head tipped to one side.

"No-o-o-o?" he asked, and Kate felt her face grow red. "You talk much nonsense. A sea lion makes me lose one day's fishing. Without fish, I starve. And you say they do no harm. Maybe not you. That is true. But me they harm very much. And that is important to me. When it is necessary to decide which is important, Louie or the sea lion, I choose Louie every time. Even a sea lion can understand that."

Kate had stood there feeling small and ignorant as Louie had gone on talking. By the time he had finished, she wished with all her heart that the planks of the wharf might close over her head, hiding her from public view. Louie was bent over his work again, seeming to have forgotten her entirely. She was glad when Vic took leave and started on his way again. Her goodbye to Louie's bowed shoulders was a timid murmur.

Louie didn't bother to look up. "Oh, I see you again lots of times," he said. Kate thought it the nicest goodbye she had ever heard.

"There's Leo," cried Vic suddenly, throwing an excited look over his shoulder and breaking into a run.

Kate followed him blindly, wishing she possessed his knack of dodging cars, people, and coiled ropes as if they had not been there. All at once there was a shout. Kate stopped so suddenly she almost lost her balance and went down.

"Hey, look where you're going. What do you think my nets are, a carpet for your feet, eh?"

Kate was standing where the shout had stopped her, right in the middle of a long length of orange-brown netting. A young man, a tall young man, bronzed and handsome, with a head of black and crisply curling hair, was roaring right at her and grinning happily. His teeth were very white against his tanned skin. He couldn't be really angry and smile like that, she thought. But even as she watched him, the smile vanished, his brows drew together fiercely, and his dark eyes glared.

"Jump! Beat it, or I throw you into the ocean," he yelled, and started towards Kate.

Panic gave power to her legs. With a mighty leap, she cleared the nets, coming down onto the wharf planking with such force that the soles of her feet stung. There was a roar of laughter that might have been heard in China. Kate felt rage take complete possession of her whole being. So this was the wonderful Leo of whom Vic was so proud! This was the big brother who was the best fisherman in the bay! Well, he was also the rudest. Leo, indeed! She hated him.

"What are you fooling around here for?" Now he was bullying Vic who was opening his mouth to reply. "Don't say a word," commanded Leo. "I know. You think maybe I take you and your girl friend for a ride, eh?"

He looked from Vic to Kate. "You pick a red head this time," he commented. "Red heads have bad tempers. Ain't that right, eh? Why do you look so mad?" He was grinning at Kate again.

This was really too much. Would he never stop insulting her? She could feel tears stinging her eyes. She turned her back on Leo and started blindly along the way she had come. She wanted to run, but the wharf was too wobbly through her tears. If only she could get away from this place she'd never come near it again. Never.

"We're Friends"

But Kate didn't get away. A brown arm shot out and seized her, and a deeply contrite voice said from somewhere above her bent head, "Aw, now, you must not mind me." Leo's free hand took hold of her chin, and tilted

her face back. "See, now, I am not really a bad guy. I just make a fool of myself sometimes. Vic is tough. All the kids I know, they're all tough. I forget maybe you are different. You must not cry, please."

Kate looked into his troubled face and deep into his dark eyes. She had never seen kinder eyes. And now they were troubled because she was troubled. She sniffed loudly, remembering she hadn't brought a handkerchief. Instantly, Leo let go of her chin. Fishing into a back pocket of his jeans, he handed her a flaming red bandanna.

"Here," he said, "it is perhaps fishy, but not too bad. Use it. I give it to you. A peace offering, eh?"

He held her at arm's length and looked eagerly, questioningly into her eyes. "Say we are friends."

Kate took the bandanna and wiped her eyes and nose. "Sure," she said. "We're friends."

"O.K.," yelled Leo, giving her a slap on the shoulder that nearly knocked the wind out of her. "That's swell. Now all is made right again, and I take you for a ride."

With a bound, he was back at the wharf side, working with some ropes. "Come on, you kids," he called, and vanished below. "Let's go." Vic followed.

In a moment, both Leo and Vic were standing in the boat tied to a float down below. Stairs led to the float, and it didn't take Kate very long to travel down them. In an instant, she was standing on the float with the sides of Leo's boat rubbing against it except when a swell rolled under them and lifted the boat a good two feet away. Kate started to wonder just how she would ever time her jump to land herself into the boat before the water drew it away again.

"Give me your hands," commanded Leo, reaching

toward her. She laid her hands in his. As his strong fingers closed over hers, she knew that as long as Leo was around, she had nothing to fear. He would get her safely into the boat.

"Jump," he yelled. Obeying blindly, Kate jumped, to feel herself lifted out over the water in a quick swing. The next thing she knew, there she was in the boat with Leo beside her. Vic was already seated in the stern sheets.

Leo started the motor. With a steady *put-put-put*, they began slowly to back away from the wharf. Kate lifted her eyes to the people fishing along its edge. They were all watching, and it made her feel full of importance. She would have been surprised to have known that several sitting idly there thought her red head made a pretty spot of color against the blue sea.

As soon as they were clear, Leo spun the wheel and the little craft headed into the open bay. This was Kate's very first boat ride, although she didn't say so. Vic and Leo were too much at home on the water for her to risk such a confession.

"Can we go around the point to the lighthouse?" Vic shouted over the coughing of the motor.

Leo nodded and turned their course toward the stretch of land reaching like a long arm into the bay. It was fun to be so close to the water without being actually in it, Kate thought, watching the soapy bubbles that floated in their wake. The farther they got from the wharf, the more the bow plunged up and down. Once, when a swell lifted them and let them fall back into its trough, there was such a heavy plop that spray was flung like rain into their faces.

"Hey, whatcha trying to do?" yelled Vic.

But Leo only laughed and said, "We baptize Kate with salt water. Now she is a real sailor."

Kate, watching the water roll away from them in great oily swells, wondered what a storm at sea would be like. Surely no boat as tiny as this could last long in a storm. After only a little hesitation, she asked Leo about it.

"Sure, I get caught in storms, but a storm is as nothing to my *Lena*. This is my girl friend," patting the boat, "and she is always true to me." Leo threw back his head and laughed mightily. "*Lena* and I, we don't worry about storms. We don't worry about nothing so long as the fish run, eh Vic?"

He looked around to discover that Vic had a line over the side and was hanging half-way into the water to watch it.

Instantly, Leo's face became wild and excited. "Are you crazy?" he yelled. "You can't trawl at this speed. We go too fast."

"I know," said Vic, pulling himself back into the boat and grinning sheepishly at Leo. "But I just like to play I'll get one."

Leo flung up his hands. His handsome face beamed. "There is a true fisherman," he said to Kate. "No Corsatti but would fish in a bucket if he had nothing better. Wherever there is water, they must have a line in it. Always fishermen. Always poor. Always happy."

Lighthouse Point

Off Lighthouse Point they saw a few sea lions gliding through the water as if they were water themselves. Kate had never seen anything so effortless as the ease of their swimming. Leo stopped the motor and the three sat quietly and watched them. Now there was no sound but the water slapping the boat's sides. Once in a while one of the sea lions would blow the water from his nostrils with a snort that sounded unnaturally loud.

"Louie found a baby one in his net this morning," Kate said, very quietly.

"Old Louie had a pipe dream," returned Leo. "This is a little early for baby sea lions."

"Yeh, Leo, he said he saw it." Vic came scrambling over from the stern to lend support to Kate's words.

"I know," said Leo, nodding, his narrowed eyes on the

rocks where two sea lions lay sunning themselves. "But it is funny."

"You won't kill it, will you?" asked Kate.

"Sea lions are bad business," replied Leo.

"But this is just a baby," argued Kate.

"Babies grow up," affirmed Leo.

"Where is it now?" asked Vic.

"It is here," said Leo. Reaching forward, he drew from under the bow sheets a gunny sack tied with rope at one end.

"You had it all the time?" demanded Kate, too astonished to speak sensibly.

"Sure. I took it away from old Louie to show it to Vic. Anyway, that's what I let him think. He was going to kill it and I sure don't blame him any. But me, I get all soft inside when I see it. It's too little. I cannot bear to hurt little things. I guess I got no sense."

"Oh, yes," Kate was saying inside herself, as she watched Leo cutting the rope. "You've got more sense than anyone I know."

Carefully, Leo rolled back the sack to reveal a little snout from which stiff whiskers bristled up. Followed bulging eyes and a fat little body covered with fur so fine and sleek it looked like skin instead of fur. It struggled under Leo's hands, its flippers trying to brace themselves against the thwarts. But he held it firmly while the two children bent over to look closely at it. Kate thought it was the most lovable thing she had ever seen. She longed to take it in her arms and hug it. It looked so like a baby and so little and helpless, she quite understood how even a fisherman like Leo could take pity on it. But, then, Louie had wanted to kill it and he, too, was a fisherman. She was suddenly terribly glad that Leo possessed more heart than good sense.

"I guess we're close enough in now," said Leo at last, measuring the distance to shore. Kate noticed that they had drifted quite close to the point. "Look out, you kids, I'm going to put him over the side."

Carefully, Leo's great brown hands circled the soft body. More quickly than Kate's eyes could follow him, he lifted the baby sea lion into the sea. Instantly it dove, reappearing a few seconds later at a safe distance from the boat.

"I hope its old lady is among that crowd over there," he said. "I got a good hunch she is."

Kate looked at him. No wonder Vic spoke with such pride of this big brother. He had planned all along to bring the little sea lion out here. He had just waited for them to go along, too. Leo was kind. He was kind and good. She liked him. With all her heart, she liked him.

After that, they put about and started back toward the wharf. Just before they got there, Leo cut the motor. The boat's momentum carried them gently up to the float.

"Hey, you kids," Leo called them to him as they were making ready to jump to the float. "Don't say anything about the sea lion up there," jerking his chin toward the row of feet over their heads. "They'd think I was one first-class sap."

"No," promised Vic and Kate together. "We won't."

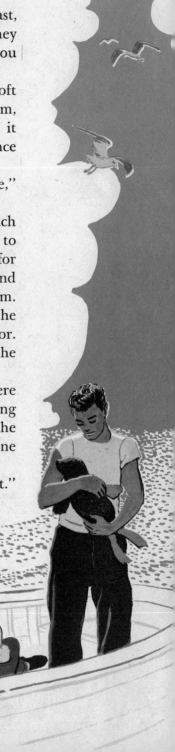

Sweet Potato in My Hand and a Possum by the Tail

Leon Wilson

The boy Cody Capshaw, his father Milt, and his sister Omalia were attending the Old-Time Fiddlers Contest in Liberty Grove, with their friend Uncle Jeff Applegate. Uncle Jeff was a noted fiddler in these mountain parts, and Cody himself had recently learned to fiddle and planned to play in the contest. But the Capshaws' cow, Maud, stung by a particularly large horsefly, had wrecked Cody's homemade fiddle. So Cody had just come along to watch.

After a sizable helping of apple pie with cheese and vanilla ice cream, Cody was ready to push on and hear music. So was Uncle Jeff. "Come on, folks," he said. "Let's slide out of here and get to the courthouse before they give out the prizes."

Omalia had never seen Uncle Jeff so excited. "Why, he's as perky as I was when I passed into the third grade!" she whispered to Milt.

The gay sound of a fiddle reached Omalia's ears when her ears were midway between the Busy Bee Restaurant and the big brick courthouse in the center of the town.

Uncle Jeff heard the music too, and his bow arm began going up and down in time with it. "That's Jack Swaggerty playin' that piece," Uncle Jeff declared, "or my name ain't Jefferson Applegate."

"Good night, you can't see *that* far!" Omalia exclaimed. All she could see, up under the shady trees on the lawn, was a big crowd of mostly men. And all she could see of the men was their backs. Omalia guessed that the man who was fiddling was in the middle of the crowd, with everyone watching him.

"Sugar," Uncle Jeff said, "I don't have to see to know. My ears inform me that's Jack Swaggerty."

Omalia grabbed Uncle Jeff's hand as they reached the crowd. There were so many people around she thought she might get lost. People were even crowding to look out the courthouse windows, two and three floors up. Every tree on the lawn had boys—small boys and some not so small—in its branches.

After a few minutes of following Uncle Jeff around and between folks, Omalia found herself in front of a platform that was handsomely decorated with looping streamers of red, white and blue cloth.

"Told you that was Jack, didn't I?" Uncle Jeff reminded Omalia.

Omalia was so busy noticing everything, she didn't hear Uncle Jeff. Four serious-faced men were on the

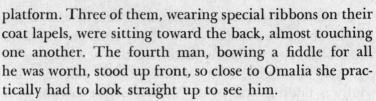

platform. Three of them, wearing special ribbons on their
coat lapels, were sitting toward the back, almost touching
one another. The fourth man, bowing a fiddle for all
he was worth, stood up front, so close to Omalia she prac-
tically had to look straight up to see him.

But now, talk about disappointments! The minute
Omalia got used to looking so high, the man quit playing.

People clapped and cheered. The fiddler nodded and
grinned. Omalia liked the way his gold teeth sparkled.

One of the three men with the ribbons on now began
standing. It seemed to Omalia he got taller and taller,
and thinner and thinner, till he was the tallest man she
had ever seen. Then he spoke. "You just had the treat
of hearin' Contestant Number Four, Jack Swaggerty,
the pride of Sequatchie County," he announced in a dry,
buzzing sort of voice that sounded to Omalia like someone
sawing the end off a plank.

"Them three are the judges," Uncle Jeff whispered.
"The one talkin' is Jim Lowdermilk."

When Mr. Lowdermilk stepped forward and put his
hands on the railing and leaned over it and looked down
at Omalia, she wondered if he was going to snap in two,
he was so exceedingly slender. To her amazement, Mr.
Lowdermilk gave her a big solemn wink. Then he said
to the crowd in that wood-sawing voice, "We're favored
with a delegation from Cumberland Mountain. That's
fine. That's lovely. The way we want it. Folks bringin'
their music from the earth's four corners. We'll hear the
next contestant now, for we got a big wash to hang."

"That's Jim's way of telling us there's lots of fiddlers,"
Uncle Jeff explained.

A fat man, fanning himself with his hat, pulled himself

together a little and invited Omalia to sit on the end of the bench he mostly occupied. After Omalia sat, she looked for Cody and Milt and saw them standing not far off. Up to now, the contest had been too exciting for Omalia to think about them.

Omalia thought that Cody's eyes, as he watched the doings on the platform, would hardly have been brighter looking at a Christmas tree. She began to feel gloomy remembering the dreadful picture of Cody's fiddle hanging on Maud's horn. She was beginning to understand, now, how much taking part in this contest would have meant to Cody.

Uncle Jeff nudged Omalia. "See the one with the ear trumpet? He's Denvil McDermott."

Omalia, looking where Uncle Jeff pointed, saw that one of the judges, a little man with a chubby face and the merriest eyes, had the end of a horn stuck in his ear.

"What's he doin' that for?" she wanted to know.

"That helps Denvil catch what's goin' on," Uncle Jeff

said. "He's listened to so much fiddle music for so many years, he's wore the edge off his hearin'."

Omalia didn't know whether this was a joke or not. When Uncle Jeff said, "Deaf or not, Denvil's still the best judge of music in Tennessee," she was glad she hadn't laughed.

"Soapsuds Over the Fence"

Mr. Lowdermilk introduced the next fiddler, George Green of Dripping Spring.

"I reckon I'll try to play you 'Soapsuds Over the Fence,'" Mr. Green said in a little old hard-to-follow whisper of a voice. Almost no one heard him.

"Stronger if you please, Mr. Green," Jim Lowdermilk said.

Omalia watched Mr. Lowdermilk put.something in front of Mr. Green that looked like a hornets' nest on a broomstick. "Try again now," Mr. Lowdermilk said. George Green, looking embarrassed, opened his mouth from here to yonder and boomed out, " 'Soapsuds Over the Fence.' "

This time, a man with what looked like a telephone set covering his ears jumped up at one side of the platform and flapped his hands up and down.

"I reckon we got you *too* strong that time," Mr. Lowdermilk said. Everyone laughed, and poor Mr. Green squirmed. "What's it all about?" Omalia wanted to know.

"I could be mistaken," Uncle Jeff whispered, "but I *believe* they're broadcastin' this here jamboree over the radio."

"It's a fact they are," the fat man sitting beside Omalia said. "I could have sat home and heard every note of this.

I could have had my comfort and let somebody else have all these seats."

Omalia watched Jim Lowdermilk adjust the microphone to suit Mr. Green's peculiar voice. Then she heard him say, "Let's just hear the name of your piece once again, if you don't mind—not too loud, not too soft."

Mr. Green looked as embarrassed as a duck in a mud puddle. "I done already talked so much about that piece, I lost interest in playin' it," he said. "I'm going to play you 'Buckin' Mule in Cumberland Gap' instead."

"Rear back and let him buck!" cried a small barefooted boy sitting in a tree almost over Omalia's head.

Mr. Green began playing and Omalia believed she was hearing, not one, but two fiddles. "George is a double-noted player," Uncle Jeff explained. "That is, he covers two strings at once and makes about twice the music we ordinary fellows make."

When George Green finished "Buckin' Mule," he played two more numbers, "Billy in the Low Ground" and "Way Down Yonder." When he finished, the crowd went wild with delight. The fat man beside Omalia yelled, "Hurrah for Drippin' Spring!"

Jim Lowdermilk stepped forward again and said in that sawing voice Omalia liked so much, "Them sweet strains you all enjoyed were rendered by Contestant Number Five, Mr. George Green. I now take pleasure in presenting our oldest contestant—"

Mr. Lowdermilk went on talking. That is, Omalia could see his mouth opening and shutting. But she couldn't hear a word he was saying because the crowd began shouting, "Come on Bart! We want Bart!"

The little boy in the tree over Omalia's head nearly fell, he got so excited. Uncle Jeff clapped his hands. The fat man clapped and whistled and stomped.

Mr. Lowdermilk didn't seem to mind being interrupted. In fact, he grinned and nodded as he waved his lanky hands toward the side of the platform where the steps were. Coming up, fiddle and bow in hand, was the oldest man Omalia guessed she had ever seen. He was so old he made Uncle Jeff look like a schoolboy.

"Mr. Bartley Golightly from Mossy Ledge!" Jim Lowdermilk shouted. The crowd clapped and cheered.

Omalia had to laugh, the two men made such a funny picture. Jim Lowdermilk was so tall and thin. Mr. Golightly, as round as a dumpling, was hardly half as tall. And though Mr. Golightly's round smooth head didn't have a hair on it, he was an exceptionally hairy man. It was all on his jaw and neck, ear to ear—the longest, thickest, whitest beard Omalia had ever seen.

When Mr. Golightly sat down, he put his fiddle on his knees, took a comb from his pocket, and neatly parted his beard in two equal halves.

"What in the world is he doin' that for?" Omalia had to know.

"Just you wait—you'll see," Uncle Jeff whispered.

Mr. Golightly picked up half his silky beard and tossed it over his right shoulder. Then he lifted the other half and tossed it over his left shoulder.

"You *got* to tell me, Uncle Jeff," Omalia whispered.

Uncle Jeff began, "Bart does that because—"

But at the same time, Jim Lowdermilk opened up again. Said he, "I see numbers of young people here who have not been with us in years past."

Omalia, looking up, saw that Mr. Lowdermilk was looking smack at her! Then he turned his lanky face in Cody's direction. Then at some of the boys in the trees.

"I'd like to tell these youngsters," Mr. Lowdermilk buzzed on, "that Bart Golightly has been fiddling a long, long time. Can any of you small ones tell me who the seventeenth president of the United States was?"

Omalia began counting, using fingers. About the time she reached Martin Van Buren, Cody put his hand up. He said in a loud voice, "It's whoever's next after Abe Lincoln."

"Andrew Johnson!" cried another boy.

"Andrew Johnson, the tailor of Greeneville, Tennessee," Jim Lowdermilk said, looking pleased because his

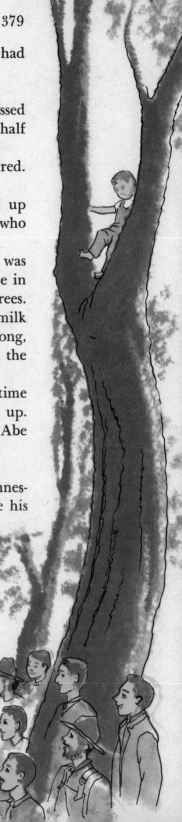

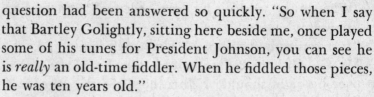

question had been answered so quickly. "So when I say that Bartley Golightly, sitting here beside me, once played some of his tunes for President Johnson, you can see he is *really* an old-time fiddler. When he fiddled those pieces, he was ten years old."

Omalia began figuring, trying to see how old this made Mr. Golightly. Mr. Lowdermilk came to everybody's rescue by saying, "So that means our fiddlin' friend is ninety-three years old."

Some man in the crowd called out good-naturedly, "Think you're going to win this year, Bart?"

The little old man smiled between the halves of his beard. "Bless your heart," he said, "I'm fixin' to try for all I'm worth."

While the crowd laughed, Omalia poked Uncle Jeff. "Why does he do that to his whiskers?"

"Don't you see?" Uncle Jeff said. "So they won't interfere with his music."

When Omalia looked at Mr. Golightly again, he had his fiddle and bow up ready to play in the space left clear by the removal of his beard.

"Name your first tune for us, Bart," Jim Lowdermilk said.

"Well," said the old man, "that Mr. Green that was up here a minute ago said he'd play 'Soapsuds Over the Fence' and then he never done it. I believe I'll pitch 'em over for you."

An Ill Wind

And down went the old man's bow, full of dash and drive. Omalia thought this was about the best fiddling she had ever heard. But the trouble was, the music lasted about twenty-five notes and then something unexpected happened. A little old summer breeze blowing through Liberty Grove picked just this minute to whip around the corner of the courthouse and set the leaves of all the trees tinkling. It blew the two halves of Mr. Golightly's beard off his shoulders. One minute the old man was making music. The next minute his beard was so absolutely snarled with his bow and fiddle he couldn't move either one of them.

The crowd gasped and moaned. Tongues clucked in sympathy. The three judges clustered around Mr. Golightly and tried to untangle him. The breeze, however, had done an excellent job.

"Friends," Jim Lowdermilk said, his face as long as a carrot. "Sure saddens me to say it, but I got to inform you Contestant Number Six is plumb out of commission. We'll have to move on now and hear from our next and final contestant, Number Seven."

As Omalia watched poor Mr. Golightly struggling with his whiskers, she said, "Oh, dear!" For the old man had begun to cry. Omalia could see the tears running down his face. "It's so sad," she said, watching the three judges lift Mr. Golightly right in his chair and carry him off the platform—chair, fiddle, bow, whiskers, and all.

"Yeah, it's sad," the fat man agreed. "But old Bart's had this trouble before. He ought to tied weights on them fly-about whiskers and kept them back out of his way. A man as old as he is ought to have that much sense."

Omalia, looking over by the corner of the courthouse, could see Mr. Golightly's friends and family gathering to untangle him. "I guess I know exactly how bad that poor man feels," she said to herself. "He can't be a bit

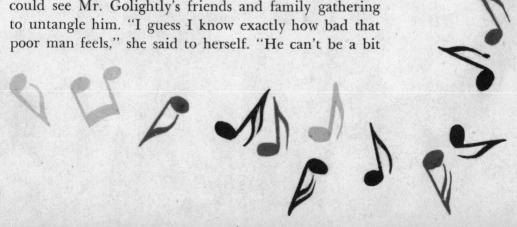

happier than my brother Cody when Maud put him out of commission."

"Presenting Contestant Number Seven," said Jim Lowdermilk. "Mr. Jefferson Applegate of Cumberland Mountain."

Hearing this, Omalia forgot about Mr. Golightly and looked back at the platform in a hurry. Sure enough, there stood Uncle Jeff. He stepped to the railing and asked the crowd a question. "Will you think little of me if I take my coat off?"

The crowd said no in a variety of ways. "Take it off and throw it away!" cried a boy in one of the trees.

Uncle Jeff grinned and handed Mr. Lowdermilk his fiddle and bow so he could make himself comfortable.

"Wow!" exclaimed the fat man. "Your friend Applegate sure makes a colorful picture, don't he?"

Omalia giggled. What the fat man said was true. With his green trousers, pink-striped shirt, blue arm garters, and that dot-and-stripe tie that made Omalia's eyes almost cross, Uncle Jeff looked a good deal like an Easter rabbit.

"I'll try to play you the first tune my granddaddy ever taught me," Uncle Jeff told the crowd. "I been playin' it sixty-four years and haven't wearied of it yet. It's that old 'Cacklin' Hen.'"

Omalia hopped with delight, for this piece was her favorite. She had spasms every time Uncle Jeff made the biddy cluck and squawk. When Uncle Jeff finished the piece, she wore her hands out clapping for him.

Uncle Jeff fiddled two more pieces. First, "Injun Et the Woodcock." The tune went so fast that Omalia could hardly see the bow shooting up and down.

The fat man said, "That's a better number than his first one. Got more move to it."

Uncle Jeff's third piece was "Doc and Sally." He felt so good as he played it, stamping his feet, that he sang a stanza and made everyone laugh. Folks cheered and whooped and there were cries of "Give Applegate the prize!"

Omalia looked at her brother. Cody was applauding as hard as he could. He was grinning from ear to ear.

When the crowd got quiet again, Jim Lowdermilk said, "We judges have been studying the wind conditions and we unanimously agree that the man from Mossy Ledge is entitled to another try."

Well, Omalia and everyone else looked over where the steps were. Here came Mr. Golightly all over again, smiling as if nothing had gone amiss. *This* time, his troublesome beard was already parted and back of his shoulders.

"Got it fixed good, Bart?" someone in the crowd asked.

The old man said, "My little great-granddaughter taken care of me. She said I ought to have no more trouble." He turned around. Omalia and about eighty

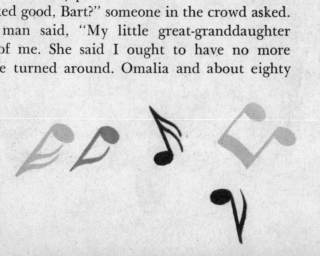

more people took the giggles, for the two ends of Mr.
Golightly's beard were tied together with his great-granddaughter's pink hair ribbon!

"I believe I can now safely undertake that piece I tried
before and didn't finish," Mr. Golightly said. He began
"Soapsuds Over the Fence."

It was lovely music. Much as Omalia doted on Uncle
Jeff's "Cacklin' Hen," she admired Mr. Golightly's
"Soapsuds" more. Seemed to Omalia that Mr. Golightly
was outfiddling everybody. Mr. Golightly played two
more numbers, "Soldier's Joy" and "Cripple Creek." And
then the great Fourth of July contest was over.

Jim Lowdermilk's face was one of the longest in sight,
and there were dozens of long ones. "I know we'd all be
happy stayin' on till dark, listenin' to this rare treat,"
Mr. Lowdermilk told the crowd. "But lots of us got

cows to milk and chickens to feed and pigs to tend and wood to fetch." He shook his head sadly.

A Fiddler After All

"Accordin' to what Jeff Applegate tells me," Mr. Lowdermilk went on, "we got another fiddler you'd enjoy hearing. While we're making up our minds about the prizes, I'm going to ask Mr. Cody Capshaw to step on the platform."

When Omalia heard this, she got such a lump of excitement in her throat she nearly choked. She looked around for Cody. Milt was standing alone.

Then she looked at the platform. Sure enough, there was Cody, looking only about twenty-four inches high as he stood beside long Mr. Lowdermilk.

"He's my brother," Omalia informed the fat man. But she was so excited she didn't say it loud enough. The fat man asked Cody a question. "Youngster," he said, "I see you got a bow. Where's the rest of your outfit?"

"Our cow ruined it," Cody said. Cody didn't intend this answer to be a joke. When folks finished laughing, he said seriously, "What I told you is true. I made me a fiddle and yesterday our cow put it on like a fancy hat. I'd be proud to play you-all a tune, but I'll have to ask one of you musicians to lend me something to play it on."

Mr. Lowdermilk handed Cody a fiddle that someone had passed him. "Loan me your rosin a minute, Mr. Green, if you'll be so obligin'," Cody said.

George Green, standing next to Milt, handed Cody a chunk of rosin through the railing. Cody began scooting his bow over it. "Reckon I'll play you 'Old Joe Clark,'" he said.

Cody hadn't fiddled many notes before the boys in the trees began cheering. "He's sure got it!" one of them hollered. "Come on, Capshaw!" another one cried.

Cody dragged his bow like he was dragging a log chain over a hill. He stomped the beat so you could hear him half a block away. And he opened up and sang:

> *"I wish I was in Arkansas*
> *Sittin' on a rail,*
> *Sweet potato in my hand*
> *And a possum by the tail.*
> *Fare you well, Old Joe Clark,*
> *Fare you well, I'm gone;*
> *Fare you well, Old Joe Clark,*
> *Good-by Betsy Brown!"*

When Cody finished, the crowd went wild. "Play it over again!" someone shouted. "Give us 'Alabama Gals.'" "Play 'Fire on the Mountain, Run, Boys, Run.'" "How about 'Sourwood Mountain'?"

Everybody wanted another tune. Jim Lowdermilk gave Cody the go-ahead sign, so Cody put up his bow and did his best to please.

Cody finished his second piece and Mr. Lowdermilk had to raise his hands and beg for quiet. "Going to say the name of this fiddler again," he told the crowd. "I want you to remember it. Cody Capshaw of Cumberland Mountain."

Then Mr. Lowdermilk said unexpectedly, "I'm going to ask this young man's sister if she also plays." Whereupon, he looked over the railing and in that buzz-saw voice asked gently, "Miss Capshaw, do you play?"

"N-no sir!" Omalia stammered, wishing she could

quickly turn into a beetle under a leaf so no one could see her.

Mr. Lowdermilk's face became extra long. "Oh, too bad," he said. "Maybe your brother will teach you so you can play for us next Fourth of July."

"Yes, sir," Omalia said. "The next time my brother says 'frog' I'm going to jump."

The fat man and Mr. Lowdermilk laughed and Mr. Lowdermilk said to the crowd, "I'm going to repeat that remark so you can all hear it. Mr. Capshaw's young sister says the next time her brother says 'frog' she's going to jump."

Everyone rocked with laughter. Omalia wished she hadn't said it. She felt so foolish with everyone laughing at her.

"Before we turn Mr. Capshaw loose," Mr. Lowdermilk went on, "I believe many people would like to ask him the same question that occurs to me. And that is—" Mr. Lowdermilk lowered his chin to look down at Cody. "How come you're such an expert? I believe these young people here and the ones listening on the radio would be interested. All right, sir, let's hear."

Cody grabbed his hair and tugged it to help himself think. He also gulped. Also, he worked his toes in his shiny shoes. You see, Cody didn't know *why* he was a fiddler. He figured he might hit on the reason if he started talking, so he said, "Well, I reckon having a teacher like Uncle Jeff is better than half of it. And I reckon the rest of it is havin' a natural craving for music."

Omalia thought Cody's answer wasn't much account, though she couldn't think of a better one. Mr. Lowdermilk, however, was delighted. "A natural craving for

music," he repeated. "Mr. Capshaw, saying that puts you right in with these big fellows like Applegate and Bart Golightly and George Green."

The judges were now ready to announce the winners. Denvil McDermott, the one with the ear trumpet, did the talking. "Been judging this affair since 1927," he said in a dry, crumpling-paper sort of voice, "and truly believe we never have had the talent we've heard today. In 1932 I sat here and watched Clyde Skinner hold his fiddle upside down and draw sweet strains from it. In 1943 I heard Jerry Cooke play left-handed. Three years ago the best man was Marlin Thomas playin' that cigar-box fiddle. But ladies and gents, girls and boys, today's bunch of fiddlers is the best yet."

Mr. McDermott was a happy man. He consulted the paper in his hand. "Now the prizes, and we'll all go home and be back here one year from today, rain or shine." Mr. McDermott began reading from his paper, "For top-notch double-note playing, third prize to George Green. For general all-around excellence, second prize to Jefferson Applegate. For being the best beginner we judges have heard in years, special honorable mention to Cody Capshaw. And for being the finest and longest-playing fiddler in Tennessee, first prize to Bart Golightly."

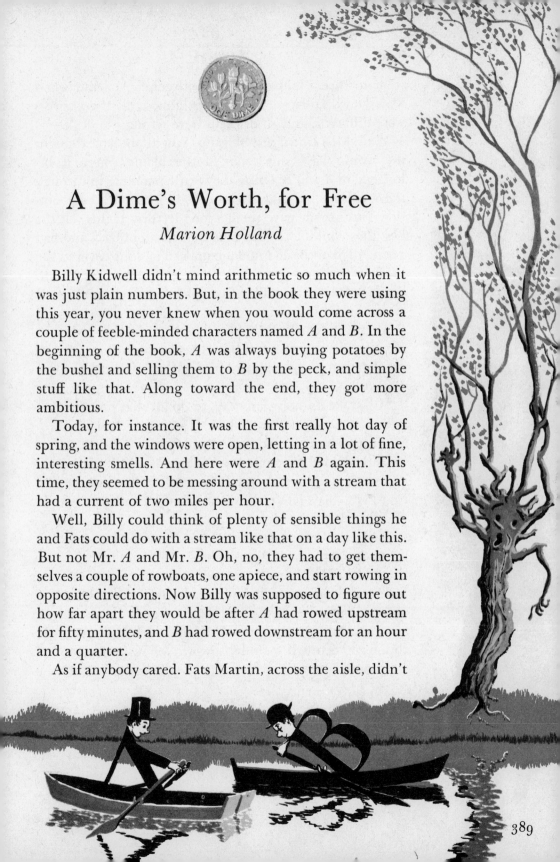

A Dime's Worth, for Free

Marion Holland

Billy Kidwell didn't mind arithmetic so much when it was just plain numbers. But, in the book they were using this year, you never knew when you would come across a couple of feeble-minded characters named *A* and *B*. In the beginning of the book, *A* was always buying potatoes by the bushel and selling them to *B* by the peck, and simple stuff like that. Along toward the end, they got more ambitious.

Today, for instance. It was the first really hot day of spring, and the windows were open, letting in a lot of fine, interesting smells. And here were *A* and *B* again. This time, they seemed to be messing around with a stream that had a current of two miles per hour.

Well, Billy could think of plenty of sensible things he and Fats could do with a stream like that on a day like this. But not Mr. *A* and Mr. *B*. Oh, no, they had to get themselves a couple of rowboats, one apiece, and start rowing in opposite directions. Now Billy was supposed to figure out how far apart they would be after *A* had rowed upstream for fifty minutes, and *B* had rowed downstream for an hour and a quarter.

As if anybody cared. Fats Martin, across the aisle, didn't

seem to care. Neither did anybody else. At least, when Miss Dowd collected the papers, almost all the answers were different, and all of them were wrong.

Well, Miss Dowd just blew up. You might have thought she would have put some of the blame where it belonged, on *A* and *B*. Or on the weather coming in through the windows and making everybody just itch to get outside. But no, she gave them a long lecture. If this was the best they could do, it was time they all went back and had a good drill on Basic Fundamentals. Then she covered the whole front blackboard with long columns of figures, to be copied down and added up for homework and turned in tomorrow morning.

At three o'clock, Billy and Fats left school together in silence. The sun was still hot. The breeze still smelled of wet dirt and plum trees in bloom. But the whole day was ruined.

"It'll take an hour, anyway, to do all that homework," said Billy finally, aiming a kick at a stone.

"Or two hours," said Fats gloomily.

Billy folded his homework paper as small as possible and stuck it in his jacket. His fingers found a dime he had forgotten. "Say, let's go down to Schultz's and get a couple of dill pickles," he said.

"Or jelly beans," suggested Fats. Fats had not earned his name on a diet of dill pickles.

Schultz's Delicatessen was cool and dark and smelled of pickles and cinnamon and new magazines. Around the first of the month, there was usually quite a crowd at the magazine rack. For two cents' worth of lemon drops, a fast reader could get through a dollar's worth of magazines in an afternoon.

Today the place was empty. All the magazines were old and limp looking. There wouldn't be any new ones in for at least a week.

"Well, gentlemen, what can I do for you?" asked Mr. Schultz, the way he always did.

Billy and Fats were still arguing. Dill pickles were two for a dime, but they were six cents apiece. If Billy bought a dill pickle, Fats would only have four cents left for jelly beans.

Then the phone rang, and Mr. Schultz answered it. After a minute, Billy and Fats quit arguing to listen. Mr. Schultz's red face got redder and redder. He shouted so loud they couldn't understand one word he was saying, except that it was about Emil. Emil was Mr. Schultz's grandson, who drove the delivery truck. Mr. Schultz slammed the phone down and groaned.

"What's the matter?" asked Billy in alarm. "Is Emil sick?"

"No!" roared Mr. Schultz. "But he will be, when I get hold of him! Twice already he parks the truck by a fireplug, and the police warn him. Now he does it again, and they take him to the station house. So now I got to go pay the fine before they let him go. If I don't go, who makes the afternoon deliveries? Nobody, that's who!" He threw his white apron on the floor, and jammed his hat on the back of his head.

"So hurry up!" he shouted. "Pickles or jelly beans, make up your minds. I got to lock up."

"Jelly beans," said Billy hastily. Mr. Schultz weighed them out, rang up the dime on the cash register, and shooed them toward the door.

It was then that Billy had his big idea. "Look, Mr.

Schultz," he said eagerly, "we'll mind the store for you. I bet we know the price of everything in here. Don't we, Fats?"

"We ought to," mumbled Fats, his mouth full of jelly beans.

Mr. Schultz rubbed his nose and looked doubtful.

"What's the matter?" asked Billy. "Don't you trust us with your money?"

"Sure, sure," said Mr. Schultz. "I know you boys. With my money I trust you, like my own self. But . . ." His eyes swept doubtfully over the candy bars and salted peanuts, over the glass case of pickles and spiced ham and cheese. "All right," he said finally. "And look, when I get back, I give you a dime's worth for free, each, anything you want. But not till I get back—O.K.?"

"O. K.," they agreed, and Mr. Schultz hurried out.

"A dime's worth for free!" cried Fats. "Come on. Let's pick it out."

But Billy headed straight for the cash register. "We got to hurry," he said. "Somebody might come in."

Billy Rings the Bell

Fats' round pink face turned pale. "Hey," he said hoarsely. "Have you gone crazy? What you doing?"

"Homework," replied Billy, pulling the paper out of his pocket. "Look here. You punch the keys for each number. After you punch off the whole problem, you punch the key marked Total, and the answer jumps up, all added up. See?"

Fats saw. "Hot diggety." he remarked in awe. "But it comes out in dollars and cents. What about that?"

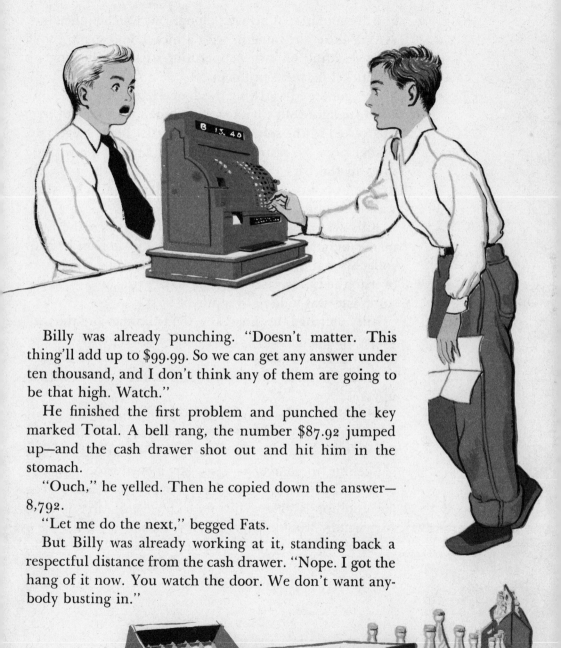

Billy was already punching. "Doesn't matter. This thing'll add up to $99.99. So we can get any answer under ten thousand, and I don't think any of them are going to be that high. Watch."

He finished the first problem and punched the key marked Total. A bell rang, the number $87.92 jumped up—and the cash drawer shot out and hit him in the stomach.

"Ouch," he yelled. Then he copied down the answer—8,792.

"Let me do the next," begged Fats.

But Billy was already working at it, standing back a respectful distance from the cash drawer. "Nope. I got the hang of it now. You watch the door. We don't want anybody busting in."

Billy got faster as he went along. Fats watched the door. A very little girl came in with a nickel, and spent a long time deciding on two peppermint sticks. Billy rang up the nickel between problems.

Fats got bored watching the door. He wandered around, trying to figure out what to take a dime's worth of, for free. He looked in the soft drink cooler—root beer, ginger ale, orange pop. No raspberry. He poked among the wooden cases in the back, where Mr. Schultz kept the pop. He dragged up a couple of empties to stand on, to see what was in the top case.

Billy was ringing up the last problem when the little man came in. In spite of the heat, the little man had his collar turned up, and his hands in his pockets. He drifted over to the candy case and glanced toward the rear of the store. Fats was hidden by a pile of boxes.

Billy punched the Total key, the bell rang, and the cash drawer popped open. Billy reached for his pencil to copy down the last answer.

"Leave it open, kid," said a gruff voice. "This is a stick-up, see?"

It was just like the movies. With one hand still in his pocket, the man reached across and scooped all the bills out of the cash drawer. It seemed to Billy that this must be happening to somebody else. He looked around for a weapon, but there was nothing within reach but a glass jar of lollipops. "Hey," he said feebly, "you can't do that. Mr. Schultz wouldn't like it. Hey, Fats!"

"Shuddup," snarled the little man as if he meant it. Billy shut up. Fats, balanced on a pile of boxes with a bottle of raspberry pop in each hand, heard his name and looked

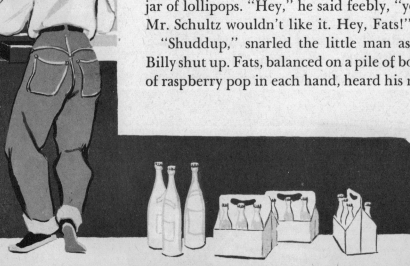

toward the front of the store. The sight that met his eyes unbalanced him completely. The boxes shifted under his feet, and he let go of one bottle to grab for support. The bottle hit the cement floor and exploded. With a yell, Fats dropped the other bottle. The two explosions echoed like gunshots.

The little man whirled to face the rear of the store. "Drop that gun!" he shouted. "I got you covered!"

This was too much for Fats. He lost his balance and fell, bringing down with him a cascade of pop bottles. It sounded like machine-gun fire, and the howl of anguish and surprise that Fats let out when he hit the floor sounded like nothing human.

The hold-up man turned and ran for the front door. With great presence of mind, Billy threw the glass jar of lollipops at his retreating back. It missed and shattered against the side of the door, just as the door opened and Mr. Schultz and Emil and Officer Maloney walked in. The hold-up man plunged head first into Officer Maloney's wide blue middle.

"Look out!" yelled Billy. "He's got a gun!"

Everything was pretty confused for a few minutes. Mr. Schultz was wringing his hands and shouting, "What's going on here?" Billy was explaining that it was a stick-up. Officer Maloney had handcuffs on the man and was going through his pockets, pulling out a gun and one-dollar bills

and five-dollar bills and ten-dollar bills. And every time people moved, their feet scrunched on broken glass and lollipops.

Right in the middle of it, Fats staggered up to the front of the store with his shirt front all red, and red drops splattering from the tips of his fingers.

"Get a doctor!" roared Mr. Schultz. "He's shot!"

"Am I?" asked Fats faintly, and held up one dripping hand. He licked a finger. "No, it's raspberry pop."

"My raspberry pop," groaned Mr. Schultz, noticing the mess in the back of the store for the first time.

A Couple of Heroes

Billy and Fats were pretty pleased when Emil had to stay and clean up the wreckage. They were witnesses and had to go with Mr. Schultz and Officer Maloney and the prisoner to the station house. There, they had to tell the whole story over and over. People kept interrupting to ask questions, while the sergeant at the desk wrote it all down. In the end, somehow, the sergeant seemed to get the idea that Fats had exploded the bottles on purpose to scare the holdup man away, and that Billy had kept him from making a getaway by stunning him with the jar of lollipops.

Even Mr. Schultz seemed to think that they had done all right. Pretty soon they began to think so too.

"Hey, how does it feel to be a hero?" whispered Billy to Fats.

Billy was anxious to get home and start acting like a hero. But suddenly Fats had to remember the dime's worth,

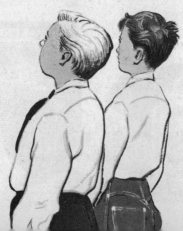

for free, that they never got. So when Mr. Schultz and Officer Maloney went back to the delicatessen, they went along, too.

Billy and Fats looked over the shelves and counters while Mr. Schultz checked the cash register with Officer Maloney. They could hear Mr. Schultz start to splutter. But they didn't pay any attention until Officer Maloney called to them.

"Looks as if you boys did a pretty brisk business here while Mr. Schultz was gone," he said, looking at them in a rather peculiar fashion.

"No, sir," said Billy. "Just one nickel's worth of peppermint sticks."

"Then how does it happen that the total on the register shows that somebody sold $6,948.72 worth of merchandise today?" asked Officer Maloney.

Well, then it all came out. Billy showed them the homework paper, and explained how he had just taken a short cut on the arithmetic homework. "Gosh, sir," he said, squirming. "I never knew the register kept a total of *all* the numbers rung up on it."

Officer Maloney just looked at them for a long, long time. While he was looking, they began to feel less and less like heroes, and more natural.

Finally, he said, "Mr. Schultz has to know how much money ought to be in the register, in order to make sure that he gets the right amount back again. Ordinarily, he could tell by adding the amount he knows was there last night to the amount the tape says he sold today. I can think of only one way to get this straightened out. You boys take that homework paper, and add together the answers to all the problems. Then take that total, and subtract it from the amount shown on the register tape. Check your answers with each other. Keep on until you are sure you have them correct."

He got them each a pencil and a big sheet of paper, and pulled two chairs up to the candy counter. "And when you are quite finished," he said cheerfully, "Mr. Schultz will be delighted to give you each a dime's worth of anything, for free."

"Yes, sir," said Billy and Fats. They sat down and started to work.

"Hey, how does it feel to be a hero?" whispered Fats to Billy.

Glossary

This glossary, or small dictionary, contains the more unusual words from the stories in this book. Usually, only the meaning is given which fits the word the first time it is used. The "key" at the bottom of the pages helps to show how each word is pronounced. The regular dictionary should be used to find meanings of other words you find difficult, or other meanings for the words given here.

A

a·ban'don (a·băn'dŭn). Carefree manner.

a·bash' (a·băsh'). To shame or embarrass.

ab·rupt' (ăb·rŭpt'). Short, sudden.

ac·com'mo·da'tion (a·kŏm'ô·dā'shŭn). Lodgings; room and board.

ac·cus'tomed [to] (a·kŭs'tŭmd). Used or adjusted [to].

ad·just' (a·jŭst'). To set just right; to make something work at its best.

af'fa·ble (ăf'a·b'l). Mild and kindly; sociable.

af·fec'tion·ate (a·fĕk'shŭn·ĭt). Warm and friendly, loving.

af·firm' (a·fûrm'). To say firmly, to assert.

ag'o·ny (ăg'ô·nĭ). Great pain or suffering.

al'der (ôl'dĕr). One of several shrubs and trees of the birch family.

al'ti·tude (ăl'tĭ·tūd). Height, elevation.

am'ple (ăm'p'l). Abundant.

an'guish (ăng'gwĭsh). Severe pain.

an·tic'i·pa'tion (ăn·tĭs'ĭ·pā'shŭn). Act of looking forward to something, usually with pleasure.

ant'ler (ănt'lĕr). Horn of a deer.

a·ro'ma (a·rō'ma). Pleasant smell.

as·cend' (a·sĕnd'). To mount or climb.

as·sume' (a·sūm'). To pretend to have, to put on.

as·trol'o·ger (ăs·trŏl'ô·jĕr). Person who tells fortunes by the stars.

aught (ôt). Anything.

aus·pi'cious (ôs·pĭsh'ŭs). Promising success, favorable.

au'to·mat'ic (ô'tô·măt'ĭk). Done without thought or plan; self-acting, as a machine.

B

bal'last (băl'ast). Anything heavy put in the bottom of a ship to steady it.

bam·boo' (băm·boo'). A kind of woody, tropical grass used for fishpoles, canes, etc.

bar'ley (bär'lĭ). A kind of grain.

bar'ri·er (băr'ĭ·ēr). Fence to prevent attack by an enemy.

bar'ter (bär'tĕr). To trade or exchange.

bas'ic fun'da·men'tals (bās'ĭk fŭn'da·mĕn'tălz). Simple but very important steps or processes; knowledge or skills one must have mastered before he can do real work of any kind.

bask (bask). To lie contentedly in the warmth of the sun.

ā, āte; a, furnace; ă, ăt; a, appear; â, câre; ä, cär; a, pass; a, sofa; ē, bē; ê, bĕgin; ĕ, lĕt; ĕ, silĕnt; ē, watĕr; ē, hēre; ī, hīde; ĭ, hĭd; ĭ, cabĭn; ō, hōpe; ô, ômit; ŏ, hŏp; ŏ, cŏntain; ô, ôr; ô, sôft; oo, food; oo, foot; oi, oil; ou, out; ū, ūse; û, ûnite; ŭ, ŭs; û, circŭs; û, fûr; tu, nature; du, verdure; th, thin; th, than.

baste (bāst). To sew with long, loose stitches in order to get a good fit before sewing in permanent form.

bat'ter (băt'ẽr). Cake or muffin dough.

ba·zaar' (bȧ·zär'). Asiatic outdoor market place.

be·deck' (bė·děk'). To adorn or decorate.

be·drag'gle (bė·drăg''l). To make wet and dirty as if by dragging on the ground.

be·fall' (bė·fôl'). To happen.

bel'fry (běl'frĭ). Tower for a bell.

be·stow' [on] (bė·stō'). To give.

bide (bīd). To wait for; to remain in a place.

bilge wa'ter (bĭlj wô'tẽr). Water in the bottom of a boat.

bil'low (bĭl'ō). A wave.

bit'tern (bĭt'ẽrn). Kind of heron or marsh bird.

blank (blăngk). Appearing dazed or confused.

blend (blĕnd). To mix.

blithe (blīth). Gay, cheerful.

blub'ber (blŭb'ẽr). To weep noisily.

bod'ice (bŏd'ĭs). Girl's laced garment, like a jacket, but tight-fitting.

boun'ty (boun'tĭ). Cash reward for killing harmful animals.

bra'ces (brās'ĕz). Suspenders.

bra'zier (brā'zhẽr). Pan for holding burning coals.

brief case (brēf kās). Flat leather bag for carrying unfolded papers.

brink (brĭngk). Edge, bank.

bro·cade' (brȯ·kād'). Cloth with a raised design woven of silk, silver, or gold thread.

by'play' (bī'plā'). Action apart from the main events.

C

cac'tus (kăk'tŭs). One of various desert plants usually having spines or thorns but no leaves.

ca·lam'i·ty (kȧ·lăm'ĭ·tĭ). Deep distress or misfortune.

can'ny (kăn'ĭ). Cautious.

can'o·py (kăn'ȯ·pĭ). Covering carried on poles over a person of high rank, or fixed above a throne or a bed.

car'a·van (kăr'ȧ·văn). Group of merchants traveling together for safety through dangerous places.

car'cass (kär'kȧs). Dead body of an animal, especially when cleaned or dressed as food.

cas·cade' (kăs·kād'). Small waterfall.

case'ment (kās'měnt). Window on hinges, opening like a door.

cas'u·al (kăzh'ů·ăl). Happening by chance, not planned.

cav'al·ry (kăv'ăl·rĭ). Soldiers who fight on horseback.

cham'ber·lain (chām'bẽr·lĭn). King's attendant, high official in a king's court.

chant'ey (shăn'tĭ). Song which sailors sing as they work.

chasm (kăz'm). Canyon, gorge.

cin'na·mon (sĭn'ȧ·mŭn). A spice made from the bark of a tropical tree.

clam'ber (klăm'bẽr). To climb, using both hands and feet.

ā, āte; â, furnȧce; ă, ăt; ȧ, ȧppear; â, câre; ä, cär; ȧ, pȧss; ȧ, sofȧ; ē, bē; ė, bėgin; ĕ, lĕt; ẽ, silẽnt; ē, watẽr; ẹ, hẹre; ī, hīde; ĭ, hĭd; ĭ, cabĭn; ō, hōpe;

clout (klout). Target in archery.

cob′ble (kŏb″l). To make a road surface of round stones; to mend or repair.

cock′a·too′ (kŏk′a̲·tōō′). Australian parrot.

cod′dle (kŏd″l). To treat with too much kindness.

colo′nel (kûr′nĕl). Army officer just below brigadier general in rank.

come′ly (kŭm′lĭ). Pleasing to the sight.

com′i·cal (kŏm′ĭ·kăl). Amusing, laughable.

com·pact′ (kŏm·păkt′). Crowded closely together.

com′pli·ments (kŏm′plĭ·mĕntz). Formal greeting.

con′jure [up] (kŭn′jẽr). To imagine, see with the mind.

con′ster·na′tion (kŏn′stẽr·nā′shŭn). Dismay, terror.

con·test′ant (kŏn·tĕs′tănt). Person who competes or contends with another, as for a prize.

con·tract′ (kŏn·trăkt′). To grow shorter or tighter.

con′trite (kŏn′trīt). Very sorry or repentant.

con·vic′tion (kŏn·vĭk′shŭn). Firm belief, fixed opinion.

con·vul′sive (kŏn·vŭl′sĭv). Violent and jerky in movement.

cote (kōt). House or shelter for doves.

cou′lee (kōō′lĭ). Narrow valley or gully with steep sides.

cour′ti·er (kōr′tĭ·ẽr). One who is in attendance at the court of a king.

cow (kou). To fill with fear.

craft′y (kráf′tĭ). Cunning, skillful at deceiving others.

crest (krĕst). Tuft of feathers on the head of some birds.

crisp (krĭsp). Sharp and clear, distinct; also, short and decided.

curd (kûrd). Solid part of sour milk.

cur′ry (kûr′ĭ). To clean a horse with a metal comb.

czar′das (chär′däsh). Hungarian dance.

D

da′is (dā′ĭs). Raised platform for the most important people in a gathering.

daz′zle (dăz″l). To confuse with brilliance or show.

ded′i·cate (dĕd′ĭ·kāt). To give time and energy to some noble purpose; to devote.

deed (dēd). Legal paper naming the owner of a piece of land and stating what rights to its use, if any, other people may have.

de·fend′ant (dė·fĕn′dănt). Person who is being tried in a court of law.

del′e·ga′tion (dĕl′ė·gā′shŭn). Group of people who represent a larger group.

den′im (dĕn′ĭm). Heavy cotton cloth used for work clothes.

des′o·late (dĕs′ô·lĭt). Deserted, and therefore gloomy.

de·test′a·ble (dė·tĕs′ta·b'l). Arousing hate or strong dislike.

de·vo′tion (dė·vō′shŭn). Deep liking, regard, or love.

di·min′u·tive (dĭ·mĭn′u·tĭv). Tiny.

ô, ômit; ŏ, hŏp; ǒ, cǒntain; ô, ôr; ô, sôft; ōō, fōōd; ŏŏ, fŏŏt; oi, oil; ou, out; ū, ūse; û, ûnite; ŭ, ŭs; u̲, circu̲s; û, fûr; tu̲, natu̲re; du̲, verdu̲re; th, thin; ~~th, than~~.

din'ghy (dĭng'gĭ). Small, light rowboat.

dire (dīr). Foretelling trouble.

dis·patch' (dĭs·păch'). Important official message.

dis·play' (dĭs·plā'). To spread out or show in such a way as to attract attention.

dis·suade' (dĭ·swād'). To persuade a person not to do something.

down (doun). Open, grassy upland.

drought (drout). Long period of dry weather, lack of rain.

dum'my (dŭm'ĭ). Not real, not genuine.

E

ea'sel (ē'z'l). Framework or support to hold a picture upright.

em'er·ald (ĕm'ēr·ăld). Green.

en·am'el (ĕn·ăm'ĕl). Smooth, shiny coating for the surface of metal or glass objects.

ep'i·sode (ĕp'ĭ·sōd). A happening or event.

e·rect' (ê·rĕkt'). Straight up and down.

er'mine (ûr'mĭn). Costly white fur of the Arctic weasel.

es·tab'lish (ĕs·tăb'lĭsh). To create and put on a lasting basis, to found.

e·ven'tu·al·ly (ê·vĕn'tu̱·ăl·lĭ). At last, finally.

ex·ceed'ing (ĕk·sēd'ĭng). Unusual, extraordinary.

F

fan'cy (făn'sĭ). To like.

fang (făng). Long, pointed tooth of a snake, dog, or other animal.

fa'tal (fā'tăl). Causing ruin or destruction.

fath'om (făth'ŭm). Sailor's measure of length equal to six feet.

file (fīl). To make written application for ownership of land which the government is offering for sale.

fleck (flĕk). To spot, to dot.

flim'sy (flĭm'zĭ). Not strong, weak.

flour'ish (flûr'ĭsh). To wave or swing about.

for'ward (fôr'wērd). Bold, too eager.

foun'der (foun'dēr). To become filled with water and sink.

fox'glove' (fŏks'glŭv'). Plant with spikes of white or purple flowers.

frag'ile (frăj'ĭl). Frail, weak.

fri'ar (frī'ēr). Member of a Roman Catholic religious order.

friz (frĭz). To form into small curls.

froth (frôth). Foam.

fun'da·men'tals. (See **basic fundamentals.**)

fun'gus (fŭng'gŭs). Leafless plant, like a toadstool or a mushroom, which grows on leafy plants or in rotting material.

furl (fûrl). To fold or roll tightly.

G

gal'le·on (găl'ê·ŭn). Sailing vessel in the time of Columbus.

gape (gāp). To open wide.

gar'land (gär'lănd). Wreath.

gaud'y (gôd'ĭ). Too bright in color.

gen'er·a'tion (jĕn'ēr·ā'shŭn). Group that follows or precedes another age-group through life, as children follow their parents.

ā, āte;   â, furnâce;   ă, ăt;   ă, ăppear;   â, câre;   ä, cär;   a̟, pa̟ss;   a̦, sofa̦;   ē, bē; ê, bêgin;   ĕ, lĕt;   ĕ, silĕnt;   ē, watēr;   ē̦, hē̦re;   ī, hīde;   ĭ, hĭd;   i̦, cabi̦n;   ō, hōpe;

gen′ial (jēn′yăl). Cheerful, kindly.

gid′dy (gĭd′ĭ). Dizzy.

gin′ger·ly (jĭn′jēr·lĭ). Cautiously.

glaze (glāz). To coat with a thin, glassy layer; also, the glassy coating put on pottery.

go′pher (gō′fēr). Small, destructive ground squirrel of the prairies.

gos′sa·mer (gŏs′a·mēr). Cloth very light in weight, as if woven from the threads of a cobweb.

guile (gīl). Clever deceit or treachery.

gul′ly (gŭl′ĭ). Small valley with steep sides cut by a flood.

H

han′ker (hăng′kēr). To want very much.

ha′zel (hā′z'l). Bush or small tree that bears a tasty nut.

heark′en (här′kĕn). To listen, to heed.

her′ald (hĕr′ăld). Person who makes announcements or carries messages.

herb (ûrb). One of several plants used to flavor food.

her′it·age (hĕr′ĭ·tĭj). Birthright; a thing or a right passed on from parents to their children.

hes′i·tant (hĕz′ĭ·tănt). Uncertain, undecided.

ho·ri′zon (hô·rī′z'n). The line where earth and sky seem to meet.

hos′tile (hŏs′tĭl). Unfriendly.

I

il·lu′sion (ĭ·lū′zhŭn). False or deceiving appearance.

im′ple·ment (ĭm′plĕ·mĕnt). Tool.

im′pulse (ĭm′pŭls). Sudden desire or inclination.

in′di·cate (ĭn′dĭ·kāt). To point out.

in·dul′gent (ĭn·dŭl′jĕnt). Not strict; too willing to grant favors.

in′so·lence (ĭn′sô·lĕns). Insulting behavior or speech.

in·spect′ (ĭn·spĕkt′). To examine.

in·tense′ (ĭn·tĕns′). Very much, very great.

J

jab′ber (jăb′ēr). To talk rapidly or in such a manner that another person cannot understand what is said.

jer′kin (jûr′kĭn). Jacket.

ju′bi·lant (jōō′bĭ·lănt). Very happy.

junc′tion (jŭngk′shŭn). Place where two things meet or join.

L

la·goon′ (là·gōōn′). Body of water, usually small and shallow.

la′ma (lä′mȧ). Priest of an Asiatic religion.

lank′y (lăngk′ĭ). Long and thin.

la·pel′ (lȧ·pĕl′). The folded over, front part of a coat collar.

lash (lăsh). To strike violently.

league (lēg). Measure of distance, about three miles.

lee (lē). That side of anything which is sheltered from the wind.

lor′ry (lŏr′ĭ). Large truck.

lust (lŭst). Great desire, longing.

M

mag′pie′ (măg′pī′). Black and white bird related to the jays.

mar′i·ner (măr′ĭ·nēr). Sailor.

ô, ômit; ŏ, hŏp; ȯ, cŏntain; ô, ôr; ộ, sŏft; ōō, fōōd; ŏŏ, fŏŏt; oi, oil; ou, out; ū, ūse; û, ûnite; ŭ, ŭs; u̇, circu̇s; û, fûr; tu̇, natu̇re; du̇, verdu̇re; th, thin; th, ~~th~~an.

ma′tron (mā′trŭn). Motherly woman.

me·dal′lion (mê·dăl′yŭn). Large medal.

mel′low (mĕl′ō). Soft, pure in color, ripe.

mer′chan·dise (mûr′chăn·dīz). To sell goods.

mi′grate (mī′grāt). To go from one region to another as the seasons change, as birds do.

mim′ic (mĭm′ĭk). Imitator.

mirth (mûrth). Laughter and gaiety.

mock′er·y (mŏk′ẽr·ĭ). Scornful, insulting action.

mo·men′tum (mô·mĕn′tŭm). Tendency of any moving object to continue its motion.

mon′as·ter′y (mŏn′ăs·tẽr′ĭ). House where monks live.

mon·soon′ sea′son (mŏn·sōon′ sē′z′n). Period of heavy rains in southern Asia from April to October, when a southwest wind, called the monsoon, blows from the Indian Ocean.

moor (mōor). To fasten with ropes.

mor′ti·fy (môr′tŭ·fī). To make a person feel ashamed.

mot′ley (mŏt′lĭ). Made up of different kinds.

mus′lin (mŭz′lĭn). Fine cotton dress material.

mu′ti·ny (mū′tŭ·nĭ). To refuse to obey orders; to revolt.

N

nav′i·gate (năv′ĭ·gāt). To determine a ship's course by use of a compass or by observation of the stars.

neu′tral (nū′trăl). Being neither a friend nor an enemy.

night′in·gale (nīt′ĭn·gāl). Small European bird famous for its sweet song.

noose (nōos). Loop which binds tighter the more the rope is pulled.

nudge (nŭj). To push gently with the elbow in order to attract attention.

nymph (nĭmf). Minor goddess who appears as a beautiful girl.

O

o·a′sis (ô·ā′sĭs). Fertile spot in a desert, where there is water.

om′i·nous (ŏm′ĭ·nŭs). Threatening, foretelling evil.

O′pen ses′a·me (ō′pĕn sĕs′á·mê). A password which was first used in the story of Ali Baba and the forty thieves.

op′po·site (ŏp′ô·zĭt). As different in direction as can be—as north and south.

P

pack′et (păk′ĕt). Small package.

pan′ic (păn′ĭk). Sudden, terrifying fright.

par′a·chute (păr′á·shōot). Umbrella-shaped device which enables one to fall safely to earth from a great height.

par′al·lel (păr′ă·lĕl). Being the same distance apart at all points and thus never meeting.

par′tial (pär′shăl). Incomplete, not total.

pas′try (pās′trĭ). Food made of a rich dough like piecrust.

pe·des′tri·an (pê·dĕs′trĭ·ăn). A person who is traveling on foot.

per·ceive′ (pẽr·sēv′). To see.

per′il·ous (pĕr′ĭ·lŭs). Dangerous.

ā, āte; á, furnáce; ă, ăt; ă, ăppear; â, câre; ä, cär; á, páss; á, sofá; ē, bē; ê, bêgin; ĕ, lĕt; ĕ, silĕnt; ẽ, watẽr; ę, hęre; ī, hīde; ĭ, hĭd; ĭ, cabĭn; ō, hōpe;

per·sist' (pẽr·sĭst'). To continue in a course of thought or action, to persevere.

pe·ti'tion (pẽ·tĭsh'ŭn). To ask in a serious and formal way.

phos'pho·res'cent (fŏs'fô·rĕs'ĕnt). Glowing, giving off light but not heat.

pil'lar (pĭl'ẽr). Column.

plac'id (plăs'ĭd). Calm.

plain'tive (plān'tĭv). Sad.

ply (plī). To sail over repeatedly.

por'poise (pôr'pŭs). Sea animal somewhat like a small whale; dolphin.

pre·lim'i·nar'y (prė·lĭm'ĭ·nẽr'ĭ). Happening before the main event.

prey (prā). Victim.

pro·claim' (prô·klām'). To announce or declare publicly.

prong (prŏng). Pointed end of an antler, a fork, or a similar object.

prop'er·ty (prŏp'ẽr·tĭ). Characteristic quality or power.

pro·pose' (prô·pōz). To plan or intend; to suggest.

pro·vi'sion (prô·vĭzh'ŭn). To stock with food.

prow (prou). Front end of a ship, bow.

pry (prī). To raise or move by using a lever.

puck'er (pŭk'ẽr). To draw up into folds or wrinkles.

purse (pûrs). To draw together tightly.

Q

quar'ry (kwôr'ĭ). A hunted animal.

quest (kwĕst). Search, hunt.

queue (kū). Pigtail.

quill (kwĭl). Large, stiff feather.

quoth (kwōth). Said.

R

ra'di·ance (rā'dĭ·ăns). Brightness, brilliance.

ral'ly (răl'ĭ). To bring together again and restore to order.

rap'ture (răp'tûr). Great joy.

rau'cous (rô'kŭs). Harsh.

ra'ven (rā'vĕn). Black bird larger than a crow.

rav'en·ous (răv'ĕn·ŭs). Very hungry.

rem'e·dy (rĕm'ė·dĭ). Anything that corrects an evil; a cure.

ren'der (rĕn'dẽr). To play (music).

rep'u·ta'tion (rĕp'û·tā'shŭn). A person's character as other people judge it.

res'er·va'tion (rĕz'ẽr·vā'shŭn). Area of land set aside for Indians to live on.

res'o·lute (rĕz'ô·lūt). Firm, determined.

res'tive (rĕs'tĭv). Restless.

re·vive' (rė·vīv'). To return to life; to restore to life.

rig'id (rĭj'ĭd). Stiff.

ro·bust' (rô·bŭst'). Strong, healthy.

ros'in (rŏz'ĭn). Yellowish or brownish substance made from the sap of pine trees.

roun'de·lay (roun'dĕ·lā). Song in which a simple tune is repeated frequently.

S

sal'ly (săl'ĭ). To rush forth.

sanc'ti·mo'ni·ous (săngk'tĭ·mō'nĭ·ŭs). Pretending to be good or saintly, hypocritical.

ō, ōmit; ŏ, hŏp; ǒ, cǒntain; ô, ôr; ô, sôft; ōō, fōōd; ŏŏ, fŏŏt; oi, oil; ou, out; ū, ūse;
û, ûnite; ŭ, ŭs; ů, circŭs; û, fûr; tů, natůre; dů, verdůre; th, thin; th̶, th̶an.

san'dal·wood' (săn'dăl·wood'). Asiatic tree, the wood of which is used for carvings and cabinetwork.

sap'ling (săp'lĭng). Young tree.

sar·cas'tic (sär·kăs'tĭk). Sneering, insulting.

scut'tle (skŭt''l). To move swiftly, to scamper.

sedge (sĕj). A kind of swamp plant.

seem'ly (sēm'lĭ). Fitting, proper.

sen'try (sĕn'trĭ). Soldier acting as a guard or watchman.

se·rene' (sė·rēn'). Peaceful, cloudless.

ses'a·me (See **Open sesame.**)

sheer (shẽr). Pure, unmixed.

shoal (shōl). Place where a body of water is shallow.

sire (sīr). Father; also a title of respect used in addressing a king.

skep'ti·cal (skĕp'tĭ·kăl). Doubtful.

slith'er (slĭth'ẽr). To glide like a snake.

slough (sloo or slou). Swamp.

slug'gard (slŭg'ẽrd). Lazy person.

smear (smẽr). To cover or coat with anything sticky.

smol'der (smōl'dẽr). To burn with much smoke but little flame.

sog'gy (sŏg'ĭ). Soaked with water and therefore heavy.

Span'ish Main (spăn'ĭsh mān). Correctly, the northern coast of South America; commonly, the Caribbean Sea.

spasm (spăz'm). Sudden, brief feeling or reaction.

spec'ta·cles (spĕk'tȧ·k'lz). Eyeglasses.

spright'ly (sprīt'lĭ). Lively, gay.

squirm (skwûrm). To wiggle or twist about.

stac·ca'to (stȧ·kä'tō). Disconnected, abrupt, with breaks between successive musical tones.

stag (stăg). Adult male of certain kinds of deer.

stalk (stôk). To walk stiffly and proudly.

stal'lion (stăl'yŭn). Adult male horse.

stealth'y (stĕl'thĭ). Sly, secret.

stout (stout). Strong, sturdy.

stud (stŭd). To be set thickly together.

stu·pen'dous (stů·pĕn'dŭs). Amazing, wonderful.

sulk'y (sŭl'kĭ). Sullen, not cheerful.

sum'mon (sŭm'ŭn). To send for, to order to come.

su·perb' (sů·pûrb'). Very good.

su·pe'ri·or (sů·pẽr'ĭ·ẽr). Proud, showing a feeling of being better than other people.

sur·vey'or (sûr·vā'ẽr). One who measures land and marks boundaries.

swin'dler (swĭn'dlẽr). Person who cheats others out of money.

T

ta'bor (tā'bẽr). Small drum with one head, somewhat like a tambourine.

tal'low (tăl'ō). Animal fat used in making candles, soap, etc.

ta·ran'tu·la (tȧ·răn'tů·lȧ). Large, poisonous spider.

tart (tärt). Sharp, biting, sour.

tas'sel (tăs''l). A hanging bunch of threads, cords, etc., used as a decoration.

ā, āte; ȧ, furnȧce; ă, ăt; ǎ, ǎppear; â, câre; ä, cär; ȧ, pȧss; ȧ, sofȧ; ē, bē; ė, bėgin; ĕ, lĕt; ẽ, silẽnt; ẽ, watẽr; ẹ, hẹre; ī, hīde; ĭ, hĭd; ı̇, cabı̇n; ō, hōpe;

taunt (tônt). To jeer at, mock.

taut (tôt). Stretched tight

teal (tēl). A kind of duck.

tem'ple (tĕm'p'l). Building used for the worship of a god or gods.

thatch (thăch). Straw used to cover a roof.

thrash (thrăsh). To move about violently.

thresh'ing floor (thrĕsh'ĭng flōr). Place where wheat or other grain is beaten out from the straw.

thresh'old (thrĕsh'ōld). Doorsill.

thun'der·struck' (thŭn'dĕr·strŭk'). Amazed, astonished.

to'ken (tō'kĕn). Sign.

tor·ment' (tôr·mĕnt'). To cause very great pain (to).

troop (tro͞op). To move along in a group.

troth (trôth). Faithfulness, loyalty.

trow (trō). To think or believe.

trow'el (trou'ĕl). Tool for spreading and smoothing cement or plaster.

tu'le (to͞o'lė). A kind of bulrush or swamp plant of the southwestern United States.

tu'nic (tū'nĭk). Blouse or jacket reaching to the hips or below and usually having a belt.

tur'quoise (tûr'koiz). Precious stone, sky-blue or greenish-blue in color.

tyke (tīk). Dog.

U

u·nan'i·mous·ly (ū·năn'ĭ·mŭs·lĭ). Without a single opposing vote.

un·kempt' (ŭn·kĕmpt'). Not combed.

up·hol'ster·y (ŭp·hōl'stĕr·ĭ). Cloth used to cover furniture.

u·ten'sil (ū·tĕn'sĭl). Tool or container, especially one used in a kitchen.

V

van (văn). Wagon.

vic'tuals (vĭt''lz). Food.

vis'i·ble (vĭz'ĭ·b'l). Able to be seen.

vo'cal (vō'kăl). Having a voice.

vul'gar (vŭl'gĕr). Not refined; common or coarse.

W

weir (wēr). Fence of stakes placed in a stream to catch fish.

weird (wērd). Strange, unearthly.

whey (hwā). Watery part of sour milk.

whiff (hwĭf). Slight odor or smell noticed for only a moment; short puff of air, smoke, etc.

wick'i·up' (wĭk'ĭ·ŭp'). Kind of hut made by the Indians of the southwestern United States.

wist'ful·ness (wĭst'fo͝ol·nĕs). Deep desire for something which one is not likely to get.

wit'ti·cism (wĭt'ĭ·sĭz'm). Clever, humorous remark.

wot (wŏt). Know.

writhe (rīth). To twist the body violently, as if in pain.

wrought (rôt). Done.

Y

yak (yăk). A kind of ox common in central Asia.

yew (yo͞o). A kind of European evergreen tree. Archers use the wood to make bows.

ȯ, ȯmit; ŏ, hŏp; ỏ, cỏntain; ô, ôr; ọ, sọft; o͞o, fo͞od; o͝o, fo͝ot; oi, oil; ou, out; ū, ūse; ů, ůnite; ŭ, ŭs; ṳ, circṳs; û, fûr; tṳ, natṳre; dṳ, verdṳre; th, thin; th, than.

Acknowledgments

For their courteous permissions to use the following selections, we wish to express our gratitude and appreciation to the following authors, agents, publishers, and periodicals:

Brandt & Brandt: "Clipper Ships and Captains" from A BOOK OF AMERICANS by Rosemary and Stephen Vincent Benét, published by Rinehart & Company, Inc., copyright 1933 by Rosemary and Stephen Vincent Benét; "Afternoon on a Hill" from RENASCENCE AND OTHER POEMS by Edna St. Vincent Millay, published by Harper & Brothers, copyright 1917, 1945 by Edna St. Vincent Millay; and "Travel" from SECOND APRIL AND OTHER POEMS by Edna St. Vincent Millay, published by Harper & Brothers, copyright 1921, 1949 by Edna St. Vincent Millay.—Chatto & Windus: "Lone Dog" from SONGS TO SAVE A SOUL by Irene Rutherford McLeod, copyright 1915.—Coward-McCann, Inc.: "The Mouse" by Elizabeth Coatsworth, from COMPASS ROSE (Songs for Today Series), copyright 1929 by Coward-McCann, Inc.—Curtis Brown, Ltd.: "The Peddler" from LASSIE COME-HOME by Eric Knight, copyright 1940 by Jere Knight Lindtner, reprinted by permission of the author's estate.—Dodd, Mead & Company, Inc.: "The Sea Gypsy" from POEMS by Richard Hovey.—John Lane The Bodley Head Limited (London), and Dodd, Mead & Company, Inc.: "I Meant To Do My Work Today" from THE LONELY DANCER by Richard LeGallienne, copyright 1913, 1941 by Richard LeGallienne.—Doubleday & Company, Inc.: "Bushed" from BUSH HOLIDAY by Stephen Fennimore, copyright 1948, 1949 by Stephen Fennimore; and " 'Gator Hunt" from THE LION'S PAW by Robb White, copyright 1946 by Robb White.—Harper & Brothers: "Stuart Little's Nautical Adventure" from STUART LITTLE by E. B. White, copyright 1945 by E. B. White; and "Wolves on Silver Lake" from BY THE SHORES OF SILVER LAKE by Laura Ingalls Wilder, copyright 1939 by Harper & Brothers.—Holiday House: "At the Court of the Cadi" from PEPPERFOOT OF THURSDAY MARKET by Robert Davis, copyright 1941.—Henry Holt and Company, Inc.: "Silver" and "The Little Green Orchard" from COLLECTED POEMS by Walter de la Mare, copyright 1920 by Henry Holt and Company, Inc., 1948 by Walter de la Mare.—Houghton Mifflin Company: "The Sandhill Crane" from CHILDREN SING IN THE FAR WEST by Mary Austin, copyright 1928 by Mary Austin.—Albert Whitman & Co.: "Pecos Bill and the Cyclone" from PECOS BILL by James Cloyd Bowman, published by Albert Whitman, Chicago, 1937.—Alfred A. Knopf, Inc.: "A Dime's Worth, for Free" by Marion Holland, copyright 1949, 1952 by Marion Holland.—Little, Brown & Company: "By Kite String Across Grand Canyon" from MC WHINNEY'S JAUNT by Robert Lawson, copyright 1951 by Robert Lawson; "This Is My Rock" from FAR AND FEW by David McCord, copyright 1929 by David McCord; and "Eletelephony" from TIRRA LIRRA by Laura E. Richards, copyright 1918, 1930, 1932 by Laura E. Richards.—The Macmillan Company: "Be Jubilant, My Feet" from MAGICAL MELONS by Carol R. Brink, copyright 1939; "The Wilderness Is Tamed" from AWAY GOES SALLY by Elizabeth Coatsworth, copyright 1934; "The Pirate Cook" from RHYMES ABOUT THE COUNTRY by Marchette Gaylord Chute, copyright 1925; "The Young Calves" from SALTWATER FARM by Robert P. Tristram Coffin, copyright 1937; and "Night" from STARS TONIGHT by Sara Teasdale, copyright 1930.—Dr. John Masefield, O.M., The Society of Authors, and The Macmillan Company: "Tewkesbury Road" from STORY OF A ROUNDHOUSE by John Masefield, copyright 1932.—Miss Nancy McIntosh, owner of the copyright, and Macmillan & Co., Ltd.: "The Song of the Pirate King" from THE PIRATES OF PENZANCE in The Savoy Operas by Sir W. S. Gilbert.—Clifford H. Meigs: "If I Were a One-Legged Pirate" by Mildred Plew Meigs, from Child Life.—Price Waterhouse & Co.: "Overheard on a Saltmarsh" from CHILDREN OF LOVE by Harold Monro, copyright 1913 by Poetry Bookshop.—Laura E. Richards: "Antonio" from Child Life, by permission of the author's estate.—Charles Scribner's Sons: "Hans and Gretel Find a Friend" from HANS BRINKER by Mary Mapes Dodge; "The Shooting Match at Nottingham Town" from MERRY ADVENTURES OF ROBIN HOOD by Howard Pyle; and "The Mother Teal and the Overland Route," selection adapted by permission of the publisher from LIVES OF THE HUNTED by Ernest Thompson Seton, copyright 1901, 1929 by Ernest Thompson Seton.—Simon and Schuster, Inc.: "Bambi and The Enemy," selection adapted by permission of the publisher from BAMBI by Felix Salten, copyright 1928 by Simon and Schuster, Inc.—Story Parade, Inc., for the following, copyright in the years indicated by Story Parade, Inc.: "The Big Green Umbrella" and "Wisdom of Solomon" by Elizabeth Coatsworth (1944, 1947); "The Pudding That Broke Up the Preaching" by Ellis Credle (1948); "Rococo Skates" by Marjorie Fischer (1936); "Smoky" by Marion Holland (1947); "Nail Soup" by Christine M. Kowalski (1948); and "Whitey's Sunday Horse" by Glen Rounds (1941).—The Viking Press, Inc.: "The Baby Sea Lion" from SENSIBLE KATE by Doris Gates, copyright 1943 by Doris Gates; "The Doughnuts" from HOMER PRICE by Robert McCloskey, copyright 1943 by Robert McCloskey; "A Red-Gold Terrier from Lhasa" from DAUGHTER OF THE MOUNTAINS by Louise Rankin, copyright 1948 by Louise S. Rankin; "The Wedding" from THE SINGING TREE by Kate Seredy, copyright 1939 by Kate Seredy; (excerpts adapted from the originals by permission of the publisher); and "Evening Hymn" from SONG IN THE MEADOW by Elizabeth Madox Roberts, copyright 1940 by Elizabeth Madox Roberts.—Franklin Watts, Inc.: "Sweet Potato in My Hand and a Possum by the Tail" from THIS BOY CODY AND HIS FRIENDS by Leon Wilson, copyright 1952 by Leon Wilson.—James W. Shearer: "Green Moth" from SKIPPING ALONG ALONE by Winifred Welles, copyright 1931 by The Macmillan Company, by permission of the author's estate.—Edgar Wyatt: "Kit Carson and the General," copyright 1953 by Story Parade, Inc., by permission of the author.